ELECTRONIC

ENGINEERING PRINCIPLES

By

JOHN D. RYDER, Ph.D.

Professor of Electrical Engineering
Head, Department of Electrical Engineering
University of Illinois

SECOND EDITION

PRENTICE-HALL, INC.

New York

Second Edition

First Printing........................*December, 1952*
Second Printing...........................*June, 1953*

PREFACE TO SECOND EDITION

In preparing a second edition of this book, it has seemed desirable to introduce new and timely material as required by the dynamic nature of electronics, without a major increase in the overall size of the book. The material has been carefully reviewed, and rewritten in many places, and some reduction has been made in line with modern considerations of its relative importance. However, the organization of the book has been substantially preserved, with the exception of the treatment of electron emission, which has been consolidated into one chapter.

As a result, it has been found possible to introduce enlarged treatment of numerous subjects, particularly a more general treatment of amplifiers, and to expand the section on feedback. In line with modern trends, a wholly new chapter on solid-state devices and the transistor has been incorporated. New problems and new illustrations have been added to most chapters.

The general concept of the book as a fundamental and thorough treatment of basic electronics has been retained. The circuit concept of electronic tubes has been stressed, but only after consideration of the physical and nonlinear limitations of the devices. The use of calculus and a-c circuit analysis thus become desirable prerequisites to study in the electronic area.

J. D. RYDER

PREFACE TO THE FIRST EDITION

The author has been convinced for a considerable time that electronics has outgrown its position as a subordinate field of communications or radio engineering, and should be treated independently as *electronic engineering*. So considered, it becomes applicable to all electrical engineering, involving as it does theories of conduction, simple atomic structure, and generalized circuit analysis with linear and nonlinear circuit elements. Thus, electronic engineering is fundamental to all power or radio applications of electron tubes, but is not necessarily a part of either field.

A most important factor in the study of electron tubes is an understanding of the advantages and limitations of electron tubes as electric circuit elements. Such an understanding requires knowledge of the physical background involved in emission, space charge, and gaseous conduction phenomena, without requiring a complete course in kinetic theory. Also needed is an electric circuit background that goes beyond the limitations of sinusoidal voltages and has included a grounding in the common network theorems. This book endeavors to supply the physical fundamentals needed for an understanding of electron tubes, but must depend on other courses for the basic alternating-current network theory required. Mathematics through simple differential equations is assumed, since this is also needed for the circuit theory.

The material has been chosen to present the electron tube as a useful engineering device. Theory and applications are closely grouped, and applications are chosen largely from the industrial field, since radio applications frequently are treated in a subsequent course.

The author wishes to express his appreciation to Doctor W. L. Everitt, of the University of Illinois, for discussion and counsel, and to Doctor W. B. Boast and Professor W. L. Cassell of the staff of this department for many helpful suggestions. Acknowledgement is also made to the *RCA Receiving Tube Manual* for the inspiration for Figures 8-8, 8-10, and 8-11.

J. D. RYDER

CONTENTS

v

tions at the Cathode Surface. The Space-Charge Equation. Departures from Theory. Transit Time. Effect of Transit Time. Power Loss in the Diode.

nation of Amplitude Distortion. Intermodulation Distortion. The Plate Load for Maximum Power Output. The Push-Pull Class A Amplifier. Graphical Analysis of the Push-Pull Amplifier. The Class AB Push-Pull Amplifier. The Class B Push-Pull Amplifier. Amplifiers with Reactive Loads.

PHYSICAL CONSTANTS

e = charge on the electron = 1.602×10^{-19} coulomb.

m = mass of the electron at rest = 9.106×10^{-31} kilogram (kg).

e/m = charge to mass ratio for the electron at rest = 1.759×10^{11} coulombs/kg.

c = velocity of light = 2.99776×10^8 meters per second $\cong 3 \times 10^8$ meters per second.

h = Planck's constant = 6.624×10^{-34} joule-second.

k = Boltzmann's constant = 1.380×10^{-23} joule per °K.

N = Avogadro's number = 6.024×10^{23} molecules per mole.

A = Angstrom unit = 10^{-10} meter.

ϵ_v = space permittivity = $10^7/4\pi c^2$ = 8.85×10^{-12}.

ev = electron volt = 1.602×10^{-19} joule.

One atomic weight = 1.65×10^{-27} kilogram. (Atomic weights on the physical scale are relative to the weight of the oxygen isotope O^{16} taken as equal to 16.)

CHAPTER 1

THE FUNDAMENTAL PARTICLES
OF ELECTRONICS

*Electronics is the science which deals with devices operating by passage
of electric charges through gas or space, and with the circuits in which
such devices are operated.*

In addition to the devices directly covered by the definition above,
there is now available another group of devices, among which are
the crystal rectifier, the barrier-layer devices, and the transistor,
which depend on the complex movement of electric charges in
semiconductors. While not specifically covered by the above definition, yet they frequently enter the thinking of the electronics
engineer, and in the future will probably be classed as electronic
devices because of the similarity of performance and of circuit
design.

1-1. Early History

Modern electronic science is usually considered as having been
born in 1883 with the discovery of the *Edison effect* by Thomas A.
Edison. During one of his experiments with his newborn incandescent lamp, Edison discovered that when a small metal plate was
sealed into the lamp and made positive with respect to the heated
filament, an electric current would flow in the wire leading to the
plate. When the polarity of the applied potential was reversed,
the flow of current through the space inside the lamp ceased. Edison, interested largely in his incandescent lamp, did not pursue the
matter further.

Sir William H. Preece in England, in 1884, further investigated
the Edison effect. He found the current magnitude to be influenced by the voltage between the filament and plate, the temperature of the filament, and its distance from the plate. He rightly

assumed the current to be carried by negative particles, now called electrons.

Around 1885, Elihu Thomson invented the magnetic blowout for an arc and applied it to prevent burning of contacts on starters for electric street railway cars. This was an early application of electron ballistics, in which the force on an electronic arc stream in a magnetic field was used to stretch and break or blow out the arc.

J. A. Fleming, circa 1897, applied the Edison effect to the rectification, or detection, of radio signals, obtaining increased sensitivity and stability over the crystal and electrolytic detectors then in use. In 1907, Lee DeForest added the grid or control element to the Fleming diode, making a sensitive electrostatic relay, the triode tube. This device started the science of electronics on its present path.

Galvanometer

Fig. 1-1. Form of circuit and tube used to show the Edison effect.

1-2. The Electron

Later experiments showed that the current flowing in the Edison effect was due to a procession of small negatively charged particles. Sir J. J. Thomson discovered similar small charges in early research on cathode rays, and it was proposed that they be named *electrons*, a term invented by G. Johnstone Stoney. This name was generally accepted and applied to the negatively charged particle of electricity, now considered the basic particle in the science of electronics.

The electron is the smallest known unit of electricity. At times it is convenient to think of it as a tiny particle, but at other times the wave properties which it has been found to possess lead to a more satisfactory explanation of experimental results. No satisfactory explanation of this dual character exists as yet. The concept chosen for discussion of particular phenomena is usually that which leads to the most satisfactory explanation.

Thomson's early experiments showed that every electron carried the same charge per unit of mass (e/m). About 1910, Robert A.

Millikan measured the electric charge on the electron and found it to be constant. This charge is now believed to be 1.602×10^{-19} coulomb, and since e/m has been measured as 1.759×10^{11} coulombs per kilogram, the mass of an electron can be found to be 9.106×10^{-31} kilogram.

It is thought that electric-current flow in solids, gases, and vacuum is due to the movement of electric charges. Benjamin Franklin was one of the first to propose that an electric current be thought of as an electric-fluid flow from positive to negative terminal in a metallic circuit external to the source. The technique of electrical engineering has been built on this concept, which is now known to be reversed, the negative electrons actually flowing from negative to positive in the external circuit. The customary usage is too well established to be overcome, and although unfortunate, need cause no difficulty. In this text, when *electric currents* are referred to, the customary direction is meant; when the reference is to *electronic currents*, the flow of electrons from negative to positive is to be considered.

1-3. Theories of Atomic Structure

In the late nineteenth century, the atom was believed to be the smallest indivisible particle of matter. Sir J. J. Thomson conceived

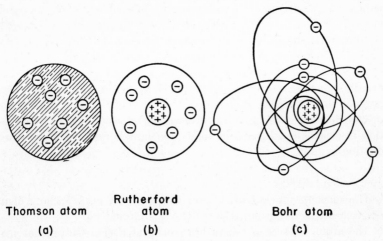

Thomson atom

(a)

Rutherford atom

(b)

Bohr atom

(c)

Fig. 1-2. Structure of the atom as proposed in various early theories.

the atom as a sphere of positive electric charge having negative charges scattered throughout, much like raisins in a muffin. Sir Ernest Rutherford showed by experiment that such an arrangement was not correct, and suggested that an atom might consist of a core or *nucleus* of positive charge, surrounded by a static cloud of negative charges, sufficient in number to render the atom electrically neutral.

Niels Bohr proposed a dynamic atom model somewhat like the solar system, in contrast to the previously proposed static models. The negative charges of the Bohr atom were considered as in motion in orbits about a central nucleus of positive charge. The number of negative electrons was assumed equal to the atomic number of the element, and for a normal atom, the negative charge of these electrons was exactly balanced by the positive charge of the nucleus.

Such an atom is largely empty space, the single electron of the hydrogen atom having a normal orbit of approximately 10^{-8} cm, with a nucleus of nominal diameter 10^{-13} cm having a single positive charge.

Bohr's atomic theory was successfully used to explain line spectra, x rays, electric current conduction through gases, and other phenomena. However, certain other experimental phenomena could not be fully explained by the Bohr theory. Efforts to employ the Bohr atom model in explanation of these phenomena have led to various modifications in the definiteness of the geometry of the Bohr model. Thus the negative charges have been assigned wave as well as particle properties, energy values have been substituted for the elaborate orbits, and the mathematical formulation of wave mechanics has been developed.

Although much of the positive physical picture supplied by the original Bohr model has been lost, these recent developments have provided a more satisfactory conception of an atom, and of its function in electric conduction in solids and liquids and electronic conduction in gases.

1-4. Other Particles

The nucleus appears to contain two kinds of particles in which are concentrated the positive electric charge and most of the mass of the atom. These particles have been identified through atom-cracking experiments and given appropriate names.

The *proton* is a particle carrying a positive electric charge which is numerically equal to the negative charge of the electron. The proton has a mass approximately that of the hydrogen atom H^1, whose nucleus consists only of one proton.

The *neutron* carries zero electric charge and has a mass 0.08 per cent larger than that of the proton. Neutrons are present in the nuclei of all atoms except hydrogen H^1. The neutron and proton constitute the building blocks of the nucleus, and contribute mass, and charge and mass, respectively.

Certain other particles are of interest, although they apparently do not contribute individually to the properties of the atom.

The *positron*, sometimes called the *positive electron*, has a mass equal to that of the electron and a positive charge equal to that of the proton. It occurs in the free state very rarely, usually as the result of atomic disintegration in artificial radioactive materials, wherein the following event is believed to take place:

$$\text{proton} \rightarrow \text{neutron} + \text{positron} + \text{neutrino}.$$

The positron appears to have an average life of only a few billionths of a second (10^{-9} sec) for when it comes close to a negative electron they join and mutually annihilate one another or disappear, with the conversion of their masses into radiant energy (gamma rays). It has been shown experimentally that the inverse process also occurs: that is, there may be production of particles from radiant energy. If a radiation of sufficiently high energy is passed through matter, electrons and positrons are generated. The material substance of the particles is created by transformation of the energy in accordance with the Einstein relation

$$\text{energy} = \text{mass} \times c^2,$$

where c is the velocity of light.

The *neutrino*, mentioned above, is a hypothetical particle of no charge and almost zero mass. Its existence has been postulated in order to introduce the proper amount of momentum and energy to balance the above equation for the disintegration of the proton, ensuring conservation of energy and momentum during this event. No direct evidence of the existence of the neutrino has yet been found.

Still another particle of importance in atomic or nuclear theory is the *mesotron* (or *meson*), which was discovered in 1936, in connection with work on cosmic rays. There appear to be two types of mesotrons, a heavy particle of mass about 285 times that of an electron, and a lighter particle of mass about 215 times that of an electron. Either type may occur with positive or negative charges. The exact function of the mesotron is not yet understood.

The *photon*, although not a unit from which matter is constructed, is important as a fundamental particle. It is a bundle of radiant energy; and although it cannot be considered as having a material substance or mass, yet by use of the Einstein relation given above, it may be considered as having a radiation mass equivalent to its energy. The amount of this energy is dependent on the frequency, or *color*, of the radiation. Our visible heat, light, radio waves, and x rays are all groups, or bunches, of photons. It has become necessary to think of light energy coming in the form of particles as well as in waves in order to explain satisfactorily many of the phenomena encountered in modern atomic physics. This is the same sort of dual viewpoint which must be employed in discussing the properties of the electron.

TABLE 1

THE FUNDAMENTAL PARTICLES

Name	Mass*	Electric Charge	Other Properties
Electron..........	1/1820 atomic unit	−1 unit	
Proton............	1.0076 atomic units	+1 unit	
Neutron..........	1.00893 atomic units	0	
Positron..........	1/1820 atomic unit	+1 unit	
Neutrino.........	Almost zero	0	Momentum and energy
Mesotron.........	Approximately 285 or 215 electron masses	±	Energy
Photon............	...	0	Electromagnetic radiation

* The atomic unit of mass on the physical scale is 1/16 that of the oxygen atom O^{16}, or very nearly that of the hydrogen atom H^1.

REFERENCES

1. Rutherford, E., *Phil. Mag.*, **21**, 669 (1911).
2. Richtmyer, F. K., and Kennard, E. H., *Introduction to Modern Physics*, 4th ed., McGraw-Hill Book Company, Inc., New York, 1947.

3. Huggins, M. L., "Structure of Atoms and Molecules, Electron Theory of Valence," *Elec. Eng.*, **53,** 851 (1934).
4. Waterman, A. T., "Fundamental Properties of the Electron," *Trans. AIEE*, **53,** 3 (1934).
5. Millikan, R. A., *The Electron*, University of Chicago Press, Chicago, 1917.
6. Kennelly, A. E., "Recent Developments in Electrical Units," *Elec. Eng.*, **58,** 78 (1939).
7. Stranathan, J. D., *The Particles of Modern Physics*, The Blakiston Company, Philadelphia, 1942.
8. Millikan, R. A., *Electrons (+ and −), Protons, Photons, Neutrons, Mesotrons and Cosmic Rays*, University of Chicago Press, Chicago, 1947.

CHAPTER 2

THE MOVEMENT OF CHARGED PARTICLES IN FIELDS

Electronic devices operate through motion of electrons or other charged particles, under the action of electric and magnetic fields. A knowledge of the motions of charged particles is important to a study of electronics because without that knowledge a basic understanding of modern and complex electron tubes cannot be achieved. Actually the basic principles are simple, stemming from the ordinary laws of dynamics, modified in a simple manner to account for accelerations other than that of gravity.

While many of the situations discussed in this chapter may appear complicated, it can be seen that basically they express the action of charged particles in electric fields, in magnetic fields, or in combinations of the two. Complications introduced are a result of of the orientation of the fields rather than as a result of the fields themselves.

2-1. Dynamics of a Particle

Newton's second law of motion states: *The time-rate of change of momentum of a body is proportional to the applied force and takes place in the direction in which the force acts.*

Mathematically this may be stated as

$$f = \frac{d(m\boldsymbol{v})}{dt},$$

and, if the mass of the body is a constant,

$$f = m\frac{d\boldsymbol{v}}{dt} = m\boldsymbol{a}, \tag{2-1}$$

since the acceleration is the rate of change of velocity. When m is

8

in kilograms and a is in meters per second^2, f is in newtons. If the acceleration is known, the instantaneous velocity may be determined by use of

$$\frac{dv}{dt} = a$$

or
$$v = \int_0^t a\, dt + v_0 \qquad \text{m/sec} \qquad (2\text{-}2)$$

if the velocity at $t = 0$ is called v_0. This form of the equation applies whether a is constant or variable with time.

Since distance is obtained as

$$s = \int v\, dt,$$

another integration of Eq. 2-2 yields

$$s = \int_0^t \int_0^t a\, dt\, dt + \int_0^t v_0\, dt + s_0 \qquad \text{m} \qquad (2\text{-}3)$$

if the initial position is s_0 at $t = 0$.

This expression allows the determination of the position of a body of mass m at any time t when the body is subjected to an acceleration a or a force f. If the force acting is constant, the acceleration is likewise constant, and Eqs. 2-2 and 2-3 reduce to the usual forms

$$v = at + v_0, \qquad \text{m/sec} \qquad (2\text{-}4)$$

$$s = \frac{at^2}{2} + v_0 t + s_0. \qquad \text{m.} \qquad (2\text{-}5)$$

During a time interval dt, the work done on a mass moving in direction ds with velocity v, as in Fig. 2-1, is

$$dw = f \cos \alpha\, ds = m\, \frac{dv}{dt}\, v\, dt = mv\, dv,$$

where α is the angle between the direction of the motion ds and the direction of the force f. If the velocity is altered from v_0 to a new value v, the total work done, or the kinetic energy given to the body of mass m is

$$\text{K.E.} = \int_{v_0}^v mv\, dv = \frac{m(v^2 - v_0^2)}{2} \qquad \text{joules} \qquad (2\text{-}6)$$

if m is assumed independent of velocity.   This result is not dependent on acceleration remaining constant, nor is it dependent on the direction of the velocity.   If mass is in kilograms and velocity in meters per second, the resultant energy is in joules.

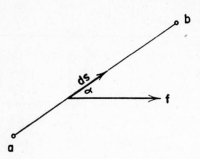

Fig. 2-1.   Work done by force f in direction ds is $f\,ds\cos\alpha$.

For a body moving with peripheral velocity v in a circular path as in Fig. 2-2, $v\,dt$ is the distance moved along the arc in time dt.   The angle $d\theta$ is defined as

$$d\theta = \frac{v\,dt}{r}.$$

The angular velocity ω, in radians per second, is defined so that

$$\omega = \frac{d\theta}{dt} = \frac{v}{r} \qquad \text{radians/sec,} \qquad (2\text{-}7)$$

v and r being in consistent units.

In uniform circular motion, an acceleration is acting toward the center of rotation.   By Newton's law, a force directed toward the center must then be present, and this is called a *centripetal* force.   If the rotating mass is to remain in equilibrium in the circular path,

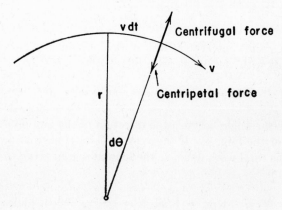

Fig. 2-2.   Forces existing in circular motion of a particle.

the centripetal force must be balanced by an outward-directed or *centrifugal* force.

Referring to Fig. 2-3, if $d\theta$ becomes infinitesimal, v_1 approaches v, and the change in velocity dv is perpendicular to a line bisecting $d\theta$.

Then

$$dv = v \, d\theta,$$

and dividing by dt gives as the center-directed acceleration

$$a = \frac{dv}{dt} = v\frac{d\theta}{dt} = \frac{v^2}{r} = r\omega^2, \quad (2\text{-}8)$$

following use of Eq. 2-7. The centripetal force, or opposing centrifugal force, may then be written as

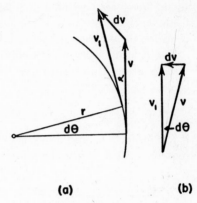

(a)   **(b)**

Fig. 2-3. Relations between linear and angular velocity.

$$f_c = ma = \frac{mv^2}{r} = mr\omega^2 \qquad \text{newtons.} \qquad (2\text{-}9)$$

These few statements from the dynamics of a particle will be useful in studying the motion of electric charges in electric and magnetic fields.

2-2. Acceleration of an Electron in an Electric Field

An electric current is measured by the amount of electric charge passing through a given cross section of a region per second. In metallic conductors a very large number (high density) of electrons move very slowly through the material. Conduction in gas or space, where the electrons are freed of the confinement and interference to movement inherent in a solid conductor, occurs usually with a relatively small number (low density) of electrons or other charges moving very rapidly.

Because of this low density, and since the concept of a rigid conductor is absent in electronic paths, it is convenient to consider the actions of individual electrons or other charges in understanding the operation of electronic devices. Restricting the discussion to electrons, it is usual to assume that the number of electrons per unit volume of the path, or the charge density, is low, and it is also frequently desirable to assume that the electrons move in such a high vacuum that there will be no collisions with gas atoms. Gravitational forces are neglected as small, in comparison with the effects of fields on the electrons. Actually, of course, there are many devices in which these assumptions must be modified.

The field intensity in an electric field, equal to the negative of the voltage gradient, is defined as the force acting per unit of positive charge, or in general

$$\mathcal{E} = \frac{f}{q} \qquad \text{v/m,} \qquad (2\text{-}10)$$

if f is in newtons and q in coulombs. The direction of the field intensity is taken as the direction of the force on the positive charge.

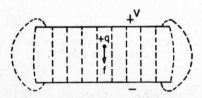

Fig. 2-4. Force f on a positive charge q in a uniform electric field.

Since a positive charge will be attracted to the negative electrode, the force f and field intensity $\mathcal{E}$ are directed from positive to negative electrode, as in Fig. 2-4.

An electron carries a negative charge of 1.60×10^{-19} coulomb, a magnitude here referred to as e. Since the charge is negative, the force exerted on an electron in an electric field will be directed toward the positive electrode, in the direction of the potential gradient, or opposite to the defined positive direction of the electric field intensity. If the direction of electronic motion is thus reasoned physically, there is no need to carry a negative sign on e. The force f_e on an electron in an electric field is then

$$f_e = e\mathcal{E} \qquad (2\text{-}11)$$

exerted in the direction of the potential gradient.

The electron will then experience an acceleration in the electric field, and Newton's second law allows this to be written as

$$a = \frac{dv}{dt} = \frac{e\mathcal{E}}{m} \qquad \text{m/sec}^2. \qquad (2\text{-}12)$$

This acceleration is directed along the field flux lines and toward the positive electrode. Equation 2-12 is of fundamental importance in predicting the motion of electrons in electric fields.

2-3. Velocity of an Electron in an Electric Field

Assume that an electron is released at point P (x_0,y_0), Fig. 2-5, with a wholly upward initial velocity, v_{0y}. Acting in the region is a uniform electric field $\mathcal{E}_y$ directed in the $-y$ direction, due to a potential difference which is positive toward $+y$. Then it is possible to state

$$a_y = \frac{dv_y}{dt} = \frac{e\mathcal{E}_y}{m}. \qquad (2\text{-}13)$$

The velocity in the y direction at any time t can be written from Eq. 2-2 as

$$v_y = \int_0^t \frac{e\mathcal{E}_y}{m}\,dt + v_{0y}.$$

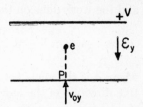

Fig. 2-5. Path of an electron in a uniform electric field.

If $\mathcal{E}_y$ is not a function of time,

$$v_y = \frac{e\mathcal{E}_y}{m}\,t + v_{0y}. \qquad (2\text{-}14)$$

The y coordinate of position at any time t can be obtained by integration of Eq. 2-14 as

$$y = \int_0^t \frac{e\mathcal{E}_y t}{m}\,dt + v_{0y}t + y_0.$$

If $\mathcal{E}_y$ is not a time function,

$$y = \frac{e\mathcal{E}_y t^2}{2m} + v_{0y}t + y_0. \qquad (2\text{-}15)$$

This is the usual law of the falling body, with the acceleration of gravity replaced by the acceleration of the electron in the field.

If the potential difference applied to the electrodes is a function of time, for example $e = E_m \sin \omega t$, the field intensity will likewise be a time function. This function may be substituted in the expression for acceleration, and if the resulting equations are integrated properly, the correct results will be obtained.

2-4. Energy Acquired by an Electron

When an electron is accelerated in an electric field, work is done upon it, and its kinetic energy is increased. The work done to move the charge from point A to a point B of higher positive potential, in a field of intensity $\mathcal{E}$, is equal to the kinetic energy acquired by the electron. From Eq. 2-11,

$$f_e = e\mathcal{E},$$

and the work done on the electron by this force will be given by

$$W = \int_A^B f_e \cos \alpha \, ds, \tag{2-16}$$

where α is the angle between the direction of the force and the positive direction of the movement ds. For the case in which the movement of the negative electron $(-e)$ is in the direction of the force (the electron is being attracted toward a positive electrode), the angle α is zero. Then

$$W = -\int_A^B e\mathcal{E} \, ds.$$

By reason of the work done on the electron, its velocity will have been changed, and the kinetic energy acquired by the electron will be

$$W = \frac{m(v^2 - v_0^2)}{2} = -e\int_A^B \mathcal{E} \, ds. \tag{2-17}$$

The negative integral of the field intensity is equal to the potential V between A and B, so that

$$W = \frac{m(v^2 - v_0^2)}{2} = Ve \qquad \text{joules.} \tag{2-18}$$

Equation 2-18 states the energy acquired by an electron in moving or "falling" through a potential V. If an electron starts at a point of zero potential and moves to a point of 100 v higher potential, it has acquired an energy of

$$W = 100 \times 1.60 \times 10^{-19} = 1.60 \times 10^{-17} \text{ joule.}$$

It makes no difference in what length of time the passage from A to B occurs, or over what path the electron moves. If a potential difference exists between A and B, the energy received by the electron in moving from A to B is given by Eq. 2-18, since in a conservative field the work integral is independent of the path.

If the initial velocity, v_0, of the electron is zero, the final velocity can be calculated as

$$v = \sqrt{2Ve/m} \qquad \text{m/sec.} \qquad (2\text{-}19)$$

This is the velocity gained by an electron in starting at rest and moving through a potential of V volts.

2-5. Sources of Energy; Current Flow

When a change is made in the velocity of an electron in transit, its kinetic energy is changed and the energy converted must be supplied by, or be delivered to, the external circuit or electrodes. During the movement of an electron in space toward a positive electrode as in Fig. 2-6, the electron is accelerated and increases its kinetic energy. An electron approaching a positive electrode induces a positive charge on that electrode or forces a free electron from the electrode into the external circuit. This effect is felt by the electrons in all the circuit conductors, as the electrons are given a slight movement in the direction of the negative electrode. The movement of this induced charge is an electric current throughout the entire circuit. If the movement

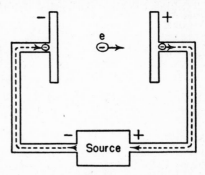

Fig. 2-6. Electron flow in an external circuit by motion of an electron in the space between a pair of electrodes.

is viewed as an electronic current, it is seen that it flows out of the negative source terminal and represents a flow of energy out of the source.

As the electron comes very close to the positive electrode, it has succeeded in forcing a charge redistribution in the external circuit, prepared a place for itself on the positive electrode, and filled the place left on the negative electrode when it migrated therefrom. When the electron strikes the electrode, the forces are neutralized, the system is in electrical balance, and current and energy transfer stop. Even if the electron never reaches the electrode, a current and energy transfer have still taken place.

While the electron is in flight in the field, a current exists in the external circuit and supplies energy to, or takes energy from, the electron.   However, as soon as the electron strikes an electrode, the current ceases.   The amount of this current may be calculated from consideration of the energy transferred.   The change in energy of the electron, which is computed from $m(v^2 - v_0^2)/2$, must be derived from the external circuit.   The source of potential V, Fig. 2-6, has contributed energy of amount $W = Vq$ and this may be equated to the energy gain of the electron or

$$\frac{m(v^2 - v_0^2)}{2} = Vq = V \int_0^t i \, dt. \qquad (2\text{-}20)$$

Taking the time derivative, for the situation indicated in Fig. 2-6, gives

$$mv \frac{dv}{dt} = mav = Vi.$$

Use of Eq. 2-12 allows the current to be written as

$$i = \frac{ev\mathcal{E}}{V}.$$

If the field $\mathcal{E}$ is uniform and due to potential V, then $\mathcal{E} = -V/d$ and

$$i = -\frac{ev}{d} \qquad \text{amp.} \qquad (2\text{-}21)$$

This is the instantaneous current flowing in the external circuit when the electron is under the influence of the field or has a velocity component parallel to the field.   The concept that the electron, on striking the electrode, continues on into the external circuit as a current is obviously untrue when consideration is given to the energies involved.   Figure 2-7 shows a plot of instantaneous current in the external circuit for an electron traveling between two parallel plates separated 1 centimeter, and with a potential difference of 100 volts applied.

Although the above discussion has been in terms of transfer of energy to an electron, it is equally possible to transfer energy from an electron to an external circuit by "shooting" a moving electron into a retarding field, or causing it to approach and be decelerated by a negative electrode.   The induced current is then found to flow in such a direction as to represent energy *into* the external circuit.

In this way certain electronic devices extract energy from beams of moving electrons.

On impact with an electrode, the kinetic energy of the electron is given up and is changed to heat.   If the amount of energy per elec-

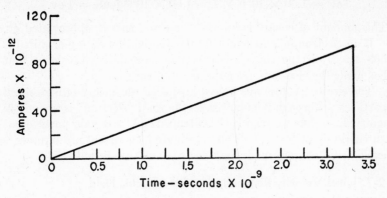

Fig. 2-7.   Instantaneous current value due to an electron traveling 1 cm between two electrodes at 100 v potential difference.

tron is great enough, some of this delivered energy may also appear as electromagnetic radiation or x rays.

A more general situation may be conceived in which there are n charges uniformly distributed in a region, all moving toward a positive electrode with velocity v.   If A is the cross-sectional area of the region,

$$J = \frac{i}{A} = \frac{nqv}{Ad},$$

where J is the current density, usually expressed in amperes per square meter.   It may be noted that nq constitutes the total charge and Ad the volume of charge in the space, so the charge density ρ is

$$\rho = \frac{nq}{Ad}.$$

Thus the current density resulting from movement of a large number of charges through a region is

$$J = \rho v. \tag{2-22}$$

If the charges are electrons the quantity ρ will take on a negative sign.

2-6. The Electron Volt

If an electron travels through a potential rise of one volt, it acquires an energy given by

$$eV = 1.60 \times 10^{-19} \times 1 = 1.60 \times 10^{-19} \text{ joule} = 1 \text{ ev}.$$

This amount of energy is known as an *electron volt*, abbreviated ev.

If an electron falls through 500 v potential, the energy acquired is 500 ev. It is the convenience of this numerical equivalence that has made the electron-volt popular as an energy unit.

The electron volt is much used in stating the energy of high-speed particles. Through popular usage, the word "electron" is frequently omitted, so that we read such statements as "a certain particle has an energy of 10,000 v." This seemingly inconsistent use of units is explained if we remember that electron volts are meant.

2-7. Initial Velocity Perpendicular to the Electric Field

The case of motion of an electron in an electric field at right angles to an initial electron velocity of v_{0x} is important in the cathode-ray tube and in other electron-deflection devices. In order to handle the problem readily, it is customary to treat the vector quantities, force, acceleration, velocity, and so forth, by use of their components along the axes of reference. The resultant motions are then the vector sums of the components.

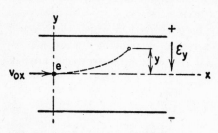

Fig. 2-8. Path of a moving electron in a uniform electric field.

Assume the initial position of the electron to be at the origin, as in Fig. 2-8, that $v_{0y} = v_{0z} = 0$, and that the uniform field has a magnitude $\mathcal{E}_y$. Then

$$a_x = \frac{dv_x}{dt} = 0, \tag{2-23}$$

$$a_y = \frac{dv_y}{dt} = \frac{e\mathcal{E}_y}{m}, \tag{2-24}$$

$$a_z = \frac{dv_z}{dt} = 0. \tag{2-25}$$

From Eq. 2-23 and the initial conditions, it is obvious that $v_x = v_{0x}$, and that there will be no motion in the z direction.

If $\mathcal{E}_y$ is assumed constant with time, then from Eq. 2-24

$$v_y = \frac{e\mathcal{E}_y t}{m}. \tag{2-26}$$

The total velocity v at any time is then the resultant of the component velocities, or

$$v = \sqrt{v_x{}^2 + v_y{}^2}.$$

By integration of Eq. 2-26 and use of the initial conditions $t = 0$, $y = 0$, the y position at any time t is

$$y = \frac{e\mathcal{E}_y t^2}{2m}. \tag{2-27}$$

Since the velocity in the x direction was constant, the distance moved along x is

$$x = v_{0x}t. \tag{2-28}$$

Combining Eqs. 2-27 and 2-28 gives

$$y = \frac{e\mathcal{E}_y}{2mv_{0x}{}^2} x^2, \tag{2-29}$$

which shows that the path of the electron is a parabola in the xy plane.

2-8. Millikan's Measurement of the Electronic Charge

Prior to 1910, attempts were made to determine the magnitude of the charge on the electron, but the results were neither accurate nor consistent. During the years 1910 to 1916, Professor R. A. Millikan, then at the University of Chicago, performed his classic oil-drop experiment and obtained a value of 4.770×10^{-10} electrostatic unit (esu), or 1.590×10^{-19} coulomb per electron. This result was very close to the now accepted value of 4.804×10^{-10} esu, or 1.602×10^{-19} coulomb, which has been obtained and checked by other experimenters using x-ray methods.

The apparatus, shown diagrammatically in Fig. 2-9, consisted of two parallel plates separated by a distance d and connected to a battery through a reversing switch. There was a small hole in the upper plate and, above this, a chamber containing an atomizer for producing an oil spray. After operation of the atomizer, an oil droplet may find its way through the hole into the space between the plates. By illumination with the strong light, the movement of the droplet may be observed and its time of fall between certain of the telescope cross hairs measured with a stop watch. If no potential is placed on the plates, the force acting on the droplet will be

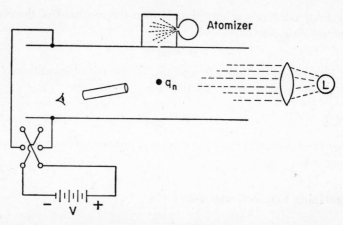

Fig. 2-9.   Apparatus as arranged for the Millikan oil-drop determination of the electronic charge.

that of gravity, which will be proportional to v_d, the downward-measured velocity:

$$\text{force} = f = mg = kv_d. \tag{2-30}$$

During the fall, the droplet may acquire an electric charge from free charges in the air, set up by passing x rays through the space for an instant. By use of the proper polarity of potential the droplet could be made to rise in the field. The net force is then proportional to an upward velocity v_u, and

$$\mathcal{E}q_u - mg = kv_u. \tag{2-31}$$

Solution of these two equations gives for the charge q_u on the droplet

$$q_u = \frac{mg}{\mathcal{E}v_d}\,(v_u + v_d). \tag{2-32}$$

If the experiment is repeated with the same particle and a different value of acquired charge $q_u{}'$, then

$$q_u' = \frac{mg}{\varepsilon v_d} (v_u' + v_d). \tag{2-33}$$

The change in charge is then

$$\Delta q = q_u' - q_u = \frac{mg}{\varepsilon v_d} (v_u' - v_u).$$

After repeating this process for a great many droplets it becomes apparent that the values of Δq are always integral multiples of some smaller number, and that none of the values of Δq are ever smaller than this number; that is

$$\Delta q = ne. \tag{2-34}$$

The least common multiple of all the ne's is obviously the value of e, the smallest indivisible unit of electricity, or the charge on the electron.

Millikan obtained the value of the mass m of the droplets from Stokes's law of motion in a viscous medium, after proving this law to be correct. For small spherical droplets falling freely in space, Stokes's law gives for the radius

$$r = \sqrt{\frac{9\eta v_d}{2g\delta}} \qquad \text{m,}$$

where η is the viscosity of the medium and δ is the density of the liquid of the drop. The mass of the droplet is then

$$m = \frac{4}{3}\pi r^3 \delta \qquad \text{kg.}$$

2-9. Electron in a Magnetic Field

The force on a current element of length ds in a magnetic field, having a current value i and oriented as in Fig. 2-10, is

$$f_m = Bi \, ds \sin \theta \qquad \text{newtons;} \tag{2-35}$$

and since current is rate of movement of charge through ds,

$$f_m = B\frac{dq}{dt} ds \sin \theta = B \, dq \frac{ds}{dt} \sin \theta.$$

Certainly the electronic charge e is an elemental charge and may be considered as dq, in which case ds/dt is the velocity of movement of this charge, and

$$f_m = Bev \sin \theta \qquad \text{newtons.} \tag{2-36}$$

This is the force on an electron moving with velocity v meters per second in a magnetic field of strength B webers per square meter,

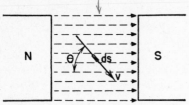

Fig. 2-10. Force on a moving electron in a magnetic field of density B and indicated direction.

where θ has meaning as the angle between the direction of ds or of the velocity of the electron, and the magnetic flux lines.

The force f_m is at right angles to the plane containing B and v, and for electrons is in the direction of movement of a right-hand screw rotated from B to v. An electron moving in the direction indicated in Fig. 2-10 will be acted upon by a force perpendicular to and into the paper.

Since this force is always perpendicular to the motion and velocity, *no work can be done on the electron by the magnetic field,* and its velocity remains unchanged except in direction. If v and B are constant, f_m is constant and will produce a constant acceleration at right angles to the velocity. A motion of this sort must be circular, and the force f_m is a centripetal force. The path is as shown in Fig. 2-11.

For the case of Fig. 2-10 the velocity component in the plane normal to the magnetic field is $v \sin \theta$. Equating the centrifugal force to the centripetal force gives

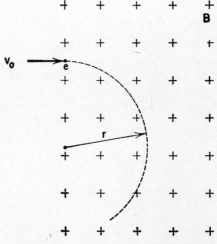

Fig. 2-11. Path of an electron moving in the plane of the page and in a magnetic field of density B directed into the page.

$$\frac{m(v \sin \theta)^2}{r} = Bev \sin \theta.$$

Solving, the radius of the circular path is found to be

$$r = \frac{mv \sin \theta}{eB} \qquad \text{m.} \qquad (2\text{-}37)$$

The peripheral velocity of the circle, $v \sin \theta$, is unchanged by the magnetic field. The angular velocity then is

$$\omega = \frac{v \sin \theta}{r} = \frac{eB}{m}. \qquad (2\text{-}38)$$

The time T for one revolution is given by

$$T = \frac{2\pi}{\omega} = \frac{2\pi m}{eB}. \qquad \text{sec.} \qquad (2\text{-}39)$$

It is interesting that this expression for the time of one revolution is independent of the peripheral velocity, being dependent only on B. This is so because the radius increases directly with peripheral velocity, a high-velocity electron traveling around a circle of large radius and taking the same time for the circuit as a low-velocity electron traveling around a circular path of small radius.

2-10. Thomson's Measurement of e/m

The factor e/m has appeared frequently in the equations of electronic motion. This ratio of charge to mass, having for the electron the value 1.76×10^{11} coulombs per kilogram, is of importance in work with all charged particles. Sir J. J. Thomson, in 1897, using an evacuated tube such as is shown in Fig. 2-12, proved that the ratio

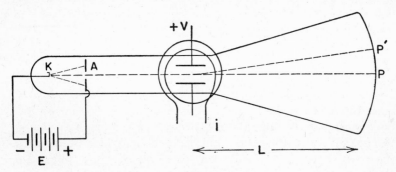

Fig. 2-12.   Demonstration of the Thomson method of measurement of e/m.

e/m is the same for all the particles or electrons in the so-called *cathode rays*. A beam of electrons is obtained in the tube by the acceleration of electrons leaving a cathode K by means of a positive potential on an anode A. In the center of the anode is a small hole, and some of the electrons pass through this hole to form a small pencil, or beam, of electrons. With no electric or magnetic fields applied, these electrons pass straight on to the fluorescent screen, where their impact at P is indicated by light given off by the material of the screen.

If a potential difference V is given to the deflection plates indicated, a field of magnitude $\mathcal{E} = -V/d$ is set up, and a force

$$f = e\mathcal{E}$$

deflects the beam of electrons upward to a new spot P' on the screen.

A magnetic field of strength B is now applied by coils mounted on each side of the tube and connected so as to produce a downward deflection of the electron beam. This gives a downward force f_m on the electrons of

$$f_m = Bev = \frac{mv^2}{r}, \tag{2-40}$$

since θ is 90°. If the strength of the field is adjusted so that the beam of electrons returns to the initial spot P, the two forces must be equal, and

$$e\mathcal{E} = Bev$$

or
$$v = \frac{\mathcal{E}}{B}, \tag{2-41}$$

allowing the determination of the velocity of the beam.

Use of Eq. 2-41 in Eq. 2-40 gives for the e/m ratio

$$\frac{e}{m} = \frac{\mathcal{E}}{rB^2}. \tag{2-42}$$

Since the radius of the magnetic deflection can be determined from the geometry of the tube, Eq. 2-42 allows computation of the charge to mass ratio of the electron; other particles may likewise be measured.

2-11. The Mass Spectrograph

If all of a group of charged particles are accelerated to a velocity v_0 by passing through a potential difference V, and then are passed through a small hole into a region containing a magnetic field perpendicular to v_0, they will be deflected into circular paths.   By Eq. 2-37 the radii of the circles are inversely proportional to the charge-to-mass ratio, so that if all particles are equally charged, the heaviest ones will have the greatest radii.

By placing a photographic plate, which will be exposed by bombardment of charged particles, as in Fig. 2-13, the radii of the paths and the masses of the particles can be measured.   Placement of collector electrodes at the points at which particles of certain mass are expected to strike allows the number of each type of particle to be measured by readings of microammeters in circuit with the collector plates.

Certain of the elements consist of mixtures of atoms differing slightly in mass.   For instance, neon, of atomic weight 20.07, is actually a mixture of 92.2 per cent atoms of atomic weight 20, 7.6 per cent atoms of weight 21, and 0.2 per cent of weight 22.   Atoms that are identical in number of electrons but

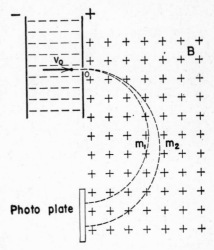

Fig. 2-13.   The principle of the mass spectrograph.

differ in mass by reason of additional neutrons in the nucleus are called *isotopes*.

By the addition of a bombardment chamber for charging the atoms, a mass spectrograph can be used for rapid chemical analysis and for the separation of isotopes.

2-12. Parallel Electric and Magnetic Fields—Focusing

An electron with velocity v_0 is projected into parallel electric and magnetic fields, of magnitudes ε and B, each directed as shown in Fig. 2-14.   The velocity v_0 makes an angle θ with respect to the alignment of the fields, as defined by the figure.

The initial component of velocity parallel to the fields is $v_0 \cos \theta$, that normal to the fields is $v_0 \sin \theta$.   Due to the two fields, the forces acting are

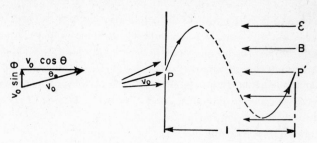

Fig. 2-14. Path of a moving electron in parallel electric and magnetic fields, showing focusing of the beam at P'.

$$f_e = e\mathcal{E}, \qquad (2\text{-}43)$$

$$f_m = Bev_0 \sin \theta. \qquad (2\text{-}44)$$

In view of the x-directed initial velocity component, Eq. 2-43 leads to

$$v_x = \frac{e\mathcal{E}}{m} t + v_0 \cos \theta$$

for the x-directed velocity, as affected by the electric field. Further integration gives

$$x = \frac{e\mathcal{E}t^2}{2m} + v_0 t \cos \theta \qquad (2\text{-}45)$$

if P is considered at the origin of the x coordinate.

The magnetic force leads to circular motion in a plane perpendicular to the magnetic field. The resultant of the two motions is a helix of variable pitch of radius

$$r = \frac{mv_0 \sin \theta}{eB}.$$

If the field $\mathcal{E} = 0$, the path is a helix of constant pitch.

In the time T taken to complete one revolution, the electron will also have moved longitudinally a distance l parallel to the field to P', owing to v_x. Since the time of a revolution, from Eq. 2-39, is $T = 2\pi m/Be$, the distance traveled during the first revolution is

$$l = \frac{2\pi m}{Be} \left(\frac{\pi \mathcal{E}}{B} + v_0 \cos \theta \right) \qquad (2\text{-}46)$$

from Eq. 2-45.

If all electrons reaching the point P have equal initial velocity v_0, and if θ is small so that $\cos \theta \cong 1$, the distance l will be the same for all electrons. If point P is considered as being a small area over which the electrons are scattered in arriving, then at P' there will be an exactly equivalent area, or image of P. This method is capable of focusing at P' a bundle of electrons arriving at P with dissimilar directions, provided that all electrons with θ large are removed by a diaphragm, as shown in Fig. 2-14. The method is used for magnetically focusing a beam of electrons in the cathode-ray tube.

2-13. Perpendicular Electric and Magnetic Fields

Assume a set of perpendicular fields, as shown in Fig. 2-15, and an electron released at $y = 0$, with a y-directed velocity only, equal to v_{0y}. The forces acting on the electron may be set down as

$$f_x = e\mathcal{E} - Bev_y = m\frac{dv_x}{dt}, \quad (2\text{-}47)$$

$$f_y = Bev_x = m\frac{dv_y}{dt}, \quad (2\text{-}48)$$

$$f_z = 0, \quad (2\text{-}49)$$

where $\mathcal{E}$ is the magnitude of the indicated electric field.

Owing to the initial velocity, or to the electric field, the electron will have a translational motion. Translation in a magnetic field causes the electron to rotate in a circular path in a plane normal to

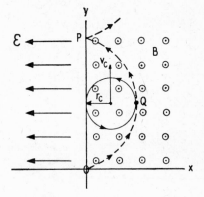

Fig. 2-15. Path of a moving electron in perpendicular electric and magnetic fields.

the magnetic field. The fact that $f_z = 0$ also indicates that the motion is confined to the xy plane. The path of the electron will be a combination of translation and rotation in a plane, and thus is cycloidal.

Differentiation of Eq. 2-47 and substitution in Eq. 2-48 gives

$$\frac{d^2 v_x}{dt^2} = -\frac{B^2 e^2}{m^2}\, v_x.$$

The solution of this differential equation can be found, under the condition that $v_x = 0$ at $t = 0$, as

$$v_x = \left(\frac{\mathcal{E}}{B} - v_{0y} \right) \sin \frac{Be}{m} t. \tag{2-50}$$

Use of this value in Eq. 2-47 gives

$$v_y = \frac{\mathcal{E}}{B} \left[1 - \left(1 - \frac{B}{\mathcal{E}} v_{0y} \right) \cos \frac{Be}{m} t \right]. \tag{2-51}$$

Under the condition that $y = 0$ at $t = 0$,

$$y = \frac{m\mathcal{E}}{B^2 e} \left[\frac{Be}{m} t - \left(1 - \frac{B}{\mathcal{E}} v_{0y} \right) \sin \frac{Be}{m} t \right]. \tag{2-52}$$

The location of the release point of the electron on the x axis is arbi-

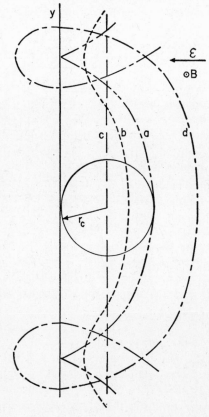

Fig. 2-16. Variations in the form of the cycloidal path.

trary, but if it be so located that at $t = 0$, $x = mv_{0y}/Be$, a desirable form of the equation for x is obtained as

$$x = \frac{m\mathcal{E}}{B^2 e}\left[1 - \left(1 - \frac{B}{\mathcal{E}}v_{0y}\right)\cos\frac{Be}{m}t\right]. \qquad (2\text{-}53)$$

Equations 2-52 and 2-53 may be recognized as the parametric equations of a cycloid of the form

$$x = r_c - r_a \cos\theta,$$
$$y = r_c\theta - r_a \sin\theta,$$

where r_c is the radius of the rolling wheel and r_a is the radius of the generating point on a spoke of the wheel. That is,

$$r_c = \frac{m\mathcal{E}}{B^2 e}, \qquad (2\text{-}54)$$

$$r_a = r_c\left(1 - \frac{B}{\mathcal{E}}v_{0y}\right). \qquad (2\text{-}55)$$

In view of the form of this last equation for the radius at the generating point, a number of interesting cases arise and are illustrated in Fig. 2-16 as follows:

1. $v_{0y} = 0$; then $r_c = r_a$, and the path of the electron is a common cycloid (a).

2. $v_{0y} < \mathcal{E}/B$, then $r_c > r_a$, and the path is that of a prolate cycloid (b).

3. $v_{0y} = \mathcal{E}/B$; then $r_a = 0$, and the path is a straight line (c).

4. $\mathcal{E}/B < v_{0y} < 2\mathcal{E}/B$, and the path is prolate but shifted by π from that of Case 2.

5. $v_{0y} > 2\mathcal{E}/B$, and the path is curtate as in (d).

Case 3 is of particular interest, since the forces due to the electric and magnetic fields are then exactly balanced. All the cases illustrate the variety of trajectories available to designers of electronic devices.

2-14. The Magnetron

A magnetic field may be combined with a radial electric field to result in the *magnetron*, originally developed by Dr. A. W. Hull. A cylindrical metal tube A has a source of electrons K axially positioned at the center, as in Fig. 2-17. Anode A is made positive with respect to K, and a magnetic field acts longitudinally as indicated.

Two accelerations will then act on an electron leaving the source
K. One, due to the radial electric field between K and A, will be
radially directed and produce a velocity v_r.
Due to the radial velocity, the magnetic field
will produce an acceleration at right angles
to v_r, and thus a tangential acceleration and
velocity will appear. These two mutually
perpendicular components will describe the
motion of the electron at any radius r, as
shown in Fig. 2-17.

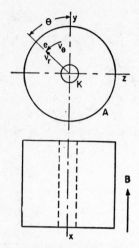

The total energy of the electron at radius r
can be computed and will be due wholly to
the radial electric field $\mathcal{E}_r$, since no work can
be done on the electron by the magnetic
field. The energy relations then are

$$\frac{m}{2}\,(v_r{}^2 + r^2\omega_\theta{}^2) = -\int_k^r e\mathcal{E}_r\,dr, \quad (2\text{-}56)$$

Fig. 2-17. Anode and
cathode arrangement of
a basic magnetron.

where r_k is the radius of the source K. In
polar coordinates it can be shown that the
magnetic field force is

$$f_\theta = ma_\theta = \frac{m}{r}\frac{d}{dt}\left(r^2\frac{d\theta}{dt}\right) = Bev_r = Be\frac{dr}{dt}.$$

Multiplying by $r\,dt$, integrating and evaluating the constant at
$r = r_k$, since $d\theta/dt = 0$ at the source surface or the electrons are
assumed as emitted normally,

$$\frac{d\theta}{dt} = \omega_\theta = \frac{Be}{2m}\left(1 - \frac{r_k{}^2}{r^2}\right), \quad (2\text{-}57)$$

and the energy expression becomes

$$\frac{m}{2}\left[v_r{}^2 + \frac{r^2B^2e^2}{4m^2}\left(1 - \frac{r_k{}^2}{r^2}\right)^2\right] = -e\int_{r_k}^r \mathcal{E}_r\,dr. \quad (2\text{-}58)$$

The right-side integral appears as V_{kr}, the potential between cathode
and r. Consequently,

$$v_r = \sqrt{\frac{2eV_{kr}}{m} - \frac{r^2B^2e^2}{4m^2}\left(1 - \frac{r_k{}^2}{r^2}\right)^2}. \quad (2\text{-}59)$$

It can be seen that some value of r may be found at which $v_r = 0$,
and at that distance the electron moves tangentially only. If this

critical value of r is less than the radius of A, no electrons reach A. For small B, a path such as (1) in Fig. 2-18 is taken, and the electron strikes the cylinder; for some larger B, the path just grazes A; and for stronger fields the path becomes that of (2).

If the potential $V_{kr} = V_A$, the anode-source potential at which grazing just occurs for $r = r_A$ can then be determined by setting $v_r = 0$ in Eq. 2-59. The result is

$$V_A = \frac{r_A{}^2 B^2 e}{8m} \left(1 - \frac{r_k{}^2}{r_A{}^2} \right)^2. \tag{2-60}$$

In many cases r_k is small with respect to r_A, and their ratio may be neglected with respect to unity.

In practice potential V_A is varied, with a fixed value of B. For

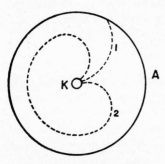

voltages less than critical the electron paths will be as at (2), Fig. 2-18, and at any instant there will be as many electrons with radial velocity components directed away from the anode as there are with radial velocity components toward the anode, and there will be no current in the anode circuit. For voltages above the critical value electrons will follow paths of the nature of (1), and current will exist in the anode circuit.

Fig. 2-18.   Possible electron paths in the magnetron.

Magnetron high-frequency generators employ this principle in the production of signals for radar and other applications.

2-15. Velocity Modulation of an Electron Beam

An important class of electron tubes for use at very high frequencies employs a principle known as *velocity modulation*. The electrons of a beam are given velocities varying in cyclic fashion and then are permitted sufficient time in transit between electrodes for the higher-velocity electrons to catch up with the preceding slower group, or to form bunches. These bunches of electrons induce currents when passing an output electrode, each bunch of electrons contributing a cycle of current. A tube designed for this purpose might have an internal construction, as in Fig. 2-19, with a beam of electrons from a heated cathode passing through holes in electrodes G_1 and G_2 into a drift space of length L, relatively free of electric fields.   The beam then passes through electrodes G_3 and G_4 to reach

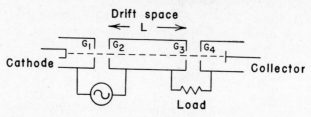

Fig. 2-19.   Electrode configuration in a velocity-modulated tube.

a positive collector.   The repulsion effects between the electrons in the beam are neglected in this analysis, as explained in Section 2-2.

Electrons in the beam are given a small velocity variation

$$v = v_0(1 - \alpha \sin \omega t)$$

as they leave electrode G_2, by a cyclic voltage applied between electrodes G_1 and G_2.   If the current passing through G_2 is i_1, the charge passing into the drift space in an increment of time dt is $i_1\, dt$.   Since there can be no accumulation of charge within the drift region, this charge must pass out through electrode G_3 at some later increment of time $d(t + \Delta t)$, where Δt is the time of transit through the drift space.   If the outward current through G_3 is called i_2, then

$$i_1\, dt = i_2\, d(t + \Delta t). \tag{2-61}$$

The time of transit through the drift space can then be obtained from the distance L and velocity v as

$$\Delta t = \frac{L}{v} = \frac{L}{v_0(1 + \alpha \sin \omega t)}.$$

If $\alpha \ll 1$, then by the approximation that

$$\frac{1}{1 \pm \alpha \sin \omega t} \cong 1 \mp \alpha \sin \omega t, \tag{2-62}$$

the expression for Δt becomes

$$\Delta t \cong \frac{L}{v_0} (1 - \alpha \sin \omega t).$$

Rewriting Eq. 2-61 as

$$i_1 = i_2 \frac{d(t + \Delta t)}{dt}$$

and taking the indicated derivative gives

$$i_1 \cong i_2 \left(1 - \frac{L\alpha\omega}{v_0} \cos \omega t \right).$$

The outgoing current i_2 then is

$$i_2 \cong \frac{i_1}{1 - \dfrac{L\alpha\omega}{v_0} \cos \omega t},$$

and if the tube is designed so that $(L\alpha\omega/v_0) \ll 1$, the approximation of Eq. 2-61 may be used once more, and

$$i_2 \cong i_1 \left(1 + \frac{L\alpha\omega}{v_0} \cos \omega t \right), \qquad (2-63)$$

which shows that an input variation of velocity has become a current variation in the electron beam as it passes electrodes G_3 and G_4 at the end of the drift space. Currents induced in these electrodes by the electron beam can be made to flow in an external resonant output or load circuit; and if a voltage proportional to the output-current variation is then fed back to electrodes G_1 and G_2 in the proper phase, the output circuit can be made to produce the original

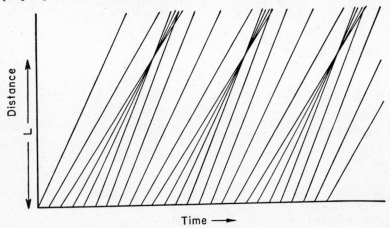

Fig. 2-20.   Distance-time diagram of electrons in the drift space.

input-velocity variation, and the device becomes an oscillator.   The *klystron* is one device operating by this principle.

Operation of the *drift space* in bunching of the electrons may be better understood through an analogy.   If several automobiles are started from a point at one-minute intervals, with velocities of successive cars having a sinusoidal variation as 40, 47, 50, 47, 40, 33, 30, 33, 40 miles per hour, and this cycle is repeated, then at some point down the road, traffic jams will develop or the cars will pass in bunches.   In Fig. 2-20, a time-vs-distance line may be considered as drawn for each car, the slope representing velocity.   It can be seen that at a distance *L*, cars in bunches of four are passing at intervals, with a few other cars widely scattered.   This is analogous to the electron-beam bunching in velocity modulation.

2-16. Mapping of Nonuniform Fields

Many types of fields actually encountered in engineering applications are not so simple as the electric field between a parallel pair of plates or as a magnetic field of parallel flux lines.   In complex fields, graphical plotting of the path taken by the electron is almost the only recourse, and even this cannot be undertaken until a map of the field flux configuration is available.

Such a map may be made by a graphical flux-plotting method, or the properties of electrolytic conduction in a model tank may be employed.

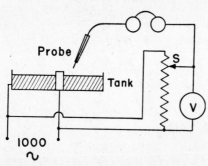

In the latter method (Ref. 5), the analogy between electric flux and current flow is utilized to obtain the configuration of the equipotential lines.   Since most electrode arrangements have an axis of symmetry, a cross section taken along this axis will yield a picture representative of the

Fig. 2-21.   Apparatus for tracing equipotential lines in the electrolytic tank.

whole.   The electrodes in this cross section are made of metal and are mounted on the bottom of a nonconducting tray upon which have been marked coordinate lines.   The tray should be filled shallowly with water.   By use of a potentiometer circuit such as is shown in

Fig. 2-21, the position of as many equipotentials as are desired may be traced out and plotted on a sheet of coordinate paper.

In still another arrangement, a double stylus is used; and by keeping the tone heard in the headphones connected between the styluses at a minimum and moving always perpendicular to the plane of the styluses, a flux line may be drawn directly.

After a field map is obtained, the paths of the electrons may be plotted if it is remembered that the electron receives a component of acceleration along the flux lines toward the plus electrode; if it has a velocity, it still is accelerated in the direction of the flux lines, with the actual path determined by the resultant of its component velocities.

A method for obtaining directly the paths followed by the electrons in electric fields depends on the analogy between the acceleration of gravity and the acceleration experienced by an electron in an electric field. A wooden model of the electrodes is made, with the height of each electrode above the base proportional to the negative value of its potential. A sheet of thin surgical rubber is then stretched tightly over the model, so that the rubber is in contact with all the electrodes. A marble rolling under gravity will then follow a path that would likewise be taken by an electron under the action of the fields. By starting the marbles at various points, the experimenter can study the behavior of different electrons. If a record is required, the paths taken by the marbles can be photographed by a moving-picture camera suspended vertically above the model.

2-17. Effect of the Relativistic Change in Mass

Newton's second law states that

$$f = \frac{d(mv)}{dt}.$$

If mass is given the possibility of varying as a function of velocity,

$$f = m\frac{dv}{dt} + v\frac{dm}{dv}\frac{dv}{dt}. \tag{2-64}$$

If mass is not a function of velocity, the right-hand term drops out, leaving the familiar form $f = ma$.

The theory of relativity requires, and it has been experimentally proved, that the masses of all bodies vary with velocity.   The actual mass of a moving body can be expressed as

$$m = \frac{m_0}{\sqrt{1 - v^2/c^2}}, \qquad (2\text{-}65)$$

where m_0 is the so-called *rest mass*, or mass at zero velocity; v is the velocity of motion; and c is the velocity of light, or 3×10^8 m/sec. This result shows that the mass is not much different from the rest mass until the velocity becomes appreciable with respect to that of light.   The difference is less than 1 per cent for electrons that have energies of less than 2500 ev.   Figure 2-22 is a plot of m/m_0, or the value of $1/\sqrt{1 - v^2/c^2}$, for various values of energy of an electron.

Applying Eq. 2-65 to the expression for force in Eq. 2-64 and taking dm/dv as required, Eq. 2-64 becomes

$$f = \frac{m_0}{(1 - v^2/c^2)^{3/2}} \frac{dv}{dt}. \qquad (2\text{-}66)$$

The energy relations give

$$W = Ve = \int_0^t f \, ds = \int_0^t fv \, dt = \int_0^v \frac{m_0 v}{(1 - v^2/c^2)^{3/2}} \, dv$$

$$= m_0 c^2 \left(\frac{1}{\sqrt{1 - v^2/c^2}} - 1 \right). \qquad (2\text{-}67)$$

Solving for the velocity,

$$v = c\sqrt{1 - \frac{1}{(Ve/m_0 c^2 + 1)^2}}. \qquad (2\text{-}68)$$

This equation permits the calculation of the actual velocity reached when the electron falls through a potential V.

The importance of the variation of m lies in the fact that the velocity of light becomes limiting for all bodies and can never be exceeded, since the mass becomes infinite at that velocity.   Electrons have been accelerated to velocities above 99.9 per cent of the velocity of light; the energy of an electron at such a velocity is above 100,000,000 ev.

In most engineering applications the voltages are low and the variation of m may be neglected.   Exceptions to this situation may arise in high-voltage cathode-ray tubes, x-ray tubes, and particle accelerators.   Figure 2-22 allows an estimation of any error intro-

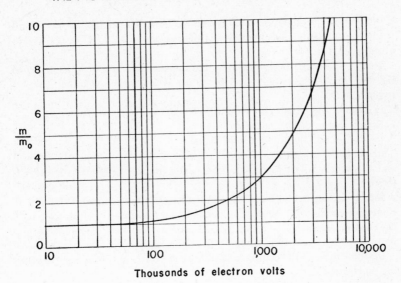

Fig. 2-22.   Relativistic variation of mass with velocity; or for the electron, the mass variation produced at a given energy.

duced.   Unless otherwise stated, relativistic variation of mass will be neglected in this text.

PROBLEMS

2-1. If unit atomic weight represents 1.65×10^{-27} kg, calculate the velocity reached by the following after acceleration by a potential of 250 v.

(a) Electron.

(b) Singly charged hydrogen ion.

(c) Singly charged mercury ion.

2-2. A singly ionized, positive Hg atom is traveling horizontally between a pair of electrodes separated 1 cm. If Hg has an atomic weight of 200, find the potential which must be applied between the parallel electrodes to overcome the gravitational forces on the ion. Is the neglect of gravity justified in ballistics problems concerning electrons and ions?

2-3. Two large parallel metal plates are horizontal and are separated a distance of 2 cm, with the upper plate being 500 v positive with respect to the lower plate. An electron with zero initial velocity is released at the center of the lower plate.

(a) What will be the velocity of the electron upon striking the upper plate?

(b) Calculate the length of time consumed by the electron in flight.

(c) How much energy is conveyed to the upper electrode?

(d) Repeat, if the initial velocity of the electron is 0.5×10^7 m per second upward.

2-4. In the preceding problem at the instant the electron is 1 cm above the lower plate, the potential on the plates is reversed in sign and changed to 300 v.

(a) Determine which electrode will be reached by the electron.

(b) Find the velocity of arrival.

(c) Determine the total time of flight.

(d) Calculate the energy of the electron at the instant of potential reversal and the energy given to the electrode upon impact. Account for the difference.

2-5. Referring to (c), Fig. 2-23, an electron of initial energy of 50 ev enters the region as shown. An applied potential on the plates is such as to cause the electron to reach a point on the dot-dash line and 1 cm above the bottom plate. At this instant the applied potential is reversed and doubled in value.

(a) Plot to scale the complete path of the electron up to the time of striking an electrode.

(b) Specify the point on an electrode at which the electron finally strikes.

(c) Find the energy delivered to the electrode when the electron strikes.

2-6. An electron with 1 ev initial energy leaves the negative plate [(a), Fig. 2-23]; passes through a small hole in a parallel electrode at +100 v and distance 2 cm, and strikes a second parallel electrode at +300 v and distance 4 cm from the starting point.

(a) Find the time of transit to the second electrode.

(b) Repeat if the initial energy is zero.

Assume that the small hole has no effect on the distribution of the electric field.

2-7. (a) Considering the electron of Problem 2-6, plot curves of current flow in the external circuits of both electrodes as a function of the time of flight.

(b) Find the net energy contributed by the +100 v electrode during the flight of the electron.

(c) How much kinetic energy is dissipated as heat on the second electrode?

2-8. An electron with initial velocity due to 50 ev, and directed upward and perpendicular to the plates, enters the field [(b), Fig. 2-23].

(a) After how much time will the electron return to the + plate?

(b) How far does the electron travel upward?

(c) How much energy, in joules, is delivered to the plate by the return of the electron?

(d) Plot a curve of current flow in the external electrode circuit vs the time of flight of the electron.

(e) How much initial energy must the electron be given to enable it to reach the upper plate?

2-9. The d-c potential of (b), Fig. 2-23 is replaced with a potential of 10 v maximum, at 10^6 cycles. If the electron is released from the lower plate at the time the potential is zero and with the top plate going positive, find the position at any subsequent time t. The initial velocity v_0 is due to an energy of 2 ev.

2-10. An electron with energy of 100 ev enters an electric field at an angle of 45 deg to the plate [(c), Fig. 2-23].

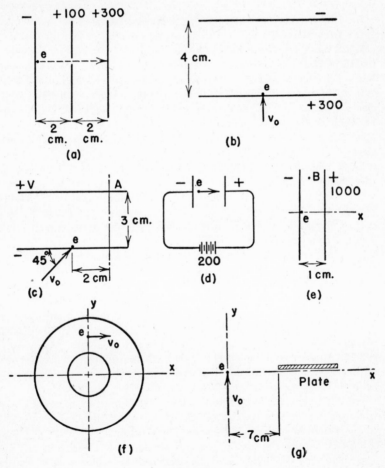

Fig. 2-23.

(a) What value of potential V will be required between the plates to make the electron hit the point A on the upper plate?

(b) How much energy will be delivered to the plate by the electron?

(c) If the potential V were furnished by a battery, find the average value of current flow from this battery during the flight of the electron.

2-11. An electron of 300 ev energy enters a magnetic field at the origin of axes.   If its initial velocity is directed along the Y axis:

(a) Find the flux density in webers per square meter and the direction of the magnetic field required to make the electron reach the point $x = 3$ cm, $y = 0, z = 0$.

(b) How long a time does it take for the electron to reach the above point?

(c) Draw the path of the electron on a set of axes.

2-12. What transverse magnetic flux density is required to act over a length of 15 cm of a horizontal electron beam to cause a vertical upward beam deflection of 2.0 cm?   The energy of the beam is 1000 v.

2-13. In copper, it is usually assumed that there is one conduction, or free electron per atom.   It has been established that there are 5×10^{22} atoms per cubic centimeter of copper.   If a piece of No. 14 B&S copper wire supplies current to a 100-w, 115-v lamp, find the average drift velocity of the electrons in the wire.

2-14. The circuit [(d), Fig. 2-23] is connected by the No. 14 B&S copper wire of Problem 2-13.   Assume that the electron had zero initial velocity.

(a) For the instant just before the electron strikes the positive plate, find its velocity.   The distance between plates is 1 cm.

(b) Compute the value of current flowing in the external circuit at the instant taken in (a).

(c) Find the drift velocity of the electrons in the copper wire at this instant and compare this value with the answer for part (a).   Explain the difference.

(d) Show that the rate of energy output by the battery at this instant is equal to the rate of increase of energy by the electron.

2-15. Plot curves of current flowing in the battery, energy output of the battery, and energy input to the electron, all against time, for the circuit of (d), Fig. 2-23, and conditions of Problem 2-14.

2-16. An electron at time $t = 0$ is released from the left-hand plate with zero velocity.   It is acted upon by the electric field and by a uniform magnetic field B perpendicular and out of the paper [(e), Fig. 2-23].

(a) What value of flux density B will be required just to prevent the electron from reaching the positive plate?

(b) Sketch the path of the electron.

2-17. A certain tube has two concentric cylinders [(f), Fig. 2-23] of 2 and 4 cm diameter.   A voltage is applied between the cylinders such that the inner cylinder is positive.   An electron is released with initial velocity in the x direction of 7×10^6 m/sec at a point P having coordinates $x = 0$, $y = 1.5$ cm as shown.

(a) What value of field intensity $\mathcal{E}$ is required at P to cause the electron to return to the same point after making the circuit?

(b) How long does it take the electron to make one circuit?

(c) What direction and density of magnetic flux would be required to replace the electric field $\mathcal{E}$ and still retain the same electron path?

2-18. A magnetic field of density 0.2 webers per sq. m. acts perpendicular and into the page in (b), Fig. 2-23. Initial electron energy is due to 200 ev.

(a) Plot the path of flight of the electron.

(b) How much time is consumed in the flight?

(c) State the energy delivered to the electrode upon impact.

2-19. An electron with 50 ev energy enters at $t = 0$ the field between two parallel electrodes at an angle of 30° to the lower plate. The plates are separated 1.0 cm, and the potential between the plates varies as $e = 100\epsilon^{0.5 \times 10^9 t}$, with the upper plate positive.

(a) Find the time taken by the electron in reaching the upper plate.

(b) Compute the velocity and energy upon arrival at the upper plate.

2-20. A mass spectrograph has a photographic plate set as shown in (g), Fig. 2-23. If positively charged particles of 500 ev energy are used, and the magnetic field has a density of 0.01 weber/sq m directed out of the paper, find the mass of particles which produced darkening of the photographic plate at a distance 1.25 cm from the left edge of the plate. Also, find the mass for the particles that produced a spot at 2.65 cm from the plate edge.

2-21. A certain electron beam has a length of 18 cm, and the energy of the electrons is due to having been accelerated by 500 v before entering the beam. A magnetic field of 10^{-4} webers per sq. m. (1 line per sq cm) acts normal to the electron beam along the whole of its length. Find the angle through which the beam is deflected.

2-22. In (c), Fig. 2-23, the potential V is zero. If v_0 is 5×10^7 m per sec, find the direction and flux density of a magnetic field which will force the electron to reach point A.

(a) Find the time of transit.

(b) What energy is delivered to the upper electrode upon impact?

(c) Find the direction and magnitude of the magnetic flux density which will return the electron to its starting point in 2×10^{-9} sec.

2-23. The potential across a certain x-ray tube is 150,000 v.

(a) If an electron starts from rest on the negative electrode, what will be its velocity on arrival at the anode?

(b) What is the mass of an electron when it strikes the positive electrode?

(c) If the total electron current through the tube is one ma, find the power delivered to the tube anode.

Use relativistic mass corrections.

2-24. The voltage V on the electrodes of (c), Fig. 2-23, is zero, but acting parallel to the electrodes is a uniform magnetic field of 300 gauss. If v_0 is due to 50 v, find the pitch and diameter of the helical electron path.

REFERENCES

1. Crowther, J. A., *Ions, Electrons and Ionizing Radiations*, 7th ed., Longmans, Green & Co., New York, 1939.
2. Lawrence, E. O., and Livingstone, M. S., "The Production of High-Speed Light Ions Without the Use of High Voltages," *Phys. Rev.*, **40**, 19 (1932).
3. Millikan, R. A., *The Electron*, University of Chicago Press, Chicago, 1917.
4. Page, L., and Adams, N. I., *Principles of Electricity*, D. Van Nostrand Company, Inc., New York, 1931.
5. McArthur, E. D., "Determining Field Distribution by Electronic Methods," *Electronics*, **4**, 192, Feb. (1932).
6. Hipple, J. A., *et al.*, "Electronics of the Mass Spectrometer," *Elec. Eng.*, **64**, 141 (1945).
7. Boast, W. B., *Principles of Electric and Magnetic Fields*, Harper & Brothers, New York, 1949.

CHAPTER 3

THE CATHODE-RAY TUBE

The cathode-ray tube is an important application of the ballistic principles of Chapter 2. It is the modern counterpart of the Crookes tube of 1879 in which the electron first made its presence known by a visible effect, by use of which x rays were discovered, and in which J. J. Thomson first measured the e/m ratio of the electron. The cathode-ray tube is now extensively used as a laboratory and production tool to investigate and visualize electric-circuit phenomena, and as a viewing device for the reception of television images and radar signals.

3-1. Focusing of Electron Beams

In an electric field, the electrons tend to accelerate along the flux lines or to move parallel and opposite to the field, since this is the direction of the force acting on them. If a configuration of electrodes is set up as in Fig. 3-1(a) and voltages are applied, the field will appear as sketched. Electrons, shot through a small hole at A with small angles of dispersion, will, on first entering the field between the cylinders, be given a small inward-directed force. Upon emerging through the curved field on the far side of the lens section, the electrons will be given a small outward-directed force due to the opposite curvature of the flux lines. However, in passing through the field the electron has been accelerated, the initial inward force acts on the electron for a longer time than the final outward force, and the net result is an inward component of velocity which will cause the electrons to emerge in a bundle at B, with final convergence of their paths at the screen C.

By variation of the potential V, the curvature of the flux lines can be shifted and the distance to the point of convergence, or focus C, altered. This is equivalent to the action of a convex lens in bring-

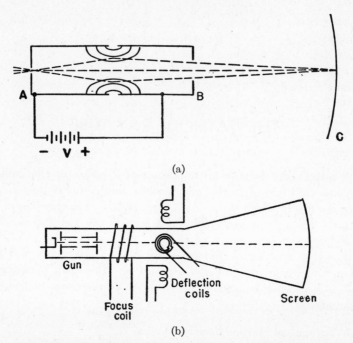

(a)

(b)

Fig. 3-1. (a) Electric field focusing of an electron beam. *A* and *B* are cross sections of a set of cylinders. (b) Magnetic focusing and deflection.

ing to a focus the light from a source. Since simple optical lenses are not well corrected near the edges, it is customary, by introduction of a diaphragm into the light path, to use light passing only through the central portion of the lens. The electron lens is also not perfect near the edges, and a diaphragm is placed at point *B* to cut off all wide-angle electrons. Designing an electron lens of this nature is more difficult than designing an optical lens because the paths of the electrons are curves, whereas light travels in straight lines.

In such work in electron optics, it becomes desirable to think of an electron as having wave properties and wavelength instead of as being a corpuscle. This wavelength has been found to be related to the velocity of the electron by

$$\lambda = \frac{h}{mv},$$

where h is Planck's constant. The higher the velocity, the shorter the wavelength. The range of wavelengths at usual velocities falls below that of visible light and into the x-ray region.

In optical systems, lens corrections are required to prevent chromatic aberration if the light rays do not all have the same wavelength (color). The electron lens likewise suffers in sharpness of focusing if λ is not the same for all electrons. Since λ is a function of the velocity and thus of the accelerating voltage, changes in this voltage may cause defocusing. Slight variations in initial velocity of the electrons are also of importance in defocusing. This latter effect may be minimized by making the final velocity very high with respect to the initial velocity.

Longitudinal magnetic fields, used in accordance with the theory of the preceding chapter, are also employed for focusing electron beams, as shown in Fig. 3-1(b). The focus coil produces a longitudinal magnetic flux, and the electrons are caused to follow a helical path. The focus is controllable by adjustment of the current flowing in the coil.

Magnification of the image is possible in such lens systems just as in optical systems. An application of this feature is made in the electron microscope in which electrons replace the visible light of the ordinary microscope. Since the electron wavelength is very considerably less than that of visible or ultraviolet light, much smaller objects may be resolved with the electron microscope than by any instrument using conventional optical systems. The electron microscope has greatly widened the sphere of work of the scientist interested in small particles or bodies.

3-2. The Electron Gun

The source of electrons in the cathode-ray tube is called an *electron gun*. In Fig. 3-2, the gun contains a heated cathode, or source of free electrons, K. The electrons leaving K pass through a hole in the grid G, which by being placed at higher or lower negative potentials can control the number of electrons passing. The electrons are accelerated by a positive potential on the focusing anode A_1, and some of the electrons enter the anode cylinder through the small hole in its end. This diaphragm serves to stop all electrons except those making a small angle with the axis of the beam.

The beam of electrons thus formed is further accelerated by the potential on the accelerating anode A_2, and is focused on the screen at the end of the tube by the electron lens set up between the first and second anodes. When the beam leaves the accelerating anode, another diaphragm is imposed in the path of the beam to cut off electrons that passed through the outer edges of the lens and were not properly focused.

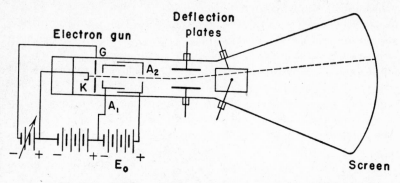

Fig. 3-2.   The electrostatically-deflected cathode-ray tube.

The number of electrons, and therefore the brightness of the spot, may be controlled by the potential on grid G; the focus, or sharpness of the spot, may be controlled by proper shaping of the electron lens by adjustment of the anode potentials.

3-3. The Cathode-Ray Tube

Although it is now known that the beam consists of electrons, these were unknown at the time of the discovery of the cathode rays

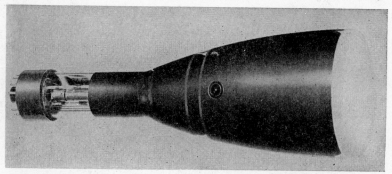

Fig. 3-3.   A typical cathode-ray tube.   (Courtesy A. B. DuMont Corp.)

by Crookes, and it was simply demonstrated that rays, or particles, were being shot out from the cathode; hence the name "cathode rays."

The complete cathode-ray tube, as shown in Fig. 3-3, consists of an evacuated space in which are an electron gun, a set of plane electrodes positioned around the beam, and a fluorescent screen. In tubes designed for magnetic deflection only, the plane electrodes may be omitted. The interior surface

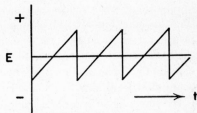

Fig. 3-4. Wave form of a sawtooth sweep voltage.

of the screen is coated with a thin, translucent layer of a material which fluoresces, or gives off flashes of light when hit by high-speed

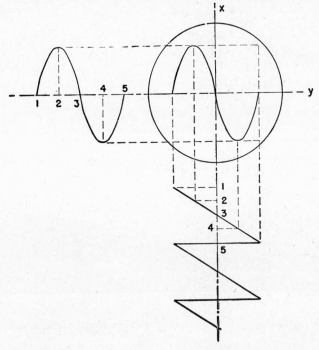

Fig. 3-5. The manner in which a sine wave can be traced on a cathode-ray screen as a time function, using a sweep voltage.

electrons, so that the location of the electron beam can be seen as a lighted spot on the screen.

If one pair of the plane electrodes is so positioned as to produce a horizontal electric field when a voltage is impressed across them, then a deflection of the beam horizontally, or along the x axis, is possible if potentials of various values and polarities are placed on this pair of electrodes. A similar pair of plates produces an electric field in the vertical direction and a vertical, or y, deflection of the beam can be produced by application of potentials to these plates. If the screen is considered as representing the xy plane, simultaneous application of potentials to both pairs of plates gives control of the spot of light in both x and y coordinates.

Since the masses of the electrons are so small, alternating potentials may be applied to the plates and the spot caused to oscillate over the screen without inertia effects at frequencies up to those of

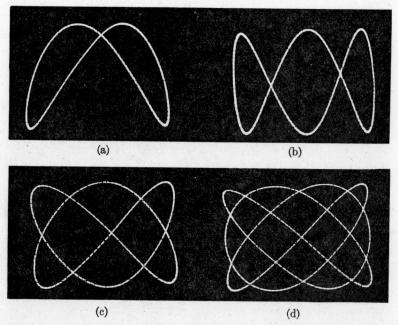

(a)   (b)

(c)   (d)

Fig. 3-6. Photographs of Lissajous figures taken directly from a cathode-ray
screen:
(a) With 2:1 frequency ratio; (b) With 3:1 frequency ratio;
(c) With 3:2 frequency ratio; (d) With 4:3 frequency ratio.

the order of 10^8 cycles per second. Since an a-c voltage is a time function, to be seen in its true wave form it must be plotted against time. This may be done by causing the x-axis deflection to vary linearly with time, moving the spot at a uniform rate across the screen, and then snapping the spot quickly back to the starting point for a recurrence of the movement. A voltage which may be applied to the x-axis plates to produce such a deflection is called a *saw-tooth wave*, or *sweep voltage*, and is shown in Fig. 3-4. If at the same time an a-c voltage whose frequency is equal to, or a multiple of, the saw-tooth recurrence frequency, is placed on the y-axis plates, the wave form of this a-c voltage will be seen traced out against time, as in Fig. 3-5.

It might be supposed that at high frequencies the movement of the spot of light would be too fast to follow with the eye; but owing

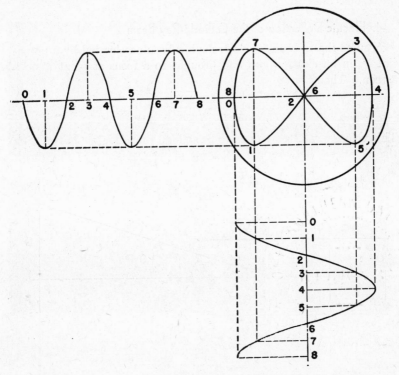

Fig. 3-7. Production of a Lissajous figure having a 2:1 frequency ratio.

to phosphorescence in the screen material and to persistence of vision in the human eye, the spot develops a tail even at low velocities, and at high rates appears as a solid-line plot of the phenomena.

Besides its use for observing wave forms of currents and voltages in electric circuits, the cathode-ray tube may be used to measure frequency by noting the figure obtained when a known frequency is applied to one set of plates and the unknown to the other. Figure 3-6 shows such patterns, and Fig. 3-7 shows a graphical method for plotting the expected screen pattern for any given set of time-varying voltages. Such patterns are called *Lissajous figures*, after an early experimenter who produced such patterns with a pendulum.

The cathode-ray tube has found applications in television reception, radar, navigational devices, computers, and other fields—wherever an electric signal must be interpreted visually, or stored for a short interval.

3-4. Electric Deflection of the Cathode-Ray Beam

Assume that a beam of electrons has been accelerated by a potential V_a in an electron gun and brought to a focus at point P on a screen. Then

$$v_0 = \sqrt{\frac{2eV_a}{m}} \qquad \text{m/sec.} \qquad (3\text{-}1)$$

This velocity will be assumed to be so high that the time in traveling the distance l_d between the deflecting plates in Fig. 3-8 is short with

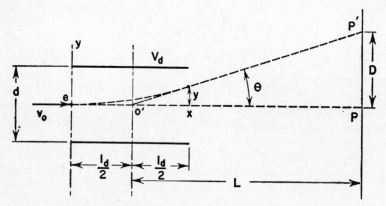

Fig. 3-8.   Electric field deflection of the cathode-ray beam.

respect to the time of a cycle of the deflecting voltage V_d, or V_d may be considered a constant for a particular electron.

The path of the electron in passing through the deflecting plates is parabolic according to Eq. 2-29. From this equation, the slope of the parabola at $x = l_d$ and consequently the slope of the straight line $o' - P'$ tangent to the parabola at $x = l_d$ is

$$\frac{dy}{dx} = \frac{e\mathcal{E}_y}{mv_{0x}^2} l_d = \tan\theta. \tag{3-2}$$

The location of o' is determined by

$$x - o' = \frac{y}{\tan\theta} = \frac{\frac{1}{2}a_y t^2}{\tan\theta}, \tag{3-3}$$

where $t = l_d/v_{0x}$. Then

$$x - o' = \frac{[(e\mathcal{E}_y/2mv_{0x}^2)l_d^2]}{[(e\mathcal{E}_y/mv_{0x}^2)l_d]} = \frac{l_d}{2}.$$

Consequently, point o' is at the center of the deflecting plates and distant L meters from the screen. The deflection D is then given by $D = L\tan\theta$ or

$$D = \frac{e\mathcal{E}_y}{mv_{0x}^2} Ll_d, \qquad\qquad \text{m,} \qquad (3\text{-}4)$$

and in view of Eq. 3-1 and the definition of $\mathcal{E}_y$,

$$D = \frac{V_d l_d L}{2dV_a} \qquad\qquad \text{m.} \qquad (3\text{-}5)$$

The deflection sensitivity is defined as the deflection per volt deflecting potential, so that

$$S_e = \frac{Ll_d}{2dV_a} \qquad\qquad \text{m/v.} \qquad (3\text{-}6)$$

The length l_d and spacing d are limited by the beam striking the plates for large deflections, and L is set by desirable mechanical size. The accelerating voltage should be high for maximum spot energy and brightness, so that any given tube is a compromise within these limitations. Customary sensitivities for laboratory tubes are of the order of 0.2-0.5 mm per volt. It should be noted that since V_d was assumed constant during the time of flight of one electron, V_d partakes of the nature of an instantaneous voltage. If a sinusoidal a-c voltage is applied, the maximum deflection will be that produced by the double peak voltage, and should be calculated accordingly.

Fringing of the electric field has been neglected above, so that actual deflections will differ slightly from the theoretical values of Eq. 3-5.   Certain empirical relations have been developed to allow for the effects of fringing and nonuniformity of the fields (Ref. 3).

3-5. Energy Sources of the Cathode-Ray Beam

Since there is an acceleration at right angles to the beam due to the deflecting potentials, the velocity of the beam leaving a set of deflecting plates is

$$v = \sqrt{v_0{}^2 + v_y{}^2}, \tag{3-7}$$

where v_y is due to the deflecting potential on the plates and is calculated from

$$V_y = \int_0^t \frac{eV_d}{md}\, dt, \tag{3-8}$$

and the limits of integration are over the time period that the electron is between the deflecting plates.   Fringing of electric flux has, of course, been neglected.

Equation 3-7 shows that the velocity of the electron has been raised; the energy likewise has been increased and the source of this energy is of interest.   As the electron approaches and enters the deflecting system, a charge is induced on the deflecting plates.   If the electron were to be undeflected, it would set up equal induced charges in the two plates, which would result in no net energy flow from the source.   However, upon deflection, the induced charges set up in the two plates are no longer equal, since the electron is approaching one plate and leaving the other, and a net flow of charge occurs in the external circuit, causing a flow of energy out of the source, which is exactly the energy given to the electron.

The total energy due to initial acceleration and to deflection is given up by the electron on impact with the screen.   Part of the energy is supplied to the atoms of the screen material and is emitted as radiant energy or light; the remainder dissipates as heat in the screen material.   Because of this heat dissipation, the cathode-ray spot should never be left stationary on the screen, because too much heat dissipated in one area will burn the screen material, resulting in a brownish color and loss of sensitivity at that point.

3-6. Magnetic Deflection of the Cathode-Ray Beam

If a pair of coils are mounted on the sides of the cathode-ray tube, causing a field transverse to the beam direction as in Fig. 3-9, the beam may be deflected by the magnetic field produced by the coil current. Assume that the magnetic field acts only over the axial distance l_m in Fig. 3-10 and that over this region B is uniform. The beam will then be deflected along a curved path of radius r and through an angle θ where

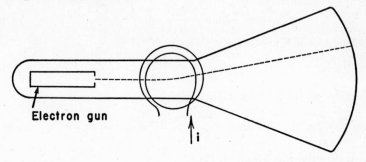

Fig. 3-9. Position of coils to produce magnetic deflection of the beam.

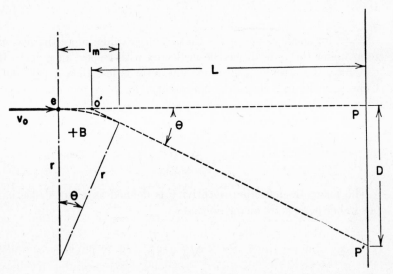

Fig. 3-10. Magnetic deflection of the cathode-ray beam.

$$\tan \theta = \frac{D}{L}. \tag{3-9}$$

Distance L is measured from the screen to the intersection of lines along the undeflected and deflected beam directions. The point o' is not, as in the electric deflection case, at the center of l_m, but the error caused by assuming it to be at the center of the field region is negligible for values of θ for which $\cos \theta$ approximates unity.

By inspection of the geometry of Fig. 3-10, it can also be seen that

$$\sin \theta = \frac{l_m}{r} \tag{3-10}$$

and by use of Eq. 2-37 for r,

$$\sin \theta = \frac{eBl_m}{mv_0}; \tag{3-11}$$

then, by use of trigonometric identities,

$$\tan \theta = \frac{eBl_m/mv_0}{\sqrt{1 - (eBl_m/mv_0)^2}}, \tag{3-12}$$

and, by equating 3-9 and 3-12,

$$D = \frac{eBl_mL/mv_0}{\sqrt{1 - (eBl_m/mv_0)^2}}. \tag{3-13}$$

Now, for small values of B—that is, large values of r—the second term under the radical may be neglected with respect to unity. If $r > 10l_m$, the error in neglecting this term is less than 1 per cent. Consequently, to a good approximation,

$$D = \frac{eBl_mL}{mv_0} \tag{3-14}$$

$$= \sqrt{\frac{e}{m}} \frac{B}{\sqrt{2V_a}} l_mL. \tag{3-15}$$

The magnetic-deflection sensitivity is defined as meter deflection per weber per square meter, so that

$$S_m = \sqrt{\frac{e}{m}} \frac{l_mL}{\sqrt{2V_a}} \quad \text{m/weber/m}^2. \tag{3-16}$$

For air-cored coils, B is directly proportional to the current flowing, and the deflection is a direct function of the coil current. Magnetic deflection ordinarily cannot be used for direct observation of the wave form of an applied voltage, since the coil current which sets up flux density B is a function of the time integral of the voltage applied to the coil.

It should be noted that the factor $\sqrt{e/m}$ appears in the expression for magnetic deflection but is not present for electric deflection. In the latter type, stray negatively charged gas atoms are deflected to the same extent as equally charged electrons, but in the electromagnetic type the deflections are smaller the greater the mass. Since the atoms have large masses relative to that of an electron, the deflections of stray charged gas atoms will be very small and will fall at or near the undeflected position of the beam. Continued bombardment of this nature is damaging to the screen, resulting in a brownish appearance near the center. This difficulty may be overcome by use of an ion trap actuated by a small permanent magnet. The electron gun is intentionally bent at an angle from the path of the electron beam, the electrons being deflected by the magnet field to follow the gun. The heavy ions are not appreciably deflected, they cannot turn the corner, and are thereby removed from the beam.

Use of a very thin aluminum coating on the inner surface of the fluorescent screen has also made tubes less sensitive to ion spotting. The coating is so thin that the small, high-velocity electrons are able to pass through it and excite the fluorescent material to visibility, whereas the much larger ions are caught by the aluminum. This coating also serves as a reflector of light and returns to the front of the tube a considerable portion of the light which would otherwise be lost into the tube interior.

Another difference between electric and magnetic deflection is noted in the effect of changes of V_a on the deflection sensitivity, since the magnetic deflection sensitivity is less affected by changing V_a, and therefore the accelerating potential can be increased to give greater spot brilliance with a smaller decrease in sensitivity for magnetic tubes than for electric-deflection tubes.

While the sensitivity is stated above in terms of unit flux density, it is more convenient for circuit design to state the sensitivity in terms of ampere turns required on the exciting coils placed against the neck of the bulb. In such terms average sensitivities may be stated as 0.5-1.0 mm deflection per ampere turn.

3-7. Fluorescent Screens

The fluorescent-screen material must be coated on the inside of the glass bulb thinly enough for the light from the electron impacts to pass through the screen and be viewed from outside the tube. A number of natural and synthetic minerals are available to produce different colors and phosphorescent properties, but only a few are in common use.

For normal laboratory observation, zinc orthosilicate is used. It gives a yellow-green color of good visual and photographic properties. The spectral characteristics are such as to give peak response at about 5200 A, which is near the maximum sensitivity of the human eye. It has considerable phosphorescence to aid the natural persistence of vision in following a rapidly moving spot.

Calcium tungstate gives a screen with a bluish trace of excellent actinic characteristics. This screen has a very short persistence time and may be used with a special camera for recording the phenomena. In this application, the spot moves in one axis only, and the film moves continuously at the desired speed on an axis at right angles to that of the spot. The film movement supplies the time axis, the film speed and sensitivity determining the maximum veloc-

TABLE 2

CATHODE-RAY TUBE FLUORESCENT SCREENS

Phosphor Number	Material	Color	Persistence	Application
P1	Zinc orthosilicate	Green	Medium short	General-purpose oscillograph
P4	Zinc sulfide	White	Short	Television
P5	Calcium tungstate	Blue	Very short	Fast photographic oscillography
P7	Zinc sulfide; zinc cadmium sulfide	Blue-white; then yellow	Very long	Radar screens
P11	Zinc sulfide	Blue	Short	Photographic oscillography
P12		Orange	Medium	Limited
P14		Blue, then orange	Long	Nonrecurrent phenomena
P15		Blue-green, ultraviolet	Short	Flying-spot scanners

ity of the spot which can be recorded. With special tubes, this velocity may reach values of several thousand miles per second. The need for short persistence of the trace is apparent, because persistence blurs the film image.

Other screen materials are available for providing extremely long persistence, and such screens usually have a yellow-colored trace. Screens with white traces have been developed as television receiving tubes in which it is desired that the picture be truly black and white. A list of standard screen designations and characteristics is given in Table 2. A *long*-persistence screen may retain a visible image from a few seconds up to several minutes, a *medium-short* persistence indicates that the useful image is retained for 20 to 30 milliseconds, whereas the *very short* persistence of the P-5 phosphor indicates a retention of less than 30 μ sec.

Since the electron beam striking the screen is carrying negative charge and the screen is insulated by the glass, the removal of this charge is necessary; otherwise the potential of the screen would fall to such a negative value as to repel the beam. Fortunately, as the electrons strike the screen they not only cause the screen to give off light but also to emit other electrons. This effect, known as *secondary emission* (see Chapter 4), may initially result in an average of more than one secondary electron being emitted per electron in the beam. This continues until the screen acquires a small positive charge, sufficient to prevent some of the secondary electrons from leaving, and thus making the charge carried away by the secondary electrons balance the arriving charge in the beam. The secondary electrons are attracted to a graphite coating over the interior bulb walls, which is connected to the second anode.

3-8. Anode Voltages

As can be seen by study of the deflection-sensitivity equations, the accelerating potential applied to the second anode is of importance in determining tube sensitivity. For high sensitivity, it should be as low as possible, but for high spot energy and brightness on the screen, the accelerating potential should be as large as possible. Since sensitivity is also a function of the deflecting plate to screen distance, high voltages are usually employed in large tubes in which the distance can be made greater to compensate for voltage increases. For very small tubes, voltages as low as 500 are employed. In ordinary laboratory equipment with 3- or 5-in. screen diameters, the anode potential will be 1500 to 2000 volts. For television and special purposes, the voltage may be 5000 to 80,000.

The higher voltages yield greater spot brightnesses, and higher spot velocities or writing speeds are possible for a given intensity of trace. The frequency of an alternating voltage or length of a transient determines the required writing speed. One method of obtaining greater brightness is to use one or more intensifier electrodes around the glass bulb between the deflection plates and the screen. These electrodes are operated at positive potentials above that of the accelerating anode and accelerate the electron beam after it has been deflected. The effect then is that of a tube with low accelerating voltage with respect to deflection sensitivity, but with high spot brightness, by reason of the acceleration received by the beam after deflection.

The cathode-ray tube is ordinarily operated by a power supply in which the positive potential connected to the second anode is grounded. The cathode of the tube is then negative, or below ground. The deflection-plate circuits are connected to the second anode, so that no axial acceleration of the beam will occur during deflection. Since the deflection-plate connections are frequently handled, grounding of the anode is a safety measure as well as a convenience in the avoidance of isolating capacitors.

3-9. Frequency Limitations

The capacitance of the deflection-plate electrodes to each other, or to the other electrodes, is usually of the order of 2 to 5 $\mu\mu$f. The reactance represented by this capacitance is large except for the very highest frequencies, so that the shunting effect of the deflection-plate system on circuits being investigated is usually negligible.

The major items affecting the input impedance of the deflecting plates are the currents due to stray electrons and to gas ions produced by collision with the electrons. Current also flows owing to acceleration of the beam toward the plates, but this is negligible in value.

At very high frequencies the deflecting voltage may not be a constant during the time of transit of one electron between the deflecting plates. This irregularity will produce an improper deflection of the beam. To prevent this aberration, the velocity of the beam may be raised by increase of V_a.

These factors limit the common laboratory cathode-ray tube to frequencies of the order of 10^7 cycles, with specially designed tubes available for very much higher frequencies. If amplifiers are used to increase the deflection-plate voltages, the frequency limits are usually fixed by amplifier design and may be much lower.

3-10. The Complete Oscillograph

The cathode-ray tube is usually used in an assemblage of apparatus called a *cathode-ray oscillograph,* arranged for easy and flexible operation.

A power unit to supply the high d-c accelerating potential, cathode heater voltages, and voltages for amplifiers is included. Amplifiers are provided so that very small voltages, of value in millivolts, may produce usable screen deflections on both x and y axes. These amplifiers must be well designed and must transmit all necessary harmonic components of the highest frequencies used without distortion of wave form or change in phase angles. An oscillator is incorporated to generate the saw-tooth linear sweep voltage, so that voltages or currents may be seen on the screen plotted as functions of time. This oscillator must provide a truly linear variation of voltage against time and a very rapid drop of voltage at the end of the cycle to return the trace to the start. This oscillator must also be variable in frequency, so that various numbers of cycles of the waves can be plotted against time. In some equipments a highly negative voltage is applied to the tube grid during this return time and the beam is completely cut off, so that the usable trace is not marred by the return trace.

Means for focusing and varying the intensity of the spot and of shifting the axes to various positions on the screen are also usually provided.

These controls result in a very flexible and rugged instrument, usable over a wide range of currents, voltages, and frequencies. The major disadvantage is that the usual instrument cannot readily show two or more waves simultaneously for an observation of phase angles. In special instruments multiple-gun tubes are employed, all operating onto a common screen, thus allowing simultaneous observation of a number of variables.

3-11. The Television Camera Tube

Devices similar to a cathode-ray tube are employed as picture pickup tubes in the television service. In these tubes a mosaic of tiny silver dots is formed on a mica card backed by a metal plate, and the optical image is focused thereon. By special sensitization, each dot gives up a number of electrons proportional to the light intensity striking it and thus assumes a positive potential, charging the tiny capacitor formed between the dot and the backing plate.

An electron gun in the tube produces an electron beam which is deflected horizontally across the mosaic by a pair of deflecting plates. After each deflection or line the beam is returned and dropped down by the width of two lines, and the deflection is repeated. After all the odd-numbered lines are scanned, the operation is repeated on the even-numbered lines until the whole optical image has been covered. As the electron beam strikes each tiny dot the capacitor between dot and backing plate is discharged, resulting in a current flow to the backing plate proportional to the dot charge, and thus to the light intensity on that particular dot. A picture consists of a composite of tiny dots, all scanned out at the rate of 30 pictures per second.

Modifications of this simple *iconoscope* have been introduced to develop a tube called the *orthicon* with more complex operating theory and greatly improved light sensitivity.

PROBLEMS

3-1. A cathode-ray tube has applied to the y deflection plates a sinusoidal 60-cycle voltage of 35 rms value. The observed deflection is a vertical line 1.76 in. long.

(a) Calculate the deflection sensitivity.

(b) If the magnetic field is assumed to act only over the region of the deflection plates, which are 0.3 in. apart and 1.0 in. long, and the accelerating potential is 2000 v, calculate the peak value of B necessary to give a magnetic deflection equal to that for (a).

3-2. The x deflecting plates of a certain cathode-ray tube are 1.5 cm long and separated 0.4 cm. The distance L is 18 cm, and the accelerating potential is 960 v.

(a) Find the screen deflection produced by a d-c voltage of 105 v.

(b) Find the flux density required over the area of the deflecting plates to produce an equal deflection magnetically.

(c) Voltage fluctuations cause the accelerating potential to drop to 900 v. Calculate the deflection for the voltage in (a) and the flux density used in (b).

3-3. The cathode-ray tube of Problem 3-2(a) has applied to the deflecting plates a sinusoidal voltage of 100 v peak and frequency of 6×10^8 cycles.

If an electron enters the deflecting plates at the voltage zero, find the deflection of this electron on the screen.

3-4. A cathode-ray tube has 1500 v accelerating potential. The electrostatic deflection plates are 1.5 cm long and separated 0.5 cm.

(a) A 60-cycle deflection potential of 100 volts is applied. Find the change in this deflection potential during the time one beam electron is between the plates.

(b) Repeat (a) if the deflection voltage has a frequency of 5×10^6 cycles.

(c) What is the highest frequency which may be used for deflection of this tube if an electron is not to remain between the plates for more than 45° of the deflection cycle?

3-5. (a) Find the velocity of the electron of Problem 3-2 on entering the deflecting plates, $V_a = 960$ v.

(b) Compute the energy in joules of the electron as it leaves the deflecting plates (electric deflection), $V_a = 960$ v after deflection by a voltage of 140 on the deflection plates.

(c) Find the value of resistance which the deflection plates represent at the instant the electron reaches the outgoing plate edge.

(d) The beam current totals 500 μa. If the spot is 0.5 mm in diameter, find the watts per square centimeter delivered to the screen by the beam with $V_a = 960$ v.

3-6. A voltage of $e_y = 100 \sin (2\pi 1000t)$ is applied to the y plates of a cathode-ray tube. On the x plates is $e_x = 120 \sin (2\pi 250t)$. If the deflection sensitivity of both sets of plates is 0.23 mm/v, what are the x and y coordinates of the electron spot on the screen at $t = 0.0002$ sec? The origin is the spot position at $t = 0$.

3-7. (a) A cathode-ray tube has an accelerating voltage of 2000 v. A magnetic field, acting over the total distance between anode and screen of 18 cm, causes a deflection of 2.0 cm on the screen. Find the density B of the field.

(b) What rms, 60-cycle voltage applied to deflection plates 1.5 cm long and separated 0.5 cm, at a distance $L = 18$ cm, will be needed to give the same deflection as in (a)?

3-8. A 40-cycle sine voltage is applied to the x plates and a 60-cycle sine voltage of equal amplitude to the y plates of a cathode-ray tube. The two waves are zero and going positive at $t = 0$. Graphically construct the complete path of the fluorescent spot on the screen.

3-9. A beam of electrons and ions, having been accelerated by 1500 volts, passes for a distance of 2.0 cm through a region with a transverse magnetic field produced by a permanent magnet. It is desired that the electrons be bent through an angle of 20°.

(a) What flux density must the magnet supply?

(b) What will be the angle of deflection of singly charged oxygen ions in passing through the same field?

3-10. Two equal 100-cycle sine voltages are applied to the plates of a cathode-ray tube. Construct the pattern seen on the screen when:

(a) The two voltages are in phase.

(b) y-plate voltage lags x-plate voltage by 60°.

(c) y-plate voltage lags x-plate voltage by 90°.

(d) y-plate voltage lags x-plate voltage by 120°.

(e) Develop a formula by which the phase angle between two waves can be computed from measurements on the pattern.

3-11. Voltages, sinusoidal in form, and of frequencies ω_1 and ω_2 are applied to the vertical and horizontal deflection plates, respectively, of a cathode-ray tube. Plot the patterns which will be seen if: $\omega_1/\omega_2 = 3$, in phase; $\omega_1/\omega_2 = 3/2$, waves displaced 90° of ω_1; $\omega_1/\omega_2 = 3/4$, waves in phase.

REFERENCES

1. *The Cathode-Ray Tube and Typical Applications*, A. B. DuMont Laboratories, Clifton, N. J., 1948.

2. MacGregor-Morris, J. T., and Henley, J. A., *Cathode-Ray Oscillography*, Chapman & Hall, Ltd., London, 1936.

3. Hintenburger, H., *Z. Physik*, **105**, 501 (1937).

4. Maloff, I. G., and Epstein, D. W., *Electron Optics in Television*, McGraw-Hill Book Company, Inc., New York, 1938.

5. Zworykin, V. K., and Morton, G. A., *Television*, John Wiley & Sons, Inc., New York, 1940.

6. Feldt, R., "Photographing Patterns on Cathode-Ray Tubes," *Electronics*, **17**, 130, February (1944).

7. Zworykin, V. K., "The Iconoscope—A Modern Version of the Electric Eye," *Proc. IRE*, **22**, 16 (1934).

8. Rose, A., Weimer, P. K., and Law, H. B., "The Image Orthicon—A Sensitive Television Pickup Tube," *Proc. IRE*, **34**, 424 (1946).

9. Soller, T., Starr, M. A., and Valley, G. E., Jr., *Cathode-Ray Tube Displays*, McGraw-Hill Book Company, Inc., New York, 1948.

CHAPTER 4

EMISSION OF ELECTRONS

The discharge of electrons from solid or liquid bodies is called *emission*. This may be incited by application of heat, strong electric fields, electromagnetic radiation (light), and by bombardment by electrons, ions, or atomic particles. The resulting electron emissions are called, respectively,

1. Thermionic emission.
2. High-field emission.
3. Photoelectric emission.
4. Secondary emission.

4-1. Electronic Behavior in Metals

The Bohr atom theory discussed briefly in Chapter 1 supposes a positively charged nucleus surrounded by a group of electrons, established in definite states, orbits, or *energy levels*, as a picture of an atom. The electrons have a number of available orbits, or levels, in which they can exist and move. There are many more possible orbits than electrons in any given atom, so that under given conditions many orbits are empty. However, an electron can exist in an atom only if it is an orbit, and no more than two electrons (having opposite directions of spin) may exist in any orbit at one time.

A particular electron, in order to occupy this orbit, or *energy level*, as it is preferably called, must have a definite amount of energy. This energy of the electron in the orbit is a result of the position, or distance, of the orbit in the force field of the positive nucleus. If the electron is given additional energy, it can take up only the exact amount required to raise its total energy to that of another level, and it then exists there. If it loses energy, it can lose only the exact amount which will allow it to drop back to a lower energy level. The

63

energy differences between levels in atoms in a gas are relatively great, and it is difficult to give electrons the additional energy required to permit a step up to a higher energy level. Under usual conditions most of the electrons in a gas atom will be found grouped in the lowest possible energy states, and the atom is then said to be in the *normal*, or *unexcited*, state.

The atomic structure of metals in the solid state is such that a great many atoms are forced very close together in a regular pattern, called a *crystal*. The interatomic forces are extremely great, since it is these forces that give the metal its physical strength. As a result of these forces, each of the original energy levels splits into a very great number of energy levels, so that the energy required for an electron to progress up from one level to the next may be very small. The effect is much as if the possible energy levels represented almost a continuous band. Application of energy, possibly in the form of heat, will then permit many of the higher-energy electrons in the atoms of the crystal to move up to still higher levels.

The distribution of energy among the different electrons of a metal has been studied extensively. The distribution function which most satisfactorily meets the physical requirements is known as the *Fermi-Dirac distribution*, originally derived on a statistical basis. This function allows us to determine the number of electrons dN per unit volume, having a certain value of energy dE at a particular temperature T. This function is of the form

$$dN = \frac{c\sqrt{E}\,dE}{\epsilon^{\frac{E-E_M}{kT}} + 1} = F\,dE \qquad (4\text{-}1)$$

and is illustrated in Fig. 4-1(a) for the value of absolute zero temperature T_0. The symbols in the equation are:

c = proportionality constant = 6.82×10^{27} electrons/m³/(ev)$^{3/2}$,
E = energy in electron volts,
k = Boltzmann's constant = 1.38×10^{-23} joule/°K,
T = temperature in degrees Kelvin (centrigrade absolute),
E_M = see below.

The curve for absolute zero temperature shows that in a metal all the energy levels up to a certain value E_M are occupied by electrons, but that no electrons exist in any level above E_M. This curve also shows that there are more electrons having high energy values than those having low values.

The curve permits a definition of absolute zero as that temperature at which the electrons are in the lowest possible energy states. It should be noted that absolute zero is not the absence of all energy, but only the condition of lowest energy.

As the temperature is raised, the higher-energy electrons which are most easily reached by external forces are given additional energy, and move to energy values above E_M. The lower-energy electrons are unaffected. At still higher temperatures more of the high-energy electrons move to still higher energies.

However, even at temperatures of 3000°K, which curve (b), Fig. 4-1 approximates for tungsten, most of the electrons are still unaffected by this added heat energy. The heat energy absorbed per unit mass per degree rise, or specific heat, is almost entirely taken up by thermal vibration of the atoms, and only a small portion is used to increase the energy levels of some of the high-energy electrons. In other words, the distribution of energy among the electrons does not change very much, even for very high temperatures.

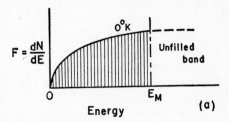

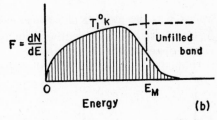

Fig. 4-1. Fermi-Dirac energy distribution of electrons in a metal (a) at 0°K., (b) at temperature T_1.

The value E_M is a characteristic of a material, frequently called the *Fermi level*. For any electron having energy $E = E_M$, the denominator of the function F of Eq. 4-1 becomes 2, for all values of T. Since E_M is a characteristic of a material, it is of use as a bench mark or measuring point for energy relations. In other words, it is a measure of the relative level of the electron energies in an atom.

For ordinary metallic conductors, E_M occurs at the top of a group or band of occupied or filled electron energy levels, at absolute zero temperature. Thus in metals, E_M is the energy of the highest-energy electron, at absolute zero temperature. It may be noted that for $T = 0°$, Eq. 4-1 reduces to

$$dN = c\sqrt{E}\, dE \qquad (4\text{-}2)$$

for values of $E < E_M$. This is known as the *completely degenerate function*, and is the parabolic equation from which the absolute zero curve is plotted in Fig. 4-1(b).

An integration of Eq. 4-2 for the T_0 curve will yield an equation from which

$$E_M = \left(\frac{3N}{2c}\right)^{2/3} = 3.64 \times 10^{-19} N^{2/3}, \qquad (4\text{-}3)$$

where N is the number of valence electrons in the material. Since N is a variable dependent on the particular metal used, E_M has values dependent on the material.

It should be noted that the distribution shown in Fig. 4-1 applies to the energy of the electrons of the crystal, regardless of the directions of the electron velocities. If an electron is to be emitted and is to leave the surface of the metal, its velocity must be directed toward the surface, or have a sufficiently large component toward the surface, to overcome the surface forces. When only the electrons having outward-directed velocities are considered, the distribution of energy among these electrons becomes like that in Fig. 4-2 for absolute zero T_0, and a higher temperature T_2. Since the curve for T_2 approaches the axis asymptotically, there will be a few electrons with very high energies. It may be possible for some of these high-energy (high-outward-velocity) electrons to pass through the surface and leave the metal.

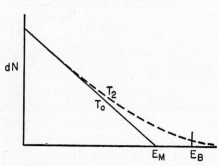

dN

Energy perpendicular to the surface

Fig. 4-2. Distribution of energy among electrons having velocity components directed normal to the surface.

4-2. Free Electrons—Current Flow in Metals

The positive charge on the nucleus sets up an electric field inside the atom. Since work is done when a charge is moved in a field, work would be done in moving an electron from the position of the nucleus to a particular orbit. This work establishes the energy level of the orbit and shows that the farther the orbit is from the nucleus, the higher the energy of that orbit. Consequently, the outermost electrons of the atom are the high-energy electrons, and it is these electrons that take up additional energy most easily. The inner electrons are rather effectively shielded from external influences by the fields of the outer electrons.

In a metallic crystal the atoms are very closely packed, and internuclear distances are of such a nature that many of the outer-orbit (high-energy) electrons are about as far from the nucleus of a neighboring atom as from their own nucleus. This arrangement is illustrated in Fig. 4-3, where

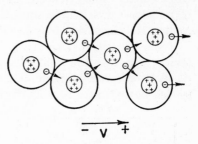

Fig. 4-3. Movements of free electrons in a metal under action of a potential.

the effective radii of the atoms are indicated but all the inner electrons are omitted for clarity. The outer electrons are acted upon by the field of their own nucleus and by a practically equal and opposite field from the nucleus of another atom, as a result of the nearly equal distances. Consequently, the two fields partially cancel and the outer electrons of the atoms are largely free of internal atomic forces. It is these electrons that are spoken of as free electrons, privileged to move about in the metal under the action of any external forces applied, and which may be emitted if given sufficient energy. If a voltage now sets up an electric field in the metal, producing a force from left to right on the electrons in Fig. 4-3, there will be a movement of these free electrons from atom to atom, and this drift will constitute an electric current in the metal.

The paths of the electrons in moving from atom to atom are erratic, and occasionally energy is lost in overcoming the field of an atom and forcing the transfer of an electron. This energy loss per unit time for the whole conductor represents the I^2R loss, and the resistance simply becomes due to the forces that are overcome in moving the free electrons from atom to atom.

The metal in crystalline form has a regular pattern, or lattice arrangement of atoms. This makes the movements of the electrons relatively easy, since the paths from atom to atom are regularized and the resistance is low. If the metal is heated, the atoms are excited and develop thermal vibrations. As a consequence the regularity of the lattice is somewhat broken up because the atoms are now in oscillation over a considerable region, and transfer of electrons becomes more difficult. These facts account for the increase of resistance with temperature, or the positive temperature coefficient of resistance shown by most metals.

It can be seen that the path of any given electron is somewhat erratic (Fig. 4-4) and unlike the path of other electrons moving in the electron current. Because of this irregularity the resistance met by one electron may be different from that met by another, yet the

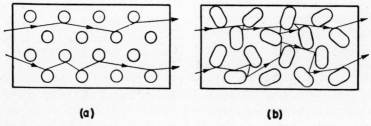

(a)   (b)

Fig. 4-4. Electron paths through a conductor: (a) ordered crystal at low temperature. (b) effect of thermal vibrations of atoms at high temperature in disrupting electron paths.

over-all resistance of the metal bar is a constant. This is so because an electron current is made up of extremely large numbers of electrons, and the statistical average of a very great number of samples is a constant. When a current of 1 amp flows, electrons pass a point at the rate of 6.3×10^{18} per second, and the energy lost by each is added into the whole, yielding a total value of energy per unit time which when divided by I^2 gives always the same *average* resistance per electron.

The economist or statistician is well satisfied if he can obtain several thousand or several tens of thousands of samples from which to draw his conclusions, but the electrical engineer is enabled to work with an average drawn from samples of the order of 10^{18} units. It is therefore to be expected that electrical engineering problems can be more exactly solved than those of economics.

4-3. The Energy Barrier at the Metal Surface

In order to determine whether it is possible for some of the high-energy free electrons to leave the surface, it is necessary to know something of the surface conditions which the electrons will encounter. It is known that work must be done by the electron to emerge from the metal. This work, or the energy given up, is known as E_B, or the *barrier energy*, since the surface effects appear as if a barrier, or wall, were erected at the metal surface over which the electrons must climb. Upon further consideration, E_B may be broken into two parts—the energy E_1 given up or work done to overcome the forces very near to the surface, and E_2, the work done in overcoming the forces at larger distances from the surface. That is,

$$E_B = E_1 + E_2. \tag{4-4}$$

Study of the work factor E_1 discloses, first, that it is very difficult to locate the surface exactly. Since the atoms will not necessarily be laid in like bricks, there will likely be a surface roughness of the order of atomic diameters. This will lead to an uncertainty of surface location of the order of 10^{-8} cm or more. The forces due to the different surface atoms will then be quite erratic in nature, and the electron must have sufficient energy to overcome these forces. Consequently, E_1 is a function of the particular metal and of its surface condition, including the effects of deposited layers of other metals and of any adsorbed gases on the surface.

The second part of the barrier energy, E_2, is used in moving the electron through the force fields existing at greater distances from the surface. At these distances the forces due to individual atoms will largely compensate. The remaining force is due to attraction from the so-called *image*, or induced surface charge. When an electron leaves a metal surface, the surface will be left with a positive charge, and an electric field will be set up between it and the surface as at (a), Fig. 4-5. Since the metal is an equipotential surface in the field, the electron will be unable to note any difference if the field of (a) is changed to that of (b). The position of the metal surface is still taken by an equipotential of the field between the two equal and opposite charges, and the flux lines (by means of which the electron comes in contact with the outside world) remain unchanged. Since the field remains the same, the force on the electron must be the same.   The plus charge at the left is called the *image charge*.

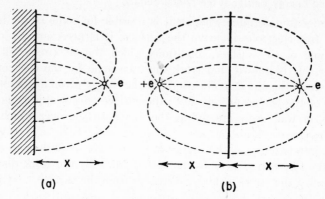

Fig. 4-5.   The electric-image principle.

Coulomb's law allows the calculation of the force on the electron $(-e)$, where

$$f = \frac{q_1 q_2}{4\pi\epsilon_v r^2} \qquad\qquad \text{newtons,} \qquad (4\text{-}5)$$

and the charge is in coulombs, r in meters, and $\epsilon_v = 10^7/4\pi c^2$, the permittivity of space

$$f_x = \frac{(+e)(-e)}{4\pi\epsilon_v (2x)^2}$$

$$= \frac{-e^2}{16\pi\epsilon_v x^2}. \qquad\qquad (4\text{-}6)$$

The negative sign indicates the force is to the left, or in the negative x direction.   The expression obviously holds only beyond some $x = x_1$ such that the surface may be considered as a true equipotential plane, or for x_1 equal to at least a few atomic diameters from the surface.

If now the electron is entirely removed from the surface, theoretically to an infinite distance, the work done against the force of Eq. 4-6 is

$$E_2 = -\int_{x_1}^{\infty} f_x \, dx$$

$$= \frac{e^2}{16\pi\epsilon_v x_1} \qquad \text{joules,} \qquad (4\text{-}7)$$

indicating that the work done is an inverse function of distance in the field of the image charge, as shown in Fig. 4-6.

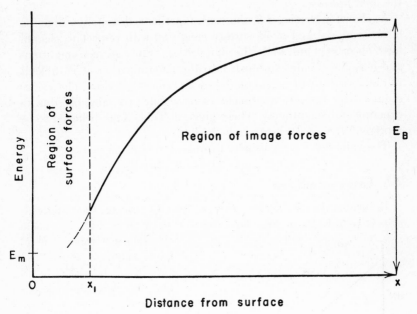

Fig. 4-6.   Energy conditions near a surface.

The total work E_B is that done by the electron in freeing itself from the binding forces of the metal. This total barrier energy E_B is seen to be dependent on the particular material and its surface condition as incorporated in E_1, and on the image forces as included in E_2. To secure emission of electrons, means must be found to raise the energy of individual electrons to the minimum level of energy E_B. If amounts of energy greater than this are supplied, the excess over E_B will appear as kinetic energy of the emitted electron.

4-4. The Work Function

Since it has already been shown that even at absolute zero in metals many electrons already have an energy near the value E_M, it is necessary only to supply an additional energy E_W, where

$$E_W = E_B - E_M \tag{4-8}$$

in order to secure emission. The value of energy E_W is known as the *work function*.

As shown in Section 4-3, the work function is definitely a function of the material and of its surface condition with respect to cleanliness, absorbed films, and other impurities. Since surface conditions and cleanliness enter so much into the determination, it is difficult to obtain consistent experimental measurements of E_W. The values obtained by various experimenters may differ considerably due to experimental conditions. Those given in Table 3 are believed to be representative of the best available data.

The values of E_W are usually expressed in electron volts.

4-5. Emission Equations

Returning to the distribution of energy among the outward-directed electrons of Fig. 4-2, which is redrawn in Fig. 4-7, some electrons at temperature T_2 have energies above the value E_B. It is these electrons which can be emitted. To find the current represented by these electrons per unit area of the surface, it is necessary to determine the equation of the distribution for a temperature T_2, integrate this equation from E_B to infinity to obtain the number of electrons passing through the surface, and multiply by the average velocity of the electrons and the charge per electron. An equation of the form

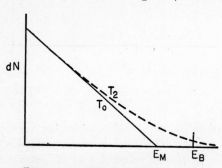

Energy perpendicular to the surface

Fig. 4-7. Energy distribution among electrons having velocity components directed toward the surface.

$$J = A_0 T^2 \epsilon^{-\frac{(E_B - E_M)e}{kT}} \qquad (4\text{-}9)$$

is the result. The factor $E_B - E_M$ can be recognized as the work function E_W. By combining terms, the equation is put into the more usual form

$$J = A_0 T^2 \epsilon^{-b_0/T} \qquad \text{amp/m}^2, \qquad (4\text{-}10)$$

where

J = current density in amp/m^2 of cathode area,

T = cathode temperature, degrees Kelvin (centigrade absolute),

$A_0 = 4\pi mek^2/h^3$ = proportionality constant, amp/m^2/deg^2,

$b_0 = eE_W/k = 11{,}600\, E_W$,

h = Planck's constant,

k = Boltzmann's constant.

An equation of this form but having the exponent of T as 1/2 was developed by O. W. Richardson in 1914. The above form of the equation was developed by S. Dushman in 1923, and is known as Dushman's equation. Since the exponential term is so large, it is difficult to determine from experiment whether the exponent of T should be 1/2 or 2, but the Dushman form is now generally accepted as having the better theoretical basis.

In theory the factor A_0 should be a universal constant for all metals, having a value of 120.4×10^4 amp/m^2/deg^2. Actually, the values of A_0 determined experimentally vary considerably, as can be seen in Table 3.

TABLE 3

VALUES OF THE EMISSION CONSTANTS

Element	A_0 (amp/m^2/deg^2)	b_0 (°K)	E_W (ev)	Melting Point (°K)
Calcium...............	60×10^4	37,100	3.2	1083
Carbon................	30×10^4	54,500	4.34	...
Cesium................	16.2×10^4	21,000	1.81	299
Copper................	65×10^4	47,000	4.1	1356
Molybdenum...........	55×10^4	49,900	4.2	2895
Nickel.................	30×10^4	58,000	4.6	1725
Tantalum..............	37×10^4	47,600	4.1	3123
Thorium...............	60×10^4	39,400	3.4	2118
Tungsten..............	60×10^4	52,400	4.52	3643
Thorium on tungsten....	3×10^4	30,500	2.6	...

Equation 4-10 may be written in the form

$$\log \frac{J}{T^2} = \log A_0 - \frac{0.4343 b_0}{T}. \qquad (4\text{-}11)$$

If the left-hand side of this equation is plotted against $1/T$, the result should be a straight line with an intercept of $\log A_0^*$ and a slope of $-0.4343 b_0$. By such a plot, values of A_0 and b_0 may be obtained experimentally for a particular material. Actually, this method does not yield good results readily because of limited possible temperature ranges, adsorbed gases, surface impurities, and difficulties of temperature measurement.

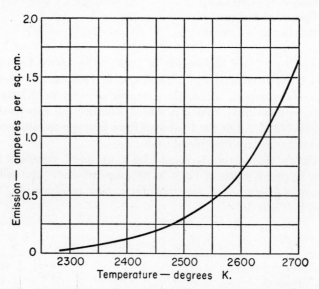

Fig. 4-8. Emitted current density vs temperature for a tungsten filament.

A plot of the Dushman relation (Eq. 4-10) gives a curve as in Fig. 4-8. This curve is for tungsten and shows that at low temperatures the emitted currents are very small. At room temperature a square centimeter of tungsten will emit one electron in about 10^{14} years. However, at higher temperatures the emitted currents may be quite

---

* In this text "log" will be used to indicate a logarithm to the base 10; "ln" to indicate use of the Naperian base.

large, the emission being a very sensitive function of temperature as a result of the exponential term in Eq. 4-10.

4-6. Energy of the Emitted Electrons

The curve of Fig. 4-7 shows that some electrons may be emitted with energies very much above that of the barrier. These electrons will have kinetic energy, or velocities, after emission. Other electrons will have just enough energy to overcome the energy barrier, and very little will remain to appear as energy of motion.

The *most probable* velocity, c_0, of the emitted electrons can be determined from the kinetic theory of gases as

$$c_0 = \sqrt{\frac{2kT}{m}} \qquad (4\text{-}12)$$

in terms of Boltzmann's constant k, the temperature T, and the mass of the electron.

By rewriting Eq. 4-12 as

$$\frac{mc_0^2}{2e} = \frac{kT}{e} = \frac{V}{2} \qquad (4\text{-}13)$$

it is possible to state the most probable energy of the electrons in the emitted electron cloud in terms of V. For a metal at 2800°K, this most probable energy is only 0.48 ev, and at the melting point of tungsten it becomes only 0.63 ev. It is seen that although the electrons actually do have residual velocities after emission, the probable value of these velocities is quite small compared with the velocities or energies developed by electrons in their movement in various types of electron tubes.

4-7. Contact Potential

It is to be expected that any two different metals would have different values of E_M; that is, the energies of the highest-energy electrons would not be the same in both metals. If bars of the two metals are joined at one end J, as in Fig. 4-9, and bar A has the highest value of E_M, then existing in A are electrons of higher energy than any in B. Since the bars are joined, the surface barrier is broken down and high-velocity electrons flow from A into B. This process continues until there are as many high-velocity electrons in

B as in A, and equilibrium is reached across the junction. The values of E_M in the two metals have then been equalized.

However, there are now more electrons than normal in B, and less than normal in A. A potential will then appear across the unconnected ends of the bars. This potential, called a contact potential, exists only across an open circuit. Since there is no continuing source of energy in the circuit, any attempt to measure this potential by current-drawing instruments is doomed to failure.

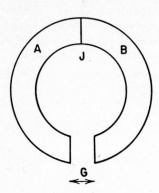

Fig. 4-9. Illustrating contact potential.

The magnitude of the contact potential can be determined by considering that, if contact is not made at J, an electron in the gap G just outside the face of A will have a potential, equal to the work function E_{WA} of A, above the level E_{MA} inside the bar A. Likewise, an electron in the gap just outside the face of B will be at a potential E_{WB} volts above the level E_{MB} inside bar B.

When the bars are joined at J, the levels E_{MA} and E_{MB} are equalized by movement of electrons from bar A to bar B. Since E_M is now the same for both electrons, the one just outside B is E_{WB} volts above the common reference E_M, and the one outside A is E_{WA} volts above the same reference. Consequently, the potential difference between the two electrons and likewise between the ends of the bars across G is

$$\text{contact P.D.} = E_{WB} - E_{WA}, \qquad (4\text{-}14)$$

or the contact potential between two metals is equal to the difference of the work functions in electron volts.

In certain electronic devices, electrodes of different materials may be connected in an external circuit with the electrodes facing each other in an electron stream. Even though no external emf is applied, the electron stream may be acted upon by the contact potential difference between the electrodes.

4-8. Thermionic Cathode Materials and Construction

The emitter electrode of a tube is called a *cathode*, since it is the negative electrode of the discharge. In *thermionic* emission, cathodes are divided into two classes, (1) filamentary and (2) equipotential, or indirectly heated. Custom and past usage permit the application of the word *filament* to both types.

In the filamentary construction a wire is heated by passage of electric current through it, and electron emission takes place directly from the wire. Such a filament is shown at (a), Fig. 4-10. Since the heating current flows directly through the wire, a potential drop of a few volts is uniformly distributed along the wire; that is, all points of the filament are not at the same potential.

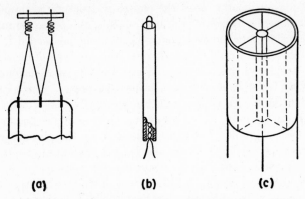

(a)   **(b)**   **(c)**

Fig. 4-10. Cathode construction: (a) filamentary; (b) radio receiving tube equipotential cathode; (c) heat-shielded cathode.

In the equipotential construction a twisted hairpin or loop of tungsten wire insulated with a baked-on refractory material is inserted in a thin-walled, hollow metal cylinder, usually made of nickel. The outside of the cylinder is coated with material which will emit the electrons. Passage of current through the tungsten heater causes the cylinder to become hot enough to emit the desired electron current. Since the emitted current is usually quite small and no heating current flows in the cylinder, there is no voltage drop along the cylinder; that is, it is equipotential. An equipotential cathode, as used in a radio receiving tube, is shown at (b), Fig. 4-10. Owing to the heat storage in the cylinder, cathodes of this type require a short heating time before they reach operating temperature. This thermal storage reduces any cyclic variations of temperature which might appear when the cathode is heated by alternating current.

A different form of construction of an equipotential cathode is the *heat-shielded* construction of (c), Fig. 4-10. Passing up inside a small metal cylinder and insulated therefrom is a tungsten heater wire. Radiating from the central cylinder are metal fins, usually nickel, welded to an outer cylinder. The fins and inside surface of the outer cylinder are coated with emitting material. Surrounding the outer cylinder are one or two additional cylinders of polished nickel, which serve as radiation shields, or thermal insulators.

The tungsten heater raises the emitting structure to proper temperature, and, by reason of the heat shields, the power to maintain this is considerably reduced under what would be needed if all the cathode area could radiate heat freely. In this type of construction the emitting area can be increased and the emission current raised without a proportionate increase in heating power. Such cathodes have been built with emission currents of the order of 600 to 1000 amp. Unfortunately, they cannot be used in high-vacuum tubes owing to excessive negative charges built up by the presence of large quantities of electrons in the spaces between the fins. In gas tubes in which positive ions exist to neutralize the negative charge, their use leads to a considerable heating-power saving and increased over-all efficiency. Heating time for heat-shielded cathodes may run from 10 sec to as much as 30 min.

The range of materials for thermionic emitters is fairly narrow. Desirable qualities are low work function, good mechanical properties at high temperature, and a high melting point, so that T in Dushman's equation may be as high as possible. Many materials with low work functions, such as cesium, have very low melting points, and hence the attainable thermionic emission is too small to be useful.

Tungsten, although its work function of 4.52 ev is not small, is desirable as an emitter because of its extremely high melting point of 3643°K. This value allows tungsten filaments to be operated at temperatures of 2500° to 2600°K without an excessive rate of evaporation of tungsten atoms with its attendant reduction of cross section. Tungsten is susceptible to *poisoning*, or reduction of emission, by thin adsorbed layers of oxygen, water vapor, and certain other gases, so that high vacuums must be maintained. Operation in atmospheres of the inert gases does no damage since bombardment of the surface by positive gas ions is not harmful.

The relative emission efficiency, defined as milliamperes of emission per watt of heating power, is in the range of 2 to 10 ma per watt. By comparison with other materials, this is considered low, so that the use of tungsten is limited to x-ray tubes, vacuum rectifiers, and a few other services.

Thoriated Tungsten. Langmuir discovered in 1913 that the addi-

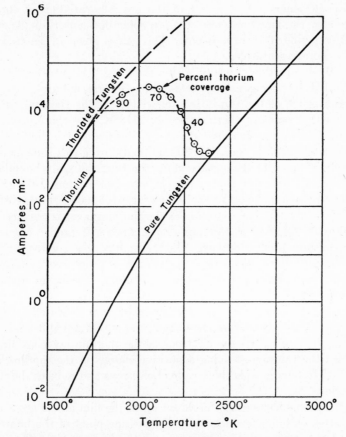

Fig. 4-11. Electron emission from thorium on tungsten as a function of temperature and per cent surface covered.

tion of 1 to 2 per cent of thoria (thorium oxide) to tungsten powder, before the usual sintering, swaging, and wiredrawing processes, resulted in a filament material of notably improved emission characteristics. The results are due to adsorption of a monatomic film of thorium atoms on the surface of the tungsten. Certain other alkali metals lead to similar results.

The variation of emission with coverage of tungsten by thorium atoms is shown in Fig. 4-11. Operation at overtemperature results in stripping the filament to pure tungsten with a drop in current of about 10^4 times. As a result of the possible variation of surface coverage, the emission constants are somewhat uncertain, varying from experiment to experiment. The values given in Table 4 are believed representative.

In the production of a tube with a thoriated filament, the filament is heated to approximately 2800°K for several minutes. In this interval some of the thoria is reduced to metallic thorium. Since the melting point of thorium is only 2118°K, any thorium on the filament surface is evaporated. Next, the filament is held at approximately 2100°K for about 30 min, and during this time metallic thorium diffuses to the surface along the tungsten grain boundaries and spreads out over the surface in an adsorbed film. Operation of the filament then at a normal temperature of 1900°K gives copious emission. Gradual evaporation of the thorium layer is balanced by additional diffusion of thorium to the surface if proper operating temperatures are maintained. Either undervoltage or overvoltage may result in loss of emission. Operation at proper voltage insures a tube life limited only by the reserve supply of thorium stored in the filament.

It may be noted that the work function of a thoriated-tungsten surface is less than tungsten at 4.52 ev, and of thorium at 3.4 ev. By use of the two metals the electrons of the thorium layer are drawn toward the tungsten, leaving a positive charge on the thorium surface. This charge aids the escape of electrons and reduces the work function.

The mechanical surface forces set up in the film are so great that operation within a few degrees of the melting point of thorium does not cause appreciable evaporation of thorium atoms. Thoriated tungsten filaments are, however, susceptible to damage by gas ions. Presence of gas in a tube operating at high voltage can cause ion bombardment of the filament, almost immediate stripping of the thorium layer, and reduction of emission to that of pure tungsten. When thoriated tungsten filaments are used in tubes operating at voltages above 3000 to 4000 it is necessary to ensure a very high vacuum. That this can be done is established by successful use of such filaments in tubes operating up to 15,000 v.

Improved operation results if, before the processing described above, the filament is heated in a hydrocarbon atmosphere, the carbon combining with the tungsten to form tungsten carbide. The presence of the carbide layer reduces thorium evaporation to one-sixth of the value before carbonization. Operation at higher temperatures with increased emission is then possible without an increase in the rate of thorium loss.

The relative emission efficiency of thoriated-tungsten filaments approximates 50 to 100 ma per watt of heating power.

Oxide-coated Materials. Wehnelt discovered as early as 1904 that emission from certain of the alkaline-earth oxides is large even at low temperatures. Large-scale commercial use of such materials did not take place until 18 years later, when oxide-coated filaments were introduced to reduce the filament power consumption of the battery-operated radio receivers of the day.

The oxide-coated cathode consists of a metal base of nickel, or alloys, coated with a layer of oxides, usually barium or strontium. Since these oxides are unstable in air, the cathodes are first coated with barium or strontium carbonates or nitrates by spraying or dipping, followed by a drying process. During evacuation the cathodes are heated and the coatings are reduced to the oxides, the gases released being removed by the vacuum pumps. By application of anode voltages so that currents are drawn from the cathode, the emission is built up or the cathode activated.

It is believed that in the activation process some of the oxide is reduced to the pure metal, which then forms an adsorbed surface layer as well as increasing the conductivity of the oxide layer by dispersal through the layer. This layer is electropositive to the base, reducing the work function by setting up a field to aid the electrons, much as in the case of thoriated tungsten.

The emission constants for oxide-coated cathodes are extremely variable but are believed to be in the range of values given in Table 4. The materials fail to show a definite value of emitted current for a

TABLE 4

CHARACTERISTICS OF CATHODE MATERIALS

Material	A_0	E_W (ev)	Emission Efficiency (ma/w)	Operating Temperature (°K)
Tungsten............	60×10^4	4.52	2-10	2500-2600
Thorium on tungsten	$*3 \times 10^4$	*2.63	50-100	1800-2000
Oxide-coated........	$*0.1 \times 10^4$	*1.0	100-1000	900-1250

* Highly variable.

particular temperature, the actual current depending to a considerable extent on the value of the applied field. If the energy barrier is considered, the shape is believed to be as in Fig. 4-12(b) in contrast to that for tungsten at (a). It is possible that in addition to

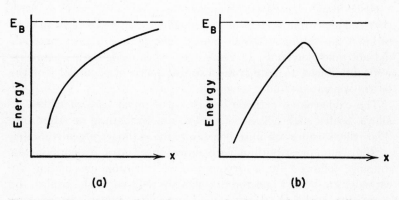

Fig. 4-12. Variations in the surface energy barrier as a function of distance x from the surface: (a) tungsten; (b) oxide-coated cathode.

electrons crossing over the barrier due to thermal energy, application of high voltages or field intensities may also pull them directly through the thin portion of the barrier. As a result, increasing the voltage may increase the emission. The peculiar barrier shape is thought to be caused by the presence of the electropositive barium layer.

Certain anomalies in oxide-cathode emission are explained if the interface between base metal and oxide is considered as electrically represented by a resistor shunted by a capacitor. The value of interface resistance is a variable dependent on operating conditions and the past history of the cathode.   The interface resistance seems due to formation of compounds between the barium and impurities in the nickel base such as silicon, aluminum, or titanium.   Emission inconsistencies in operation on short-time pulses and transients can be explained through use of the interface resistance and capacitance concept.

Oxide coatings are very susceptible to poisoning by oxygen and to damage by gas-ion bombardment.   Consequently, they are usually employed only in tubes with voltages below 1000, in which ionic energies are not likely to cause damage.

High instantaneous emissions can be obtained from oxide cathodes if short-time high-voltage pulses are applied to a tube.   These peak emissions, which may be as great as 100 amp per square centimeter, cannot be maintained, because of heating of the tube elements and release of gases.

Over 95 per cent of all radio tubes employ oxide coatings on either filaments or equipotential cathodes.   The reason is the low operating temperature, 900° to 1100°K, which requires small amounts of power for heating.   The relative emission efficiency is 100 to 1000 ma per watt.

4-9. Cathode Temperatures

The energy supplied in electrical form to a cathode will continue to raise the temperature of the cathode until a temperature is reached at which the rate of heat loss from the cathode balances the rate of heat input.   Since cathodes are usually operated in vacuum, heat can be removed from the cathode only by (1) radiation, (2) conduction along the leads, and (3) emission of electrons.   Even for tubes operated in gas, the pressure is usually so low that convection losses are small.

Lead losses are minor due to the small cross-sectional area, and usually amount to 5 per cent or less of the total cathode input. Cooling of the cathode by the energy carried away by the electrons ($2kT$) is small; the work function is also small.   The net energy therefore is computed as $2kT + eE_W$ = energy removed from the cathode per electron, in joules.   Multiplication by the number of electrons emitted per second yields the power removed in watts.   In gas tubes where the emission is very high, this small heat loss is partially compensated for by energy given the cathode by gas-ion bombardment.

As a result, the power supplied to the thermionic cathode must be almost entirely radiated to the surroundings. This requirement furnishes a means of determination of temperature where optical

TABLE 5

PROPERTIES OF TUNGSTEN*

Temp (°K)	Radiated Power Density† (w/m²)	Resistivity (ohm-meters)
500	97.1	1.056×10^{-7}
600	304	1.323×10^{-7}
700	764	1.609×10^{-7}
800	1,690	1.900×10^{-7}
900	3,220	2.194×10^{-7}
1000	6,020	2.493×10^{-7}
1100	10,270	2.794×10^{-7}
1200	16,600	3.098×10^{-7}
1300	25,700	3.408×10^{-7}
1400	38,300	3.719×10^{-7}
1500	55,200	4.036×10^{-7}
1600	77,400	4.355×10^{-7}
1700	106,200	4.678×10^{-7}
1800	141,900	5.005×10^{-7}
1900	186,400	5.335×10^{-7}
2000	240,400	5.667×10^{-7}
2100	305,000	6.006×10^{-7}
2200	382,000	6.348×10^{-7}
2300	472,000	6.691×10^{-7}
2400	577,000	7.039×10^{-7}
2500	698,000	7.391×10^{-7}
2600	838,000	7.749×10^{-7}
2700	996,000	8.104×10^{-7}
2800	1,176,000	8.470×10^{-7}
2900	1,378,000	8.833×10^{-7}
3000	1,605,000	9.204×10^{-7}

* Jones, H. A., and Langmuir, I., *Gen. Elec. Rev.*, **30**, 310, 354, 408 (1927).
† Outside a glass enclosure at a temperature of 293°K.

pyrometers are unavailable or cannot be used. Jones and Langmuir have measured very accurately for tungsten the input power per unit area of the cathode that will produce a given temperature. Such a temperature scale for tungsten is reproduced in Table 5 from the original Jones and Langmuir data. Similar tables have been prepared for thoriated tungsten, but one for oxide coatings is still uncertain owing to variations in surface conditions.

The data of Table 5, though experimentally determined, are theoretically based on the Stefan-Boltzmann radiation law,

$$W = e_T\sigma(T^4 - T_0^4) \qquad \text{v/m}^2, \qquad (4\text{-}15)$$

where

T = temperature of the cathode, °K,

T_0 = temperature of surroundings (ambient) °K,

σ = Stefan-Boltzmann constant = 5.77×10^{-8} w/m^2/deg^{4}K,

e_T = emissivity of the surface.

It is seen that Table 5 can apply only for tungsten surfaces. For other materials, e_T, the emissivity, may be radically different, since it depends on the surface conditions. Values of e_T for uncarbonized thoriated tungsten do not differ from those for pure tungsten, but for oxide-coated cathodes the emissivity is considerably different, and may vary over a wide range for cathodes prepared in different laboratories or by different processes.

Upon determination of the area of the cathode required to produce the desired emission current, the power needed to heat the cathode can be obtained by interpolation from Table 5. To this quantity 5 per cent may be added to provide for conduction losses in the leads. If the power input and area are known, the operating temperature can likewise be obtained from the table.

Example 1. A certain tungsten filament of 6 cm length and 0.01 cm diameter is to operate at a temperature of 2550°K. Find the heating power, the voltage, and current required.

$$\text{Surface area} = l\pi d = \frac{6.0}{100} \times \pi \times \frac{0.01}{100} = 0.0000188 \text{ m}^2.$$

Interpolation from the table yields 768,000 as the watts/m^2 radiated at 2550°K.

$$\text{Power} = \frac{W}{\text{m}^2} \times \text{area} = 768,000 \times 0.0000188 = 14.4 \text{ w.}$$

Addition of 5 per cent for lead losses gives

Total power input = 15.12 w.

Resistivity at 2550°K = 7.570 × 10⁻⁷ ohm-meters.

$$\text{Resistance of the filament} = \frac{\rho \times l}{\text{cross section}} = \frac{7.570 \times 10^{-7} \times \frac{8}{100}}{(\pi/4) \times (0.01/100)^2}$$

$$= 5.78 \text{ ohms.}$$

$$\text{Volts} = \sqrt{WR} = \sqrt{15.12 \times 5.78} = 9.34 \ V.$$

$$\text{Current} = \frac{V}{R} = \frac{9.34}{5.78} = 1.62 \text{ amp.}$$

This calculation neglects the voltage drop in the leads, so that the terminal voltage would have to be slightly higher.

Example 2.   The tungsten filament of Example 1 is to supply an emission current of 0.252 amp.   Find the temperature of operation.

$$I = A_0 S T^2 \epsilon^{-b_0/T}.$$

$$0.252 = 60.2 \times 10^4 \times 1.88 \times 10^{-5} T^2 \epsilon^{-52,400/T}.$$

$$2 \log T = \frac{0.4343 \times 52,400}{T} - \log \frac{11.32}{0.252}.$$

$$\log T = \frac{11,300}{T} - 0.826.$$

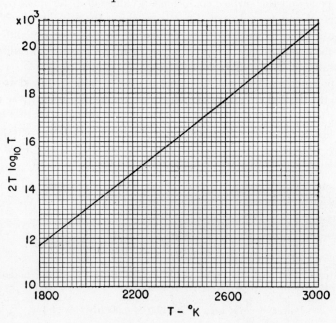

Fig. 4-13.   Plot of $2T \log T$ vs T (°K).

Try $T = 2600°K$; then

$$3.415 = 4.351 - 0.826 = 3.525.$$

Obviously the guess was low. Try $T = 2660°K$; then

$$3.425 = 4.248 - 0.826 = 3.422.$$

This is very nearly correct; the temperature should then be $2659°$ or $2658°K$.

The labor involved in the above may be reduced by rewriting Dushman's equation as

$$2T \log T = 0.4343b_0 - T \log \left(\frac{A_0 S}{I} \right).$$

Figure 4-13 may then be used to obtain values for the function on the left side of this equation.

4-10. Photoelectric Emission

It is found experimentally that emission of electrons may be caused by light striking a metal plate. Since light is a form of energy, *photoelectric* emission differs from thermal emission only in that the work function energy is supplied by light rather than by heat.

Photoelectric emission may be readily studied when the emitting plate is sealed into a vacuum tube, with a second electrode maintained at a positive potential to receive the electrons. A simple cell is shown in Fig. 4-14, in which the cathode forms the surface emitting the electrons and the anode is the receptor element.

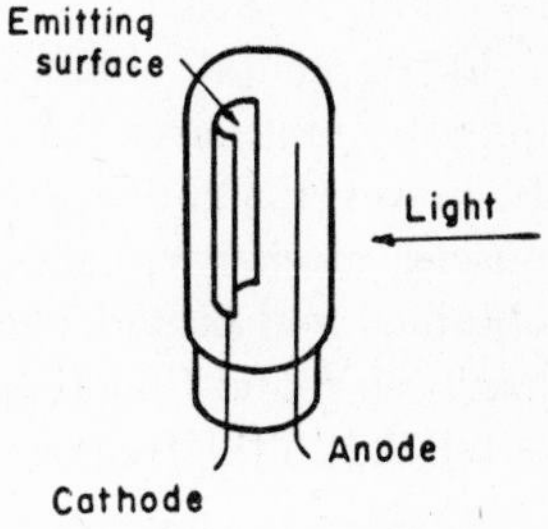

Observation of photoelectric phenomena with various intensities and sources

Fig. 4-14. Simple photo-emissive cell.

of light leads to the following conclusions concerning what takes place in the tube:

1. The number of electrons emitted per second varies linearly with the incident light intensity.
2. The maximum energy of any of the emitted electrons is a linear function of the frequency of the light.
3. The maximum energy of any of the emitted electrons is independent of the intensity of the light.
4. The emission of the electrons begins at the instant the light strikes the surface (within 10^{-9} sec).

Under the wave theory of light, the energy carried must be assumed as uniformly distributed throughout the light beam. As the intensity of light is increased the energy must increase. Therefore it would seem that the maximum kinetic energy, or velocity, of the emitted electrons would be expected to increase as the energy supplied by the light increases. That this reasoning is not valid is shown by (3) above, reinforced by (2), which shows the excess energy to be a function of frequency and not of total light energy impinging on the surface.

Again assuming the energy distributed uniformly throughout a beam of light, let the radiation from a 40-w tungsten lamp be allowed to fall on a sodium surface at a distance of one foot. Given the approximate number of atoms per square centimeter of surface and assuming that the emission might come from the top 10 layers of atoms, it can be shown (Ref. 21) that the energy reaching each sodium atom is so small that it would take 500 *days* for any one atom to accumulate enough energy to overcome the work function and emit an electron. Yet experiment shows such emission occurs in less than 10^{-9} sec!

Experimental observations listed as (3) and (4) above, consequently, are not explained on the basis of the wave theory of light. If, however, light is assumed to consist of discrete bundles, or corpuscles of energy, called *photons*, the corpuscular theory of light is obtained and provides explanation for the observed phenomena. It has been found that these photons carry an amount of energy which is related to the frequency as

$$W = hf \qquad \text{joules,} \qquad (4\text{-}16)$$

where h is Planck's constant.

If the energy of a photon is equal to, or greater than, the work function of a surface, it is possible for any photon to hit some particular surface atom with sufficient energy to cause emission of an electron. No storage of energy is needed, and emission occurs almost instantaneously with impact of the light or the photons. Also, since an increase in intensity of the light would merely increase the number of photons striking a unit area of a surface in unit time, and would not affect the energy per photon, the energy of the emitted electrons would be independent of the light intensity, thus supporting the third observation above. Since the amount of energy carried by a photon is proportional to frequency, the maximum energy of the emitted electrons can be anticipated as proportional to the frequency of the light, which explains (2) above. Increase in light intensity means more photons striking the surface per unit time, and, consequently, the number of electrons emitted will vary linearly with light intensity, as observed in (1) above.

The corpuscular theory is thus seen to provide simple explanations for all the observed data, whereas the wave theory completely fails on the last two points. However, it is not correct to conclude that the wave theory is in error. The corpuscular theory, thus far, has been unable to explain the phenomena of wave interference produced by slits and gratings. Consequently, it appears necessary to view light as having properties of both wave and corpuscle, either viewpoint being used as required to explain particular phenomena satisfactorily.

4-11. The Einstein Equation

On the basis of the law of conservation of energy, Einstein proposed the equation

$$hf = eE_W + \frac{mv^2}{2} \qquad (4\text{-}17)$$

as an explanation of the photoelectric effect. In principle, this equation states that hf, the energy of the impinging photon, is completely transferred to the emitted electron as energy, eE_W, to overcome the work function, and as kinetic energy, $mv^2/2$, of the electron after emission. Since the photon has given up all its energy, it ceases to exist and disappears.

Each photon does not necessarily produce an electron because many photons are reflected by the metal. However, it is reasonable to assume that as the number of photons increases with a brighter light, the number of photons causing emission of photo-electrons will increase in direct proportion, or (1) of the observations of the preceding section is satisfied.

The Einstein equation satisfactorily explains (2), since Equation 4-17 shows a linear relation between frequency of the light and the kinetic energy of the emitted electron. For a given surface, the term eE_W is a constant, and as the frequency of the photon increases, the excess energy contributed to the electron also increases and appears as kinetic energy.

Since the equation shows the value of kinetic energy of the electron to be dependent on the frequency of the light only, the maximum energy per electron is independent of the intensity of the light. Increased light means more photons striking the surface and more electrons emitted, but the energy of any given electron is fixed only by the energy of the individual photon which was absorbed by the atom in forcing emission of the electron. Therefore (3) of the observed data is explained.

Since eE_W is a constant for a particular surface, it is obvious that at some frequency f_0 given by

$$f_0 = \frac{eE_W}{h} \tag{4-18}$$

the current will become zero. This is a limiting or *threshold* frequency, no lower frequency having sufficient energy per photon to overcome the work function and cause emission.

Equation 4-18 furnishes a simple method of measuring the work functions of various materials by measurement of their threshold photoelectric frequency. If surfaces of high degrees of cleanliness are used, good checks can be obtained between values so obtained and those from thermionic methods. This agreement furnishes support for believing that the emissive phenomena are similar in the two cases.

4-12. Secondary Emission

It has been shown that if sufficient energy be transferred to an electron in a metal atom, the electron may be emitted. If the source of this energy is from mechanical impact of an electron or ion, the electrons emitted are called *secondary* electrons and the phenomenon is *secondary emission*. The original electrons, or other particles such as gas ions, are called *primary electrons, primary ions,* and so forth.

The phenomenon was reported by Sir Joseph Bragg in 1908, but intensive study of the subject has occurred only in recent years. The information obtained has made it possible to increase and control the emission, or to eliminate it in cases where its presence is undesirable.

To produce secondary emission, a surface of either a conductor or a nonconductor is bombarded by a high-energy beam of electrons or other particles. The secondary electrons which are knocked out of the surface, or emitted by reason of the energy contributed in mechanical form, will find their way to any electrode of higher potential in the region, and will constitute a flow of charge away from the bombarded surface, in contrast to the primary beam, which forms a charge flow to the surface.

The ratio of the number of secondary electrons emitted to the number of primary electrons, or equivalent charges, striking the surface per unit time is called δ, the *secondary-emission coefficient*. This coefficient may also be considered as the average number of secondary electrons liberated by each primary electron.

Early investigation of secondary-emission phenomena was hampered by imperfect high-vacuum technique and lack of understanding of the nature of surface impurities. More recent precision research allows the general properties of secondary emission to be summarized as follows:

1. The emission depends on the nature of the surface of the emitter.
2. The emission coefficient δ is a function of primary electron energy.
3. Velocities of the secondary electrons are small, since the emission energies are usually less than 20 ev.
4. Directions of emission are random.
5. Moderate temperature variations have no effect.

Measurements of secondary emission may be easily made with a special tube of the form indicated diagrammatically in Fig. 4-15. In this tube the electrons are accelerated by the potential on the

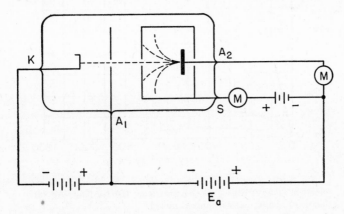

Fig. 4-15.   Measurement of secondary-emission coefficient.

first anode A_1 and are formed into a beam. The beam of electrons passes through a hole in the shield S surrounding the second anode A_2 and reaches this anode, whose surface is the subject of the test for secondary emission. Any secondary electrons emitted from the surface are attracted to the more positive shield, constituting a current flow to that electrode. The potential of the shield is sufficiently far above that of the second anode for all the secondary electrons to be attracted to the shield. The position of the first anode prevents electrons in the primary beam from reaching the shield.

Measurements of shield current and second-anode current permit calculation of the ratio δ, or the ratio of secondary to primary electrons. Variation of the energy of the electrons in the primary beam by changing the value of E_a allows the curves of Fig. 4-16 to be plotted. Various surfaces and surface conditions give different magnitudes of δ, but all surfaces show curves of the same relative shape, with a maximum δ at some particular energy of the primary

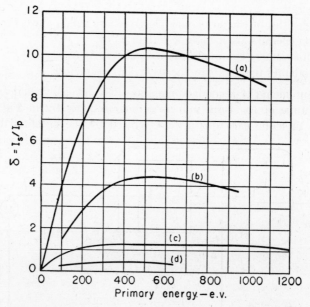

Fig. 4-16. Secondary-emission ratio as a function of primary electron energy: (a) Cs-Cs_2O-Ag surface; (b) Na-Na_2O-Ag surface; (c) nickel; (d) carbonized nickel.

beam. As the primary electron strikes the surface, it may collide with several atoms and free one or more electrons before its beam energy is entirely dissipated. When the energy of the primary electrons is increased, more collisions result and more energy is available to free or emit additional electrons. Consequently, the curve of δ rises with increased energy at first. However, as the energy of the individual primary electron is increased it penetrates further into the surface, possibly to 150 atom diameters; and although the number of collisions is increased, many of the electrons to which energy has been given are recaptured by other atoms on their way to the surface and are never emitted. As a result the curve falls at high energies. The curve then has a maximum in the neighborhood of 400 to 500 ev energy, depending on the surface and surface condition.

That the energies of the secondary electrons are small can be shown by reversing and varying the potential applied to the shield until the secondary electrons are no longer able to overcome the repelling field and reach the shield. Potentials of the order of 25 v are usually sufficient for this purpose. The average energy is usually between 5 and 10 v regardless of the energy of the primary beam.

4-13. Secondary-Emission Surfaces

Any material, metallic or nonmetallic, is capable of secondary emission, but high-emission surfaces seem to be those with low values of work function. Surface condition and treatment contribute greatly to emitting ability, since secondary emission is primarily a surface function. High-emission materials are usually composite surfaces, being in some ways similar to oxide-coated cathodes. A material having a very low emission is well-degassed graphite.

One of the better emitters, a monatomic layer of cesium on a cesium oxide layer on silver, has a maximum value of δ of over 10, as seen in Fig. 4-16. The theory of the surface action is not well understood but follows the general lines of oxide-coated-cathode theory. For cesium on cesium oxide, the work function may be reduced to about 0.5 v by proper sensitizing procedures.

The relative emission efficiency of a secondary-emission surface can be computed on an emission-per-watt basis, as for thermionic cathodes. If I_0 is the input current to the target in milliamperes, and V_0 the potential of the target, the power input to the target is

$I_0V_0/1000$ w.   The current emitted is δI_0 ma, so that the efficiency is

$$\text{emission per watt} = \frac{\delta I_0}{I_0V_0/1000} = \frac{1000}{V_0}\,\delta \qquad \text{ma/w.}$$

Relative efficiencies of the order of 60 ma per watt are obtainable, comparing with 50 to 75 ma per watt for oxide-coated cathodes. The maximum emission efficiency usually occurs at about 30 or 40 v accelerating potential on the target.

4-14. The Schottky Effect

When a positive potential is applied to the anode of a tube, a field is produced at the cathode to accelerate the electrons.   An electron at any point x in this field would have received an energy of eV joules to urge it away from the cathode, where V is the negative integral of the field intensity from cathode to x.   If then the accelerating energy given to an electron by the field is plotted as in Fig. 4-17, together with the retarding energy barrier due to the surface forces, the accelerating energy appears as a straight line, for a uniform field.

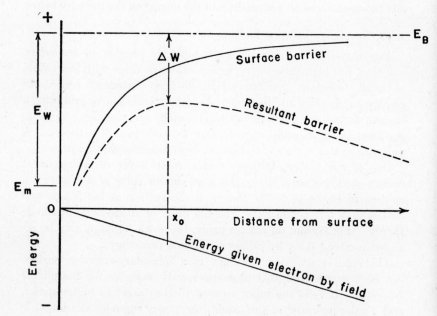

Fig. 4-17.   Lowering of the surface barrier by an electric field (Schottky effect).

Since these two effects are oppositely directed they produce a resultant surface energy barrier as shown by the dashed line. This will have a maximum at some distance x_0 from the surface.

If an electron in the metal has sufficient energy to enable it to reach x_0, it will be emitted because beyond x_0 it is under accelerating forces. The work function has then been lowered an amount ΔW, where

$$\Delta W = 2e\mathcal{E}x_0. \qquad (4\text{-}19)$$

At the point x_0, the forces on the electron are in equilibrium, or the image forces are equal to the field forces. By use of the image force from Eq. 4-6, this equilibrium gives

$$\frac{e^2}{16\pi\epsilon_v x_0^2} = e\mathcal{E}$$

or

$$x_0 = \frac{1}{4}\sqrt{\frac{e}{\mathcal{E}\epsilon_v\pi}} \qquad \text{m.} \qquad (4\text{-}20)$$

As an example, choose a field $\mathcal{E} = 100,000$ v/m. The distance x_0 to the top of the energy barrier is found to be only 6.0×10^{-8} m, or 600 A. The reduction ΔW due to the field $\mathcal{E}$ can then be calculated from the equation

$$\Delta W = 2 \times 1.60 \times 10^{-19} \times 10^5 \times 6.0 \times 10^{-8} = 19.2 \times 10^{-22} \text{ joule;}$$

and since 1 ev $= 1.60 \times 10^{-19}$ joule,

$$\Delta W = 1.20 \times 10^{-2} \text{ ev.}$$

Although this is a very small reduction in the work function, it is responsible for a noticeable increase in emission current as the applied voltage is increased.

By use of Eqs. 4-19 and 4-20, an expression for ΔW independent of x_0 can be obtained. This is

$$\Delta W = \frac{1}{2}\sqrt{\frac{e^3\mathcal{E}}{\pi\epsilon_v}} \text{ joules} = \frac{1}{2}\sqrt{\frac{e\mathcal{E}}{\pi\epsilon_v}} \text{ ev,} \qquad (4\text{-}21)$$

so that, considering this reduction, the value of the resultant work function E_W' is

$$E_W' = E_W - \frac{1}{2}\sqrt{\frac{e\mathcal{E}}{\pi\epsilon_v}}. \qquad (4\text{-}22)$$

The lowering of the work function due to an applied accelerating field is called the *Schottky effect*, after the man who first calculated its magnitude. As a result of the Schottky effect, the temperature saturation current from a thermionic cathode is to a small extent a function of the field applied to the cathode.

4-15. High-Field Emission

If the applied accelerating field at the cathode were indefinitely increased, a value might be reached at which the exponential in Eq. 4-9 would disappear, as a result of the reduction in E_B by the Schottky effect. This value can be calculated as occurring at fields of the order of 10^{10} v per meter for tungsten. However, as the field intensity is increased and the energy barrier height is lowered by ΔW, the distance to point x_0 is also reduced. At some limiting small value of x_0, it becomes possible for electrons to tunnel through the barrier as well as over it, and the emission increases to high values at fields as low as 10^8 v per meter.

This emission is called *high-field*, or *autoelectronic*, emission and is the principle employed in some types of cold-cathode devices. High-field emission is found to be independent of temperature and to follow a law

$$J = a\mathcal{E}^2\epsilon^{-b/\mathcal{E}} \qquad \text{amp/m}^2. \qquad (4\text{-}23)$$

The field between a point and a plane, or the field due to a fine wire centered in a cylinder, may reach values of high order without entailing application of unusually high voltages. For this reason, special design precautions are required in certain high-voltage x-ray and rectifier tubes, since currents of the magnitude encountered in high-field emission might damage the tubes. These precautions usually take the form of rounding all corners of the electrodes and of eliminating all sharp points at which electric fields might build up to excessive values.

PROBLEMS

4-1. Using the completely degenerate function for tungsten at 0°K, plot the energy distribution of the electrons. In computing E_M assume there are 1.23×10^{23} electrons per cubic centimeter (N).

4-2. Repeat Problem 4-1 for a tungsten temperature of 2600°K.

4-3. A ball of mass 0.2 kg is thrown vertically upward from the surface of the earth with a velocity of 60 meters per second. Find the distance which this ball may travel from the surface of the earth before being limited by the potential-energy barrier.

4-4. A certain tube has the following emission data taken:

J (amp/m²)	T (°K)	J (amp/m²)	T (°K)
0.0382	1900	6.94	2300
0.169	2000	19.52	2400
0.665	2100	50.37	2500
2.19	2200	116.9	2600
		275.1	2700

Determine by graphical means the values of the emission constants A_0 and b_0.

4-5. A thoriated-tungsten filament operating at 1950°K has an emission current of 90 ma. If a pure tungsten filament of the same length and diameter operates at the same temperature, what emission will be obtained? To what temperature must the tungsten filament be raised to secure emission equal to that of the original thoriated tungsten?

4-6. A cylindrical tungsten filament has a heated length of 1.25 in. and a diameter of 0.006 in. A cylindrical anode of 0.5 in. diameter surrounds this filament.

(a) What must be the voltage and current supplied to this filament if it is to operate at 2550°K? Assume that conduction losses are 5 per cent of the filament input.

(b) Determine the emission current obtainable at this temperature.

(c) How much additional filament length must be used if the same current is to be obtained with the filament operating at 2500°K?

4-7. The tungsten filament of a vacuum diode has a diameter of 0.009 in. and a length of 2.5 in.

(a) The filament input is 5.5 v, 5.0 amp. What is the value of the temperature-saturation current?

(b) Determine the filament operating temperature.

4-8. (a) To what value must the work function of a thoriated-tungsten surface be changed to raise the current density to 20,000 amp per square centimeter at a temperature of 2500°K?

(b) What value of field intensity could provide this reduction of work function?

4-9. The General Electric FP-400 high-vacuum diode has the following ratings and dimensions:

Filament

Material.............................. Tungsten
Voltage................................ 4.0 v
Current................................ 2.25 amp
Diameter.............................. 0.005 in.
Length................................ 1.25 in.
Lead resistance, excluding filament........ 0.08 ohm

Anode

Material.............................. Carbonized nickel
Diameter.............................. 0.620 in.

(a) Using the data on radiated power densities, calculate and plot the power radiated from the filament against T from 2000° to 2700°K.

(b) Assuming that 5 per cent of the power supplied is lost by lead heat conduction and allowing for lead resistance losses, find the temperature of the filament at rated voltage and current.

(c) Determine the resistance of the filament when it is operating at rated conditions.

(d) Calculate the emission current as a function of temperature for the range 500° to 2700°K. Plot I against T on semilog paper from 2000° to 2700°K.

4-10. A thoriated-tungsten filament is to be placed in the FP-400 diode of Problem 4-9. This material follows the tungsten radiated power table. Find the power input, and the emitted current, assuming 5 per cent losses for heat conduction, and operation at 1950°K.

4-11. A large oxide-coated cathode is to have an emission current of 100 amp when operated at 1050°K.

(a) Determine the surface area needed.

(b) Find the surface area of tungsten needed if operated at the same temperature as the oxide-coated cathode.

(c) If operated at 2500°K.

4-12. At 2400°K a tungsten filament is observed to increase its emission periodically by amounts up to 5 per cent. What change in value of work function E_W is required to explain this change?

4-13. A tungsten filament, operating at 2450°K, is to deliver an emission of 1 amp with 10 v heating potential applied. Find the filament length, diameter, current, and heating power, if conduction of heat by the filament leads is neglected.

4-14. A cylindrical anode of 1.0 in. length and 0.375 in. diameter is formed of a material having an emissivity of 0.37. Coaxial with this anode is a thoriated-tungsten filament of 1.0 in. length and 0.0075 in. diameter, operating at a temperature of 1970°K. If the anode is operated at a positive potential of 750 v and saturation current flows from the filament, find the temperature of the anode surface. (Neglect heat losses from the ends of the filament and anode cylinder and assume the ambient temperature is 293°K.)

4-15. A surface of nickel is struck by photons given off by a mercury vapor discharge, having a wavelength of 2537 A. Find the velocity of the highest-velocity electron which may be emitted.

4-16. The contact potential between two surfaces is 1.00 v, surface A

being positive to B. When surface A is struck by light of wavelength 2537 A it requires 0.46 v negative on surface B to stop the flow of current between the two surfaces.

(a) What is the work function of surface A?

(b) What threshold wavelength exists for surface A?

4-17. A cesium-surface photocell has a work function of 1.81 v.

(a) Find the threshold wave length for this surface.

(b) This surface is struck by green light of 5300 A wavelength. If electrons are emitted, what will be the maximum velocity of emission?

4-18. (a) Calculate the energy carried by photons of red light of 6439 A; yellow light of 5895 A; ultraviolet of 3302 A and 2537 A.

(b) Each of the photons of (a) strikes a sodium surface having a work function of 1.9 v. If electrons are emitted, find their velocities.

4-19. Threshold wavelengths are measured for platinum at 2570 A; potassium, 7000 A; cadmium, 3140 A; and magnesium, at 3430 A.

(a) Compute the work functions.

(b) What reversed potential would have to be applied to the tube of Fig. 4-14 just to prevent emission of electrons from each of the above materials, if the surfaces were struck by light of wavelength 5500 A?

4-20. A flash of light from the ultraviolet line of mercury at 2537 A, lasting 0.05 sec, strikes a sodium surface with area of 1.5 sq cm in a phototube. The surface has a work function of 1.9 v, and the light has a power density of 0.5 w per square centimeter. If half the photons cause the emission of an electron, find the current flowing during the flash.

4-21. If secondary electrons are emitted with average energy of 10 ev, and δ for a particular surface is 9, find the energy efficiency of emission if the primary beam has fallen through 400 v and the surface work function is 0.86 v.

REFERENCES

1. Arnold, H. D., "Phenomena in Oxide-Coated Filament Electron Tubes," *Phys. Rev.* **16,** 70 (1920).

2. Richardson, O. W., *Emission of Electricity from Hot Bodies*, 2d ed., Longmans, Green & Co., New York, 1921.

3. Langmuir, I., "The Electron Emission from Thoriated-Tungsten Filaments," *Phys. Rev.* **22,** 357 (1923).

4. Wehnelt, A., *Ann. Physik*, **14,** 425 (1904).

5. Dushman, S., "Electron Emission from Metals as a Function of Temperature," *Phys. Rev.*, **21,** 623 (1923).

6. ———— "Thermal Emission of Electrons," *International Critical Tables*, VI, 53, McGraw-Hill Book Company, Inc., New York, 1929.

7. ———— "Thermionic Emission," *Revs. Modern Phys.*, **2,** 381 (1930).

8. Jones, H. A., and Langmuir, I., "Characteristics of Tungsten Filaments as Functions of Temperature," *Gen. Elec. Rev.*, **30**, 310, 354, 408 (1927).

9. Becker, J. A., "Phenomena in Oxide-Coated Filaments," *Phys. Rev.*, **34**, 1323 (1929); **38**, 2193 (1931).

10. Reimann, A. L., *Thermionic Emission*, John Wiley & Sons, Inc., New York, 1934.

11. Prescott, C. H., and Morrison, J., "The True Temperature Scale of an Oxide-Coated Filament," *Rev. Sci. Inst.*, **10**, 36 (1939).

12. Blewett, J. P., "Properties of Oxide-Coated Cathodes," *J. Appl. Phys.*, **10**, 668, 831 (1939).

13. Coombes, E. A., "Pulsed Properties of Oxide Cathodes," *J. Appl. Phys.*, **17**, 647 (1946).

14. Marton, L., *Advances in Electronics*, Vol. 1, Academic Press, Inc., New York, 1948.

15. Eisenstein, A., "The Leaky-Condenser Oxide Cathode Interface," *J. Appl. Phys.*, **22**, 138 (1951).

16. Bartley, W. P., and White, J. E., "Characteristic Shifts in Oxide-Cathode Tubes," *Elec. Eng.*, **71**, 496 (1952).

17. Compton, K. T., and Langmuir, I., "Electrical Discharges of Gases," *Revs. Modern Phys.*, **3**, 241 (1931).

18. Campbell, N., "On Emission of Delta Rays," *Phil. Mag.*, **22**, 276 (1911).

19. Woolridge, D. E., "Theory of Secondary Emission," *Phys. Rev.*, **56**, 562 (1939).

20. Glover, A. M., "A Review of the Development of Sensitive Phototubes," *Proc. IRE*, **29**, 413 (1941).

21. Richtmyer, F. K., and Kennard, E. H., *Introduction to Modern Physics*, 4th ed., McGraw-Hill Book Company, Inc., New York, 1947.

22. Herring, C., and Nichols, M. H., "Thermionic Emission," *Revs. Modern Phys.*, **21**, 185 (1949).

CHAPTER 5

SPACE CHARGE IN VACUUM TUBES

A vacuum tube consists of an assemblage of metallic electrodes in an evacuated container. The system of terminology is based on the number of electrodes mounted in the space. When a tube consists of only two electrodes, a cathode and an anode, it is called a *diode*. As additional electrodes are added, the tube becomes in turn a *triode*, *tetrode*, *pentode*, *hexode*, and so on. The first tube of the line, both historically and in simplicity, is the diode. Since it is the basis for all the other types, many phenomena associated with all can be most conveniently studied in the diode. One such matter is that of the effects of the charges carried by the electrons in altering the potential of points in the space between cathode and anode and controlling the flow of current.

5-1. Experimental Determination of Current in a Diode

The performance characteristics of an electric device can be conveniently expressed in a volt-ampere diagram. In plotting such a curve for a simple diode consisting of a cathode surface heated to a temperature T_1, and an anode or plate, it is found that for low potentials between anode and cathode only a small current flows. This current increases as the voltage is raised, until at some particular value of voltage the current levels off, or saturates, and further large increases of voltage result in only very small current increases. This would be a curve such as is plotted for temperature T_1 in Fig. 5-1. If now the cathode temperature is raised to a value T_2 and a new curve is plotted, the lower part of the curve is identical to that for T_1, but as the saturation point for T_1 is reached the curve continues upward until it in turn saturates at a higher level of current.

The volt-ampere curve, then, consists of three regions. The first part, A to B, indicates that some electrons are emitted with sufficient energy to reach the anode without the aid of an accelerating field.

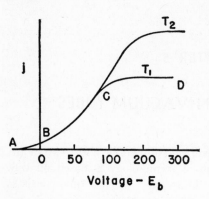

Fig. 5-1.   Volt-ampere diagram for a
diode.

In the second part, B to C, the current received at the anode is less than the current which it is known (by the Dushman equation) can be emitted from the cathode. The reason for this behavior remains to be investigated. In the region C to D all the electrons emitted are being attracted to the anode, and any further increase of current is impossible at the same temperature T_1. If the temperature is raised to T_2, a higher current is emitted, and at a higher voltage all the electrons are again attracted to the anode, and saturation is once more reached.

Actually, when the voltage is increased above the value required for saturation, the current also increases at a very slow rate, even though the Dushman equation gives only one possible value for the emitted current. This slight increase of current is due to the reduction of the work function by the Schottky effect as the applied field at the cathode is raised. For thoriated-tungsten and oxide-coated cathodes, the increase in current is much larger than predicted by the Schottky

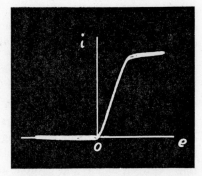

Fig. 5-2.   Oscillogram showing volt-ampere diagram of the FP-400 diode with tungsten filament.

equation, so that thoriated tungsten shows only partial saturation and oxide coatings show almost none at all.

5-2. Field Conditions at the Cathode Surface

As discussed in the previous chapter, some electrons emitted from a thermionic cathode in a vacuum possess energies in excess of the work-function value, and this excess energy appears as kinetic energy of the emitted electron. This surplus energy is of the order of 0.5 ev or less on the average, so that the resulting velocities are small.

To explain the action in the region B-C of Fig. 5-1, consider a diode without positive voltage applied to the anode. At the instant of heating the cathode, a cloud of electrons is emitted, filling the space around the cathode with negative charge. The electrons at the cathode surface are then faced with a repelling electric field due to the electrons already in the space, and the electrons having low amounts of excess energy above E_W are not emitted.

Electrons of higher excess energy overcome the repelling field and pass into space, increasing the negative charge there and raising the repelling field at the cathode surface. Equilibrium conditions will be reached when the negative charge in the space increases to the point where the repelling electric field at the cathode surface is just sufficient to prevent even the highest-energy electrons from leaving the cathode region.

If the anode is now made positive with respect to the cathode, electrons are attracted from the space cloud to the anode. This movement reduces the repelling field at the cathode surface and allows some of the highest-energy electrons to leave the cathode and enter the space. Lower-energy electrons are still unable to overcome the repelling field at the cathode surface. Equilibrium is reached at some new value of space-charge density at which the number of electrons taken by the anode is balanced by the number able to leave the cathode.

Equilibrium at any other value would lead to unstable conditions: if equilibrium were at a value of current leaving the cathode above that reaching the anode, the space charge would grow until the field at the cathode reduced the number of electrons leaving; if equilibrium were at a value of current leaving the cathode below that reaching the anode, the space charge would decrease until more electrons were permitted to leave the cathode.

If the anode voltage is increased, the repulsion due to space charge is partially canceled by the anode field, electrons having slightly lower energies are permitted to leave the cathode, and the current increases. The space-charge cloud of electrons acts as a *velocity filter*, permitting only electrons with velocities or energies above a certain minimum to leave the cathode region. The space charge also serves as a reservoir of emitted or free electrons. Since the emission of electrons from cathodes is actually quite erratic and irregular with respect to time, the space-charge reservoir acts as a surge tank to smooth out considerably the flow of electrons to the anode.

To explain the action, consider two large parallel plates separated by a distance d. If a potential is applied between the plates, the potential distribution in the space d would be as the straight line in Fig. 5-3. The slope of this line is the potential gradient $= dV/dx$. If now the left-hand, or negative, plate is raised to a high temperature, electrons are emitted from it and enter the space. The presence of the negative electrons in the space lowers the potential at all intermediate points, as is shown by the curve for space charge in Fig. 5-3. The effect of the concentration of electrons near the cathode in lowering the space potential to a negative value is shown, thereby producing a negative gradient, or repelling field (negative slope of curve), at the cathode surface. As the potential minimum is raised or lowered in value by changes in electron density or by anode potential, the repelling field or slope of the curve at the cathode surface changes, and more or fewer electrons are enabled to leave the cathode region. The potential minimum set up by the space charge is usually quite close to the cathode and is sometimes referred to as a *virtual cathode* because it may be regarded as the virtual source of the electrons flowing to the plate.

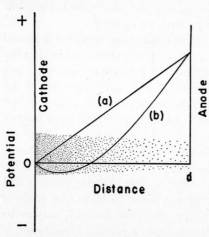

Fig. 5-3. Potential variation and electron density in a diode: (a) no space charge present; (b) with space charge.

If the anode voltage is raised, the potential minimum rises, the repelling field is decreased at the cathode surface, and the current rises. If the anode voltage is lowered, the potential minimum drops and the current decreases.

5-3. The Space-Charge Equation

In 1911 C. D. Child and in 1913 I. Langmuir (Ref. 1) independently derived the law that explains the limitation of current flow by the space charge.

Assume two very large (theoretically infinite) parallel plates positioned as shown in Fig. 5-4. Let the left-hand plate at the origin be heated to a very high temperature so that the emission will always

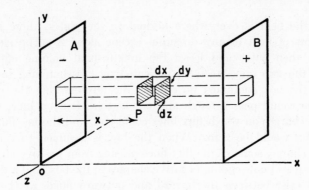

Fig. 5-4. Analysis of the parallel-plane diode with space charge.

be larger than any demands for electrons, or the current will never be temperature-saturated. The right-hand plate, or anode, is left cold and a positive potential E_b is applied with respect to the left-hand plate, or cathode. These two plates exist in a vacuum sufficiently good that no collisions of electrons with gas atoms need be considered.

Since the surfaces are so large, fringing of the electric field may be neglected, and the electric field will be uniform and everywhere perpendicular to the surfaces. Electrons that are emitted from A pass across the space under the influence of the positive potential on B and constitute a current of J amp per square meter of electrode area.

If ρ is the density of charge per unit volume at some point P, and v is the average velocity with which the charge is moving, then, since the electrons are negative charges,

$$J = -\rho v \qquad \text{amp/m}^2. \qquad (5\text{-}1)$$

Considering a volume of charge as that indicated by the infinitesimal cube of sides dx, dy, dz, shown in Fig. 5-4 at a distance x from the cathode, the negative charge enclosed in this volume is

$$dq = -\rho \, dx \, dy \, dz. \qquad (5\text{-}2)$$

Gauss's law states that the electric flux outward from a volume is equal to the total charge enclosed within the volume. The outward electric flux from the infinitesimal volume is thus given by Eq. 5-2.

Since the field is everywhere normal to the plates, there is no component of field in any direction except along x. The electric flux will then enter and leave the infinitesimal volume entirely through the two opposite faces indicated by crosshatching in Fig. 5-4. If the box contained no charge, the flux entering the right-hand face would pass through and out of the left-hand face, there being no charges on which flux lines could end, and the net flux *out* of the box would be zero. When the box is assumed to contain negative charge, some of the flux lines passing from positive charges on anode B will now end on negative charges in the box, and a difference will exist between the inward and outward fluxes at the box ends. If inward flux is designated negative and outward flux as positive, then passing *in* through the right-hand face is a total flux equal to $-D_2 \, dy \, dz$, if D_2 is the flux density over that face. Passing *out* of the left face is a total flux $D_1 \, dy \, dz$, if D_1 is the flux density over that face. The net *outward* flux, then, is

$$(D_1 - D_2) \, dy \, dz = -\rho \, dx \, dy \, dz,$$

or

$$D_2 - D_1 = \rho \, dx. \qquad (5\text{-}3)$$

The box is of elemental length in the x direction, so that the rate of change of flux density dD/dx can be stated as

$$\frac{dD}{dx} = \frac{D_2 - D_1}{dx} = \rho$$

since $(D_2 - D_1)$ is the change in flux density in the box length dx. Also, $D = \epsilon_v \mathcal{E}$ in the evacuated region ($\epsilon_v = 10^7/4\pi c^2$, the permittivity of space), so that it is possible to write

$$\frac{d\mathcal{E}}{dx} = \frac{\rho}{\epsilon_v}. \qquad (5\text{-}4)$$

Now, by definition, $\varepsilon = -dV/dx$, so that

$$\frac{d^2V}{dx^2} = -\frac{\rho}{\epsilon_v} \qquad (5\text{-}5)$$

describes the effect of the charge on the electric flux at any point P, where V is the potential of the point P in the space. This relation is known as *Poisson's equation in one dimension*.

The kinetic energy of an electron at point P is dependent on its energy of emission and the potential through which it has fallen in reaching P, or

$$\frac{mv^2}{2} = Ve + \frac{mv_0^2}{2}. \qquad (5\text{-}6)$$

Since the initial energy $mv_0^2/2$ is usually less than 1 ev, it will be small compared with the energy acquired in falling through potentials usually encountered in vacuum tubes, and may be neglected with respect to the term Ve.

Then, by use of Eqs. 5-1 and 5-6, Eq. 5-5 becomes

$$\frac{d^2V}{dx^2} = \frac{J}{\epsilon_v v} = \frac{J}{\epsilon_v \sqrt{2Ve/m}}. \qquad (5\text{-}7)$$

Multiplying both sides by $2\dfrac{dV}{dx}$,

$$2\frac{dV}{dx}\frac{d^2V}{dx^2} = \frac{2J}{\epsilon_v \sqrt{2e/m}}\, V^{-1/2} \frac{dV}{dx}.$$

Upon integration, this yields

$$\left(\frac{dV}{dx}\right)^2 = \frac{4J}{\epsilon_v \sqrt{2e/m}}\, V^{1/2} + C_1. \qquad (5\text{-}8)$$

It has already been reasoned that at the cathode surface, where the potential V is zero, there is a small negative, or repelling, field. Consequently, the constant C_1 is equal to the square of this small negative field. Experiment has shown that although this field is present, it is so small that no appreciable error is introduced into the value of current flowing if the surface field or the constant C_1 is neglected. By inspection of Fig. 5-3, it can be seen that the field (slope) with space charge is actually zero at some point very close to the cathode. In effect, then, for purposes of this analysis, the cathode surface is moved out this small distance.

Taking the square root of Eq. 5-8 and rearranging terms,

$$V^{-1/4}\, dV = \frac{2}{\sqrt[4]{2e/m}} \sqrt{\frac{J}{\epsilon_v}}\, dx.$$

Again performing an integration,

$$\frac{4}{3}\, V^{3/4} = \frac{2}{\sqrt[4]{2e/m}} \sqrt{\frac{J}{\epsilon_v}}\, x + C_2; \qquad (5\text{-}9)$$

and since at $x = 0$, $V = 0$, then $C_2 = 0$.

Then, selecting as particular values of potential and distance those at the anode, E_b and d, Eq. 5-9 may be written in terms of current density J reaching the anode as

$$J = \frac{\epsilon_v}{2.25} \sqrt{\frac{2e}{m}} \frac{E_b^{3/2}}{d^2} \qquad \text{amp/m}^2. \qquad (5\text{-}10)$$

Inserting values for the constants,

$$J = 2.34 \times 10^{-6} \frac{E_b^{3/2}}{d^2} \qquad \text{amp/m}^2, \qquad (5\text{-}11)$$

where d is the anode-cathode separation in meters. This is known as the *Langmuir-Child law*, the *three-halves power law*, or the *space-charge equation*, and applies for very large parallel-plane electrodes.

This equation predicts the value of current obtained in the region *B-C* of Fig. 5-1, and shows that the charge due to the electrons in the space is the factor that limits the current to a value less than the total emission. The Dushman equation then predicts the number of electrons that *may* be emitted from a given cathode at temperature $T;$ the Langmuir-Child law establishes the net number of electrons which actually reach the anode. The current can never be greater than the emission value, but it may be less owing to the space-charge limitation. Most vacuum-tube operation is in the region of space-charge control of the current.

The space-charge equation shows that the current is an inverse function of the square of the electrode separation; consequently, to avoid the necessity for high voltages, cathode-anode spacings are usually small. The current is also proportional to the three-halves power of the applied voltage, and this indicates that a vacuum diode is essentially a nonlinear, as well as unilateral, circuit device. It does not obey the ordinary linear circuit relations, and superposition and other network theorems either cannot be applied or must be used with special consideration. For these reasons it has been necessary to develop certain specialized methods to permit the analysis of circuits containing diodes and other vacuum tubes.

Langmuir also obtained an expression for the space-charge-limited current of a diode with long concentric cylindrical electrodes. This expression is

$$i = 14.7 \times 10^{-6} \frac{lE_b^{3/2}}{r_a \beta^2} \qquad \text{amp,} \qquad (5\text{-}12)$$

where l is the length of the cylinders and r_a is the anode radius in consistent units. Note that this equation is for total current flow and not current density.

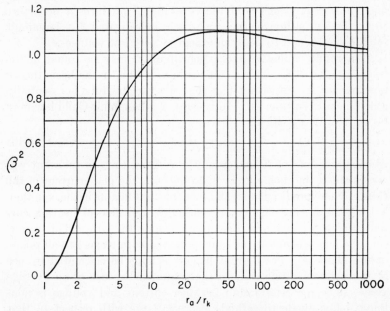

Fig. 5-5.   Values of the constant β^2.

The factor β is a function of $\log_e r_a/r_k$ (r_k being the cathode radius), which appears as a result of integrating the field differential equations in cylindrical coordinates and is expressed by a series (Ref. 2):

$$\beta = \ln \frac{r_a}{r_k} - \frac{2}{5}\left(\ln \frac{r_a}{r_k}\right)^2 + \frac{11}{120}\left(\ln \frac{r_a}{r_k}\right)^3 - \cdots .$$

Values of β^2 have been calculated for ratios of r_a/r_k, and are plotted in Fig. 5-5.

5-4. Departures from Theory

When actual diodes are tested, it is found that very few tubes have values for the constant of proportionality, or for the exponent of E_b, which exactly check those given in the theoretical Langmuir-Child relation. One of the most important reasons for this discrepancy is that no tube can be built to meet exactly the assumptions set up. A practical tube cannot have infinite plane electrodes or infinitely long cylindrical electrodes and some fringing of fields and changes in shape are unavoidable. Presence of residual gas atoms also produces deviation from theory by electron-atom collisions and ionization. Neglect of the constant C_1 produces a departure from theory, although this has been investigated by Langmuir (Ref. 4) and found to be small except at very low voltages.

As a result, values of the exponent of E_b may be found in the range of 1.3 to 1.8. This result neither invalidates the basic theory nor changes the important fact that the vacuum tube is essentially a nonlinear circuit device. In general, the Langmuir-Child law may be written for a particular tube as

$$i_b = KE_b{}^a, \tag{5-13}$$

where the values of K and a may vary from tube to tube but will center about the theoretical values, and i_b is the plate current of the tube. Therefore K includes all other constant factors in the equation.

In tubes having filamentary cathodes, the flow of heating current produces a potential distribution along the wire. This means that the anode is not at the same potential with respect to all points of the filament. The current flowing cannot be calculated by use of the voltage to one end, to the center, or by use of an average value, since the relationship between current and voltage is nonlinear. For anode to cathode voltages large with respect to that of the filament, the effect may be neglected, but for anode to cathode voltages of the order of the filament voltage, the exponent a takes on the value $5/2$.

If Eq. 5-13 is rewritten as

$$\log i_b = \log K + a \log E_b, \tag{5-14}$$

data taken on a particular tube and plotted on log-log paper should yield a straight line. Determination of the slope and intercept of this line will yield values for K and a.

5-5. Transit Time

Equation 5-11 states the relation between current density and potential at the anode. If Eq. 5-9 is solved for J and this result is equated to the value of current density in Eq. 5-11, then since the current density at all points in the space must be equal, there results

$$\frac{V^{3/2}}{x^2} = \frac{E_b^{3/2}}{d^2}.$$

Solving for V gives the potential at any point x in the space as

$$V = E_b \left(\frac{x}{d}\right)^{4/3} \qquad \text{v.} \qquad (5\text{-}15)$$

This potential distribution does not reflect the potential minimum (due to the electron concentration near the cathode) because the constant C_1 was dropped in the derivation. Had it been determined, the potential distribution predicted in Eq. 5-15 would be of the form of the space-charge distribution in Fig. 5-3.

Since $v = \sqrt{2Ve/m}$, from Eq. 5-15 the velocity at any point is

$$v = \sqrt{\frac{2eE_b}{m}} \left(\frac{x}{d}\right)^{2/3} = \frac{dx}{dt}, \qquad (5\text{-}16)$$

and integration over the full *transit time* gives

$$t_1 = \frac{d}{\dfrac{\sqrt{\dfrac{2eE_b}{m}}}{3}} = \frac{d}{v_{\text{av}}} \qquad (5\text{-}17)$$

as the transit time for the electron.

In a vacuum tube with a cathode-anode spacing of 2 mm and anode voltage of 100 v, the transit time is found to be 0.001 μsec, which is equal to the time of a cycle of a 1000-megacycle wave.

5-6. Effects of Transit Time

The space-charge law was derived for steady-state conditions under the assumption that the potential acting during the flight of an electron is constant. Under such equilibrium conditions, the space charge is stable and constant, and the current density is given by $-\rho v$ at any point in the space.

Changes in space charge, and position and depth of the potential minimum, have been discussed as affected by changes in anode potential. Suppose that a sudden change is made, reducing the anode potential. This change calls for redistribution of charge in the space; but owing to the finite time of transit developed above, the redistribution cannot take place instantaneously.

At an instant after the change, electrons leave the cathode under influence of the new anode potential while electrons which left the cathode under the preceding value are approaching the anode. This means that the current induced in the anode circuit by the approaching electrons does not immediately change to a new value, since finite time is required for the electron flow in the space to be fully adjusted. Obviously, if the changes in anode voltage are produced by a high frequency, such that the anode voltage shifts appreciably during the time of transit of a single electron, the space conditions will always be in a transient state, and changes in current will be delayed, or the current will lag the voltage.

The readjustment, or change in the charge distribution in the space, causes an induced current to flow in the anode circuit. Since this redistribution of space charge is due to a change in potential, or field, the induced current is found proportional to the rate of change of field. The actual current in the anode circuit is that produced by the steady-state-charge motion set up before the potential change, plus the induced current. This total current is the same at all points in the circuit.

Maxwell has shown that total current through any space is made up of two parts: the ordinary conduction, or equilibrium, current and another component he has called the displacement current. This latter component is established as proportional to the time rate of change of electric field, and exists only when potentials are changing. The total current density J_t in the space of the diode is then

$$J_t = J_c + J_d = -\rho v + \epsilon_v \frac{d\mathcal{E}}{dt} \qquad (5\text{-}18)$$

At low frequencies J_d is small, since $d\mathcal{E}/dt$ is small, the important term is the steady-state current J_c, and the steady-state concept is applicable. As the frequency is raised, $d\mathcal{E}/dt$ increases, and at frequencies of 10^8 or higher the term is important. At a nominal frequency where both terms are comparable, the conduction-current term, for applied sinusoidal anode potential, becomes

$$J_c = k_1 V_m \sin \omega t.$$

The displacement-current component is a function of the rate of change of the field intensity $\mathcal{E}$. The value of $\mathcal{E}$ under the applied sinusoidal emf, with large plane electrodes assumed, is

$$\mathcal{E} = -k_2 \frac{V_m}{d} \sin \omega t.$$

Consequently, the total current density is

$$J_t = k_1 V \sin \omega t - k_2 \epsilon_v \frac{\omega V_m}{d} \cos \omega t, \tag{5-19}$$

which indicates a lag of the resultant current behind the voltage, as reasoned above.

5-7. Power Loss in the Diode

If the velocities of emission are neglected, the electrons will arrive at the anode of the diode with an energy given by

$$W = E_b e. \tag{5-20}$$

As the electrons are stopped by the impact with the anode, the energy conveyed by the electrons is converted into heat. In the use of voltages above about 50,000, a minor amount of the energy is also converted into x radiation.

The rate of arrival of energy, or the power delivered to the anode by n electrons per second, is

$$P = \frac{W}{t} = \frac{E_b n e}{t}. \tag{5-21}$$

The term ne/t, or charge delivered per second, is the current flowing, so that

$$P = E_b I_b \qquad \text{w.} \tag{5-22}$$

By use of the space-charge law for current,

$$I_b = K E_b^{3/2};$$

then $\qquad\qquad P = K E_b^{5/2} \qquad\qquad$ w. $\qquad$ (5-23)

This is the power loss in the tube due to space-current flow.

Because this total power must be removed from the anode largely by radiation, the anode area and material must be such as to be able to dissipate the received power without an excessive temperature rise. The temperature rise is limited by the melting point of the anode material, by release of gas from the metal at high temperatures and resultant loss of vacuum, and the allowable temperature rise of the glass or metal envelope of the tube. In receiving tubes the anodes are usually made of nickel blackened to improve radiation abilities, and are operated at maximum temperatures below that at which they would show any color.

In higher-power radiation-cooled transmitting tubes the anodes may be of molybdenum, tantalum, or graphite. The first two permit high dissipation rates because of their high melting points and graphite is desirable because of its high emissivity, approximating 0.9. Graphite is apt to have considerable amounts of occluded gas which must be removed by high-temperature treatment in the exhaust process; tantalum, on the other hand, actually tends to absorb gases at high temperatures and may improve the vacuum. The tubes with molybdenum or tantalum anodes are designed to operate at temperatures at which the anode will show cherry-red to bright-yellow colors.

Another class of tubes are conduction-cooled either by water or forced air. The very large high-power tubes of 5- to 100-kw ratings fall in this class. They are made usually with an external copper anode, sealed to the glass cathode insulation by special seals. The copper anode may be placed in a water jacket for water cooling or it may have copper fins through which air is blown for forced air cooling.

Since the performance of a tube is so definitely limited by operating temperature regardless of the combination of voltage and current that produce the loss and temperature rise, tubes used for appreciable power output are given ratings in terms of the allowable anode loss or plate dissipation. In this respect they differ basically from other types of electric machinery, which are usually rated in terms of power output rather than in terms of their losses.

PROBLEMS

5-1. (a) For a diode with parallel electrodes, spaced 0.5 cm and with $E_b = 300$ v, plot the variation of potential across the space under the assumption of space-charge conditions and negligible emission velocities of the electrons.

(b) Plot also the variation of electric field between cathode and anode as a function of distance.

(c) Make a similar plot of charge density, and of velocity of the electrons. What relationship between v and ρ is indicated? Why is this true?

5-2. The tungsten cathode of Problem 5-1 is at a temperature of 2500°K.

(a) Will the current be temperature- or space-charge-limited?

(b) What value of current density reaches the anode?

(c) How much power will the anode have to dissipate per unit area?

5-3. A tungsten filament of length 1.1 in. and diameter 0.009 in. is operated at the center of a cylindrical anode of 0.395 in. diameter, and 1.1 in. length. The filament operates at 2450°K. Find the anode voltage needed if the anode current is to be 3 ma.

5-4. A parallel-plane thoriated-tungsten cathode is to supply a total current of 25 amp at a temperature of 1900°K.

(a) Find the total heating power required.

(b) This value of current is flowing to a parallel-plane anode at a distance of 0.75 cm, and maintained at a positive potential with respect to the cathode. If the anode emissivity is 0.40 find the temperature reached by the anode, assuming radiation from one side only, that the cathode heat is otherwise dissipated, and that the surrounding temperature is 20°C.

5-5. The tungsten filament of a cylindrical-plate diode has a diameter of 0.009 in. and a length of 2 in. The anode diameter is 0.75 in. If 5 amp at 5 v is supplied to the filament, at what anode potential will the current become temperature-limited?

5-6. A cylindrical-plate diode, with a thoriated-tungsten filament of length 3 cm and diameter 0.06 cm, has a filament temperature of 1900°K. The anode diameter is 2 cm.

If the current through the tube is to be one-tenth of temperature saturation value, what anode-cathode voltage should be used?

5-7. A certain vacuum diode on test shows that 40 v is required to cause 200 ma anode current.

(a) How much voltage is required if the anode current is to be increased to 350 ma, assuming sufficient emission?

(b) What is the maximum current which can flow without causing the anode loss to exceed 25 w?

(c) If the anode area is 4 cm² and emissivity 0.6, what will be the anode temperature rise above a 20°C ambient, for part (b)?

5-8. Given a cylindrical tungsten filament whose length is 1 in. and diameter 0.004 in. Concentric with this filament is a tantalum anode whose diameter is 0.5 in. and length 1 in.

(a) What must be the power input to the filament if it is to operate at 2450°K?

(b) What is the temperature saturation current of this tube?

(c) What anode current will be obtained at a potential of 100 v?

5-9. A certain FP-400 diode was used to obtain the following data:

E_b (v)	I_b (ma)	E_b (v)	I_b (ma)
5.0	0.34	20.0	2.77
10.0	0.96	25.0	3.98
15.0	1.75	29.7	5.02

Determine graphically the values of the constant K and the exponent a for this tube.

5-10. A parallel-plane diode has an anode-cathode spacing of 0.25 cm. If 125 v is applied with anode positive, find:

(a) The velocity with which an electron reaches the anode.

(b) The average velocity with and without space charge.

(c) The time of transit with and without space charge present.

5-11. A filament is made of oxide-coated ribbon 0.125 in. wide, is 1.5 in. long, and is operated at 1050°K. Assuming that it approximates a plane cathode surface, what current will reach a parallel anode, spaced 0.25 in. and held at 150 v positive?

5-12. A cylindrical vacuum diode is operated under space charge conditions with anode current of 0.5 amp and anode voltage of 720 v. The anode is of molybdenum, is capable of radiating 5 w per cm² without overheating, and has the same length as the centrally located thoriated-tungsten wire filament. It may be assumed that the filament radiated power escapes from the open ends of the anode cylinder, none being radiated to the anode. Find:

(a) Anode diameter, length, and filament length. ($\beta^2 = 1.0$).

(b) Filament diameter, if operating at 1900°K.

(c) Anode temperature rise above 20°C ambient temperature, $e_T = 0.47$.

5-13. A large power tube has a water-cooled cylindrical copper anode 3.20 in. in diameter and 9.25 in. long. The filament rating is 22 v and 52 amp; the plate input to the tube is 18,000 v and 1.8 amp; but the efficiency of the tube with respect to plate input is 78 per cent. The cooling-water input is at 15°C and the outlet water is to be at 70°C.

(a) Assuming both filament and plate losses to be carried away by the cooling water, find the water flow required in liters per minute; also in gallons per minute.

(b) If the emissivity of copper is 0.32, find the temperature above a 20°C ambient to which the anode of this tube would rise if the cooling-water supply failed. Assume the anode surface to include the cylindrical area plus that of one end.

(c) What would happen to the anode?

5-14. A cylindrical-plate diode is to be built with a thoriated-tungsten filament, to give a saturation current of 250 ma. The voltage needed to overcome space charge at this value of current is to be 105, and the anode must be large enough to radiate the input under this condition at a rate of 1.3 w per square centimeter. The filament temperature is to be 1900°K. Find:

(a) The diameter and length of the anode.

(b) The filament diameter (length is to be the same as the anode). Allow 5 per cent power loss in the end connections.

(c) The filament current and voltage.

REFERENCES

1. Langmuir, I., "The Effect of Space Charge and Residual Gases on Thermionic Currents in High Vacuum," *Phys. Rev.*, **2,** 450 (1913).

2. Dow, W. G., *Fundamentals of Engineering Electronics*, John Wiley & Sons, Inc., New York, 1937.

3. Compton, K. T., and Langmuir, I., "Electrical Discharges of Gases," *Revs. Modern Phys.*, **2,** 123 (1930); **3,** 191 (1931).

4. Langmuir, I., "The Effect of Space Charge and Initial Velocities on the Potential Distribution and Thermionic Current between Parallel Plane Electrodes," *Phys. Rev.*, **21,** 419 (1923).

5. Spangenberg, K. R., *Vacuum Tubes*, McGraw-Hill Book Company, Inc., New York, 1948.

6. Spitzer, E. E., "Anode Materials for High-Vacuum Tubes," *Elec. Eng.*, **54,** 1246 (1935).

7. Ostlund, E. M., "Air Cooling Applied to External-Anode Tubes," *Electronics*, **13,** 36, June (1940).

CHAPTER 6

VACUUM DIODE RECTIFIERS

A very common application of the vacuum diode is as a rectifier of moderate amounts of alternating current into direct current, and a great percentage of radio receiving and electronic amplifying equipment is so supplied with direct current from the a-c lines. The theory and design of circuits for this use, and for removal of a-c ripple, which is undesirable in the d-c output, are considered in this chapter.

6-1. Volt-Ampere Relations; Plate Resistance

The volt-ampere characteristic of a diode was employed for the discussion of space charge in Section 5-1. As shown, space charge limits the flow of current in the vacuum diode even though the cathode is capable of emitting many more electrons. The volt-ampere curve for a vacuum diode then follows an approximate three-halves-power law. Devices such as this, which have nonlinear relations between the voltage across them and the current through them, are said to be nonlinear elements. Frequently the most satisfactory form of analysis of circuit performance of such nonlinear elements is through use of the volt-ampere characteristic.

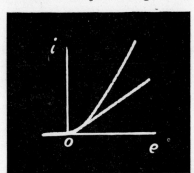

Fig. 6-1. Oscillogram of volt-ampere curve of a 6H6 diode: upper curve, static relation; lower curve, dynamic curve for $R_L = 25,000$ ohms.

Volt-ampere curves for typical diodes are shown in Figs. 6-1 and 6-4. These are called static curves, because it is implied that the diode is doing no useful work. The static curve is strictly a relation

118

between instantaneous voltage across the diode and instantaneous current through it.

A device which has a nonlinear volt-ampere characteristic presents two different forms of resistance in a circuit: *static* and *variational*.

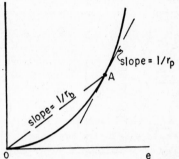

Fig. 6-2.   Volt-ampere relations and resistance for a vacuum diode.

The static resistance, or that presented to steady or direct current flow, is simply the value of a linear resistor which would pass the stated current with the stated voltage applied.   Graphically it is the reciprocal of the slope of the straight dashed line in Fig. 6-2, drawn from the origin to the point A on the curve representing the stated current.   This resistance is given the symbol r_b, where

$$r_b = \frac{e_b}{i_b}. \tag{6-1}$$

The variational resistance is that presented to changes of current. These changes must be made *along* the volt-ampere curve, so that the slope of this curve is important in determining the variational resistance.   The slope of the volt-ampere curve is given by

$$\text{slope} = \frac{di_b}{de_b} = g_p. \tag{6-2}$$

Since this quantity is dimensionally a conductance, its reciprocal is given the name *plate resistance* and the symbol r_p, or

$$r_p = \frac{de_b}{di_b}. \tag{6-3}$$

It should be noted that plate resistance is variable in general, being different for every point on the curve, and is defined only for small changes (strictly infinitesimal) of current or voltage.   In practice, r_p has meaning only for alternating or varying currents.

If the diode is connected in circuit with a resistor R, as in Fig. 6-3, and an a-c voltage is applied, useful output voltage or power may be obtained from this load as a function of the input voltage modified by the characteristics of the diode. The voltage e applied to the circuit does not appear across the diode; hence another curve is

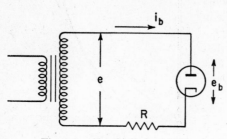

Fig. 6-3.   Simple diode circuit.

needed that relates the current through the circuit to the instantaneous voltage applied to the circuit. This curve, called a *dynamic curve*, is obtained by adding to the abscissa values of the static curve an amount that is equal to the $i_b R$ voltage drop at each current value. A typical curve is drawn in Fig. 6-4. This curve will, of necessity, have a lower slope owing to the higher total resistance. Likewise, the dynamic curve will always be more linear than the static curve as the result of adding a linear resistance R to the nonlinear resistance r_p of the diode.

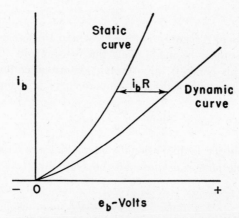

Fig. 6-4.   Volt-ampere relations for a diode.

6-2. The Half-Wave Vacuum Diode with Resistance Load

Assume that Fig. 6-5 represents the characteristics of the vacuum diode in the circuit of Fig. 6-3. If an alternating voltage of any wave form is applied, the resulting wave form of current through the diode and load R may be obtained graphically by use of the dynamic characteristic. The current flowing through the load R is seen to consist of only the positive pulses, since a current flow on the negative-anode-voltage half-cycle is impossible in a diode. The electrons cannot reach a highly negative plate, and this fact shows that the diode is a rectifier of alternating current.

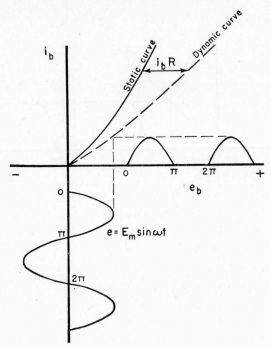

Fig. 6-5. Graphical determination of diode output-current waveform.

The single diode, or half-wave rectifier, with a resistance load, as drawn in Fig. 6-3, is not of much practical significance. However, it is so fundamental in method to the analysis of more complex circuits that it will be examined in considerable detail. In an efficient rectifier circuit, the magnitude of the load resistor R is usually many times that of the plate resistance r_p of the diode. Under such conditions the total circuit resistance is practically constant. The dynamic curve may then be assumed linear, as in Fig. 6-6, and under this assumption $r_p = r_b$.

The current for sinusoidal applied emf may be written from the circuit of Fig. 6-3 as

$$i_b = \frac{E_m}{r_p + R} \sin \omega t \qquad 0 \leq \sin \omega t \leq 1, \qquad (6\text{-}4)$$

$$i_b = 0 \qquad\qquad -1 \leq \sin \omega t \leq 0. \qquad (6\text{-}5)$$

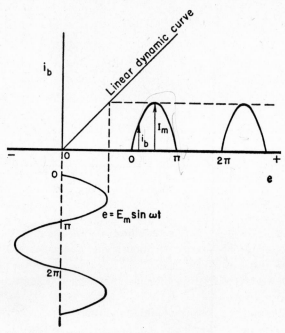

Fig. 6-6. Use of the linear approximation to the dynamic curve.

The ultimate object in the use of a rectifier is to obtain direct current from an alternating source. A d-c ammeter in series with the load will read the average value of the periodic current, or

$$E_{\text{d-c}} = \frac{1}{2\pi} \int_0^{2\pi} i_b \, d\omega t = \frac{1}{2\pi} \int_0^{\pi} \frac{E_m}{r_p + R} \sin \omega t \, d\omega t + \frac{1}{2\pi} \int_\pi^{2\pi} 0 \, d\omega t,$$

$$I_{\text{d-c}} = \frac{E_m}{\pi(r_p + R)} = \frac{E_m}{\pi}. \qquad (6\text{-}6)$$

The d-c component of voltage across the load, then, is

$$E_{\text{d-c}} = I_{\text{d-c}} R.$$

The total power input to the circuit is given by

$$P_{\text{a-c}} = I_{\text{rms}}^2(r_p + R), \tag{6-7}$$

where I_{rms} is the effective or rms value of the current pulses through the diode, or, by definition of the rms value,

$$I_{\text{rms}} = \sqrt{\frac{1}{2\pi} \int_0^{2\pi} i_b^2 \, d\omega t}$$

$$= \sqrt{\frac{1}{2\pi} \int_0^{\pi} \left(\frac{E_m}{r_p + R}\right)^2 \sin^2 \omega t \, d\omega t + \frac{1}{2\pi} \int_{\pi}^{2\pi} 0 \, d\omega t.}$$

$$I_{\text{rms}} = \frac{E_m}{2(r_p + R)} = \frac{I_m}{2}. \tag{6-8}$$

This is the value of current read by an a-c ammeter in series with the load.

A Fourier analysis of the 180° half-wave sinusoidal voltage pulses applied to the load of Fig. 6-3 yields

$$e = \frac{E_m}{\pi} + \frac{E_m}{2} \sin \omega t - \frac{2E_m}{3\pi} \cos 2\omega t - \frac{2E_m}{15\pi} \cos 4\omega t \cdots \tag{6-9}$$

as the harmonic series. The first term on the right is the average or d-c voltage. The lowest frequency and the only odd harmonic is that of the supply frequency. With these emf's applied to a resistance load, corresponding frequency terms appear in the current series.

A rectifier may be considered fundamentally a frequency converter in which one input frequency is changed to a large number of frequencies, only one of which is the desired output. This is the zero-frequency term or the d-c component. The efficiency of conversion of the input a-c power to d-c power is defined as the *rectification efficiency*, or

$$\eta_R = \frac{P_{\text{d-c}} \text{ output}}{P_{\text{a-c}} \text{ input}} \times 100\% \tag{6-10}$$

$$= \frac{\left[\dfrac{E_m}{\pi(R + r_p)}\right]^2 R \times 100\%}{\left[\dfrac{E_m}{2(R + r_p)}\right]^2 (R + r_p)} \tag{6-11}$$

$$= \frac{4}{\pi^2}\left(\frac{1}{1 + r_p/R}\right) \times 100\% = \frac{40.6\%}{1 + r_p/R}. \tag{6-12}$$

The rectification efficiency increases as r_p becomes smaller with respect to the load R, and approaches 40.6 per cent as an upper limit.

It should be noted that P_{d-c} is not all the power dissipated in the resistance load but is merely the portion due to the d-c component of rectifier output. Consideration of the terms of Eq. 6-9 indicates that currents of the harmonic frequencies will flow through the load, representing power which is unavailable as direct current. This power loss lowers the efficiency. Circuits which prevent the a-c components from flowing through the resistive load will therefore raise the efficiency of rectification. Such circuits are called *filters* and are discussed later in this chapter.

The *peak inverse voltage* is the maximum voltage appearing across the tube during the time in which the anode is negative. Insulation breakdown strength of the diode determines the allowable magnitude of this voltage. Since from the circuit of Fig. 6-3 it is apparent that during the nonconducting period the voltage e_b across the tube is equal to the applied voltage $e = E_m \sin \omega t$, then the peak inverse voltage for a half-wave rectifier is

$$\text{P.I.V.} = E_m. \tag{6-13}$$

6-3. The Full-Wave Circuit with Resistance Load

It appears from the above section that if the load could be supplied with current during the inactive cycle, the efficiency might be raised,

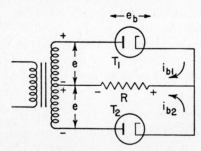

Fig. 6-7. The full-wave (biphase) circuit with resistance load.

since the harmonic components would be reduced. The full-wave or biphase circuit of Fig. 6-7 accomplishes this purpose. It consists of two half-wave circuits connected to supply a common load resistance. The additional circuit is connected so that the polarity of the a-c voltage applied to the diode is opposite to that of the first circuit. Consequently, since conduction occurs only during the half cycle in which the anode of the diode is positive, the diodes will conduct on opposite half cycles, resulting in a current wave as shown in Fig. 6-8. This wave consists of successive sine pulses, each of 180° duration. Assuming identical tubes, the tube currents can be written from the mesh equations as

$$i_{b1} = \frac{E_m}{r_p + R} \sin \omega t \\ i_{b2} = 0 \qquad\qquad\qquad 0 \leq \sin \omega t \leq 1, \qquad (6\text{-}14)$$

$$i_{b1} = 0 \\ i_{b2} = -\frac{E_m}{r_p + R} \sin \omega t \qquad -1 \leq \sin \omega t \leq 0, \qquad (6\text{-}15)$$

with the positive directions used on e as indicated in Fig. 6-7. The voltage $e = E_m \sin \omega t$ is the input for each diode, or one-half of the transformer secondary voltage. Each diode is then operating independently and under exactly the same conditions as in the half-wave circuit, only the load currents and voltages being combined.

By taking the average of the current wave in the load, the d-c current is obtained as

$$I_{\text{d-c}} = \frac{2E_m}{\pi(r_p + R)} = \frac{2I_m}{\pi}, \qquad (6\text{-}16)$$

which is twice the value of the half-wave circuit, since it is the sum of the diode currents.

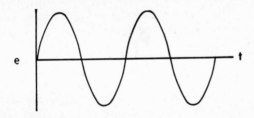

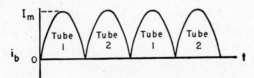

Fig. 6-8. Applied voltage and output current waves of a full-wave rectifier.

The voltage wave form applied to the load, causing the current wave forms of Fig. 6-8 to flow, may be analyzed as

$$e = \frac{2E_m}{\pi} - \frac{4E_m}{3\pi} \cos 2\omega t - \frac{4E_m}{15\pi} \cos 4\omega t - \frac{4E_m}{35\pi} \cos 6\omega t \cdots \quad (6\text{-}17)$$

In the full-wave case, the lowest frequency present is double the supply frequency, which makes removal of the harmonics with filter circuits easier. That fact, plus increased output current and improved efficiency, makes the full-wave circuit more desirable than the half-wave circuit.

By writing an instantaneous voltage equation around the outside loop of the circuit of Fig. 6-7 during the interval in which tube T_1 is nonconducting, it is found that

$$e_{b1} = 2e + e_{b2} \quad (6\text{-}18)$$

and

$$e_{b1} = -2E_m \sin \omega t + i_{b2}r_p. \quad (6\text{-}19)$$

The maximum value for e_{b1} occurs when $\omega t = 3\pi/2$; and if $E_m \gg i_{b2}r_p$, then

$$\text{P.I.V.} = 2E_m, \quad (6\text{-}20)$$

which is the highest negative voltage the diode insulation must sustain.

The full-wave circuit may use individual tubes or may employ tubes containing two diodes in one envelope, with common cathode connections. This latter arrangement saves space, but such tubes are normally made only for nominal voltages (under 3000 v P.I.V.), to avoid breakdown.

6-4. Ripple Factor

In many applications, such as supplying radio receivers and transmitters, pulsations in the direct current or voltage are very undesirable. The pulsations, or ripple, are caused by the a-c harmonic components in the voltage and current, and can be reduced by choice of rectifier circuit or by filtering of the rectifier output. The amount of remaining pulsation, or ripple, compared with the value of the direct current or voltage, is a measure of the purity of rectifier output, and is called the *ripple factor*, or

$$\text{ripple factor} = \frac{\text{effective value of a-c harmonic components}}{\text{average, or d-c component}}. \quad (6\text{-}21)$$

The current in the load of a rectifier is composed of two components: $I_{d\text{-}c}$, or the average value, and $I_{a\text{-}c}$, or the effective value of all the a-c components. Then the effective value of the total load current is

$$I_{\text{rms}} = \sqrt{I_{d\text{-}c}{}^2 + I_{a\text{-}c}{}^2}, \tag{6-22}$$

and

$$I_{a\text{-}c} = \sqrt{I_{\text{rms}}{}^2 - I_{d\text{-}c}{}^2}.$$

Use of this value in the ripple-factor expression gives

$$\text{ripple} = \frac{\sqrt{I_{\text{rms}}{}^2 - I_{d\text{-}c}{}^2}}{I_{d\text{-}c}} = \sqrt{(I_{\text{rms}}/I_{d\text{-}c})^2 - 1}. \tag{6-23}$$

The form factor F of any recurrent wave is defined as the ratio of the effective to the average value, so that the ripple factor may be expressed as

$$\text{ripple} = \sqrt{F^2 - 1}. \tag{6-24}$$

Readings obtained from a-c and d-c ammeters connected in series with the load allow determination of the ripple present in a rectifier output, unless the ripple is quite small, in which case the readings do not differ sufficiently to give accuracy.

Use of the values of I_{rms} and $I_{d\text{-}c}$ for the half-wave rectifier gives the value of 1.21, or 121 per cent, for the ripple factor of the half-wave rectifier with resistance load. The full-wave rectifier under similar conditions has a ripple factor of 0.47.

It should be noted that although Eq. 6-23 has been worked out by the use of currents, by the definition of ripple factor it is equally applicable to voltages, because the wave forms of voltage and current are identical across resistance loads.

6-5. The Shunt-Capacitor Filter

As a power source for an amplifier, radio receiver, or transmitter, a rectifier must provide direct current or voltage having a ripple factor much smaller than is obtainable directly from the rectifier, and filter circuits are employed. While reducing the ripple, filter circuits also improve the efficiency because they prevent the alternating harmonic currents from flowing in the resistance load and dissipating undesired power therein. A simple form of filter is obtained by shunting a capacitor across the resistance load of a rectifier. If the capacitance value is so chosen that $X_c \ll R$, the alternating currents find a low reactance path through the capacitor, and only a small alternating current will flow in the load to produce a ripple voltage. Such a filter is shown at (a), Fig. 6-9, as applied to a half-wave diode rectifier.

The presence of the capacitor effects a considerable change in the operating conditions of the rectifier as compared with those existing with a simple resistance load. During the time the rectifier

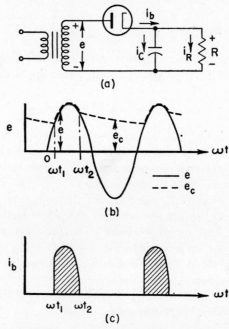

Fig. 6-9. (a) Half-wave diode rectifier with a capacitor as a filter; (b) voltage wave forms in the circuit of (a); (c) tube current wave forms.

output voltage is increasing, the capacitor charges to a voltage equal to the rectifier output, and stores energy. When the rectifier output voltage falls, the capacitor delivers energy to the load, maintaining the load voltage at a high value over a longer period of time than if the capacitor were not present. This produces a reduced ripple.

The diode delivers a pulse of current each cycle to charge the capacitor, and then acts as a switch to disconnect the source and permit the capacitor to discharge through the load. If the time constant of the filter and load circuit is long with respect to the time of a cycle, the discharge will be slow, and the voltage nearly constant over the cycle. The diode conducts for short pulses, rather than over the whole positive half cycle, and the circuit is excited by repeated current transients, as illustrated by (b) and (c), Fig. 6-9.

Since the diode plate resistance must be small in comparison with the load for good efficiency, the analysis of the circuit can be much simplified by considering the diode resistance as zero. Then, referring to Fig. 6-9(b), the voltage of the capacitor during the charging interval, ωt_1 to ωt_2, is equal to that of the supply voltage, or

$$e_C = e = E_m \sin \omega t \qquad \omega t_1 < \omega t < \omega t_2. \tag{6-25}$$

By inspection of the circuit, it can be seen that during this same time interval

$$i_b = i_C + i_R. \tag{6-26}$$

Since

$$i_R = \frac{E_m}{R} \sin \omega t \qquad \omega t_1 < \omega t < \omega t_2 \tag{6-27}$$

and

$$i_C = C \frac{de_C}{dt} = \omega C E_m \cos \omega t, \tag{6-28}$$

the rectifier tube current during the conduction interval is a pulse having a form given by

$$i_b = E_m \left(\frac{1}{R} \sin \omega t + \omega C \cos \omega t \right) \qquad \omega t_1 < \omega t < \omega t_2. \tag{6-29}$$

At ωt_2, when tube conduction ends, or $i_b = 0$, Eq. 6-26 can be written as

$$i_C = -i_R,$$

and

$$\omega C \cos \omega t_2 = -\frac{1}{R} \sin \omega t_2,$$

from which

$$\omega t_2 = \tan^{-1} (-\omega RC). \tag{6-30}$$

The angle ωt_2 lies in the second quadrant. Equation 6-29 may then be written as

$$i_b = \frac{E_m}{R} \sqrt{1 + \omega^2 R^2 C^2} \sin (\omega t + \phi),$$

where

$$\phi = \tan^{-1} (\omega RC) = \pi - \tan^{-1} (-\omega RC), \tag{6-31}$$

from which it is possible to write

$$i_b = \frac{E_m}{R} \sqrt{1 + \omega^2 R^2 C^2} \sin (\omega t_2 - \omega t) \qquad \omega t_1 < \omega t < \omega t_2 \qquad (6\text{-}32)$$

as a simplified expression for the current pulse through the diode.

Equations 6-30 and 6-32 introduce the term ωRC, a dimensionless parameter occurring frequently in the analysis of rectifier circuits with capacitance filters, and representative of the circuit conditions. Large values of ωRC may mean large capacitance or large load resistance (low current), whereas small values of ωRC mean small capacitance or low load resistance (large current). Much of the information to be obtained concerning capacitor filters will be presented in terms of ωRC.

At ωt_2 the voltage of the supply is falling faster than the capacitor can discharge through the load, and the supply voltage becomes less than e_C. The diode then has a positive cathode and ceases conduction, disconnecting the source from the load. For the period between ωt_2 and $2\pi + \omega t_1$, it can be seen that

$$-i_C = i_R$$

or
$$-C \frac{de_C}{dt} = \frac{e_C}{R},$$

from which
$$\frac{de_C}{dt} + \frac{e_C}{RC} = 0. \qquad (6\text{-}33)$$

This is the circuit differential equation and has a solution

$$e_C = A \, \epsilon^{-t/RC}.$$

At $\omega t = \omega t_2$, $e_C = E_m \sin \omega t_2$, so that, after A is evaluated,

$$e_C = E_m \sin \omega t_2 \, \epsilon^{-(\omega t - \omega t_2)/\omega RC} \qquad \omega t_2 < \omega t < (2\pi + \omega t_1) \qquad (6\text{-}34)$$

is the expression for the capacitor voltage during the discharge interval. It may be noted that for large ωRC—that is, large capacitance, or large resistance (light current load)—the exponent will be small and e_C will be more constant, or the ripple will be reduced. The ripple, therefore, *increases* with increase in current taken by the load with a simple capacitor filter.

At $\omega t_1 + 2\pi$, it can be seen from Fig. 6-9(b) that

$$e_C = E_m \sin (\omega t_1 + 2\pi),$$

and from Eq. 6-34 this becomes

$$E_m \sin \omega t_1 = E_m \sin \omega t_2 \, \epsilon^{-(\omega t_1 + 2\pi - \omega t_2)/\omega RC},$$

from which

$$\sin \omega t_1 = \sin \omega t_2 \, \epsilon^{-(\omega t_1 + 2\pi - \omega t_2)/\omega RC}. \tag{6-35}$$

This is a transcendental equation which can be solved graphically.

However, if it is assumed that the capacitor voltage at $\omega t_1 + 2\pi$ is the same as the voltage at $\omega t = 2\pi$, Eq. 6-35 may be solved for ωt_1. This assumption introduces only a small error for most load values. By this assumption, a value for the angle at which conduction in the tube starts can be found as

$$\omega t_1 = \sin^{-1}\left[\sin \omega t_2 \, \epsilon^{-(2\pi - \omega t_2)/\omega RC}\right].$$

In view of the fact that $\tan \omega t_2 = -\omega RC$, the value of $\sin \omega t_2$ can be determined, and the above equation becomes

$$\omega t_1 = \sin^{-1}\left[\frac{\omega RC}{\sqrt{1 + \omega^2 R^2 C^2}} \, \epsilon^{-(2\pi - \omega t_2)/\omega RC}\right]. \tag{6-36}$$

Curves of ωt_1 and ωt_2 as functions of ωRC are plotted in Fig. 6-10.

Having values for ωt_1 and ωt_2 as functions of ωRC, it is possible

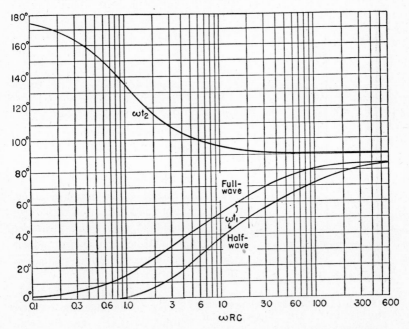

Fig. 6-10.   Variation of cut-in point ωt_1 and cut-out point ωt_2 with ωRC.

to plot typical tube-current wave forms from Eq. 6-32. Wave forms for two values of ωRC are plotted in Fig. 6-11. Note that since ωt_2 decreases and ωt_1 increases with increase in value of ωRC, the conduction angle is short for large values of capacity. At the same time, Eq. 6-32 shows that the peak amplitude of i_b increases with the value of C.

The direct voltage across the load may be obtained by averaging the voltages over a cycle. That is,

$$E_{\text{d-c}} = \frac{1}{2\pi} \int_{\omega t_1}^{\omega t_2} E_m \sin \omega t \, d\omega t + \frac{1}{2\pi} \int_{\omega t_2}^{2\pi + \omega t_1} E_m \sin \omega t_2 \, \epsilon^{-(\omega t - \omega t_2)/\omega RC} \, d\omega t.$$

After integration and substitution of Eqs. 6-35 and 6-30, this reduces to

$$E_{\text{d-c}} = \frac{E_m}{2\pi} \sqrt{1 + \omega^2 R^2 C^2} \, [1 - \cos(\omega t_2 - \omega t_1)], \qquad (6\text{-}37)$$

which relates the d-c output voltage to the peak a-c input for various values of ωRC. This value, of course, neglects the voltage drop in the diode. The ratio $E_{\text{d-c}}/E_m$ is plotted in Fig. 6-12(a) as a function of the parameter ωRC. The curve shows that for low values of C the ratio approaches $1/\pi$, the value for the half-wave rectifier with resistance load. At large values of C, the output voltage approaches the peak value of the input voltage. For good regulation with varying load, sufficient capacitance should be used to ensure operation on the upper plateau of the curve.

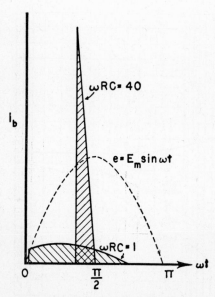

Fig. 6-11. Relative tube-current wave forms for two values of C, R remaining constant, in a half-wave rectifier with shunt capacity.

High peak currents are likely to damage the rectifier tube, so that a knowledge of the ratio of peak current to

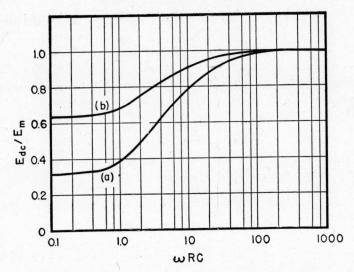

Fig. 6-12. Variation of the ratio $E_{\text{d-c}}/E_m$ with ωRC, shunt capacitance filter: (a) half-wave rectifier; (b) full-wave rectifier.

average current is desirable for rectifier design. Since

$$i_b = \frac{E_m}{R} \sqrt{1 + \omega^2 R^2 C^2} \sin (\omega t_2 - \omega t), \qquad (6\text{-}38)$$

it would appear that the maximum current I_{peak} would occur where $\omega t = \omega t_2 - \pi/2$. This is true, provided that this value of ωt lies inside the angle of conduction; otherwise I_{peak} occurs at the beginning of conduction. The wave forms of Fig. 6-11 confirm this behavior. To determine which condition applies, let i_b be maximum at t_m, so that the value of the sine in Eq. 6-38 is unity, or

$$\omega t_2 - \omega t_m = \frac{\pi}{2},$$

$$\omega t_m = \omega t_2 - \frac{\pi}{2}. \qquad (6\text{-}39)$$

The division between the two conditions occurs when the start of conduction coincides with the maximum value of Eq. 6-38, or

$$\omega t_1 = \omega t_m = \omega t_2 - \frac{\pi}{2}. \qquad (6\text{-}40)$$

Both ωt_1 and ωt_2 are functions of ωRC, so it can be found that at $\omega RC = 3.6$,

$$\omega t_2 - \omega t_1 = \frac{\pi}{2}.$$

Consequently, for all values of $\omega RC < 3.6$, the peak current occurs at $\sin(\omega t_2 - \omega t) = 1$ and is given by the expression

$$I_{peak} = \frac{E_m}{R}\sqrt{1 + \omega^2 R^2 C^2}. \tag{6-41}$$

For all values of $\omega RC > 3.6$, the peak current occurs at the beginning of conduction, or at $\omega t = \omega t_1$, and

$$I_{peak} = \frac{E_m}{R}\sqrt{1 + \omega^2 R^2 C^2}\,\sin(\omega t_2 - \omega t_1). \tag{6-42}$$

The ratio of I_{peak} to $I_{d\text{-}c}$ then may be found for $\omega RC < 3.6$ as

$$\frac{I_{peak}}{I_{d\text{-}c}} = \frac{2\pi}{1 - \cos(\omega t_2 - \omega t_1)}, \tag{6-43}$$

and for $\omega RC > 3.6$,

$$\frac{I_{peak}}{I_{d\text{-}c}} = \frac{2\pi \sin(\omega t_2 - \omega t_1)}{1 - \cos(\omega t_2 - \omega t_1)}. \tag{6-44}$$

A curve of $I_{peak}/I_{d\text{-}c}$ for the half-wave rectifier is plotted in Fig. 6-13(a).

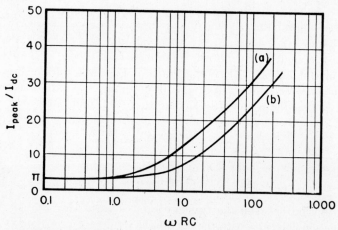

Fig. 6-13. Ratio of peak to average tube current as a function of ωRC for a shunt capacitance filter: (a) half-wave rectifier; (b) full-wave rectifier.

The ripple factor may be found by computing the rms load voltage from

$$E_{\rm rms} = \\
\sqrt{\frac{1}{2\pi} \int_{\omega t_1}^{\omega t_2} E_m{}^2 \sin^2 \omega t \, d\omega t + \frac{1}{2\pi} \int_{\omega t_2}^{2\pi + \omega t_1} E_m{}^2 \sin^2 \omega t_2 \, \epsilon^{-2(\omega t - \omega t_2)/\omega RC} \, d\omega t}$$

$$(6\text{-}45)$$

and substituting this and the value of $E_{\rm d\text{-}c}$ taken from Eq. 6-37 into the ripple equation, 6-23. The resulting expression is quite complex, so that the results are only shown plotted against ωRC in Fig. 6-14(a).

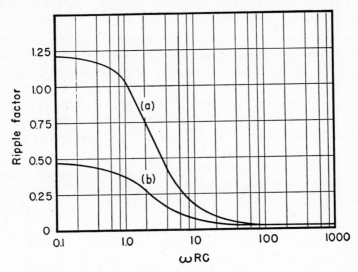

Fig. 6-14. Variation of ripple factor with ωRC, shunt capacitance filter: (a) half-wave rectifier; (b) full-wave rectifier.

On the inverse half cycle, the capacitor voltage will add directly to the a-c supply voltage, thereby raising the peak inverse voltage on a tube in the half-wave capacitor-filter circuit. Since the capacitor voltage for large ωRC is nearly equal to E_m, the peak inverse voltage on a diode at light current loads may be nearly equal to $2E_m$.

Because of the high value of ωRC needed for small ripple and good voltage regulation, and the accompanying high peak currents, the half-wave rectifier with capacitor filter is ordinarily used only for applications requiring small average currents at high voltage (R large). One such application is the supply for the anode voltages of cathode-ray tubes.

The full-wave circuit may also be used with the shunt-capacitor filter. The operation in general is similar to that of the half-wave circuit, but with the discharge time of the capacitor running only to $\pi + \omega t_1$ instead of to $2\pi + \omega t_1$. For given ωRC values, this limitation produces improved regulation and lessened ripple. The results of analysis of the full-wave circuit with shunt-capacitor filter are plotted in Figs. 6-10, 6-12, 6-13 and 6-14 for comparison with the half-wave circuit.

6-6. The Series Inductor Filter

An inductor may be used in series with the load as a filter, and may be considered as storing magnetic energy when the current is above the average value and as releasing that energy to the circuit when the current tends to fall below the average value. The inductor may also be considered as a high impedance to the alternating harmonic currents in the rectifier output, reducing the amplitude of all with respect to the d-c component, and thereby reducing the

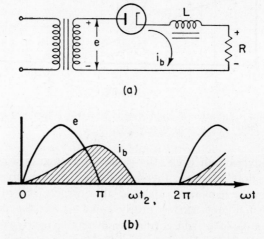

(a)

(b)

Fig. 6-15. (a) Half-wave rectifier circuit, series inductor filter; (b) current and voltage wave forms.

ripple. The circuit of a half-wave rectifier with a filter inductor L is shown in Fig. 6-15(a).

With the tube resistance again neglected as small for the sake of simplicity, the circuit emf equation may be written during the conduction interval as

$$L \frac{di}{dt} + Ri = E_m \sin \omega t, \tag{6-46}$$

which may be altered to form the usual circuit differential equation

$$\frac{di}{dt} + \frac{Ri}{L} = \frac{E_m}{L} \sin \omega t. \tag{6-47}$$

This equation has the well-known transient solution

$$i_b = B \, \epsilon^{-Rt/L} \tag{6-48}$$

and a steady-state solution given by

$$i_b = \frac{E_m}{R^2 + \omega^2 L^2} \left(R \sin \omega t - \omega L \cos \omega t \right),$$

which may also be written as

$$i_b = \frac{E_m}{\sqrt{R^2 + \omega^2 L^2}} \sin (\omega t - \theta), \tag{6-49}$$

where

$$\theta = \tan^{-1} \frac{\omega L}{R}. \tag{6-50}$$

Combining the transient and steady-state solutions gives for the current in the circuit

$$i_b = B \, \epsilon^{-Rt/L} + \frac{E_m}{\sqrt{R^2 + \omega^2 L^2}} \sin (\omega t - \theta).$$

Since in the inductive circuit with discontinuous current flow the current is always zero at the instant of closing the circuit, then when the diode connects the source to the load at $\omega t = 0$ the current i must be zero, and the constant B can be evaluated, giving

$$i_b = \frac{E_m}{\sqrt{R^2 + \omega^2 L^2}} \left[\sin (\omega t - \theta) + \epsilon^{-Rt/L} \sin \theta \right] \tag{6-51}$$

as the expression for the current pulse drawn in (b), Fig. 6-15. The circuit is then excited by repeated pulses of this form. As the inductance is increased, the exponential term decays more slowly, and current flows for considerable periods after the supply-voltage zero at $\omega t = \pi$. A positive emf is maintained on the anode of the diode after the voltage zero by reason of the $L\,di/dt$ voltage produced by a decreasing current in L. For full-wave rectifiers, it is possible to maintain current in the inductor and load at all times, the current simply commutating between tubes. A discussion of that type of circuit situation follows in Section 6-7.

If L is not sufficiently great to maintain current flow throughout the cycle, the angle of cutoff ωt_2 becomes of interest. Since negative currents are impossible in the diode, $i_b = 0$ at $\omega t = \omega t_2$. Substitution of these conditions in Eq. 6-51 gives

$$\sin(\omega t_2 - \theta) + \epsilon^{-R\omega t_2/\omega L}\sin\theta = 0. \tag{6-52}$$

After expansion and application of sine and cosine values of θ obtainable from Eq. 6-50, this becomes

$$R\sin\omega t_2 + \omega L(\epsilon^{-R\omega t_2/\omega L} - \cos\omega t_2) = 0,$$

$$\frac{R}{\omega L} = \frac{\cos\omega t_2 - \epsilon^{-R\omega t_2/\omega L}}{\sin\omega t_2}. \tag{6-53}$$

This is a transcendental equation that can be solved graphically. The results for ωt_2, the angle of conduction, are plotted as a function of the parameter $R/\omega L$ in Fig. 6-16. This curve shows the length-

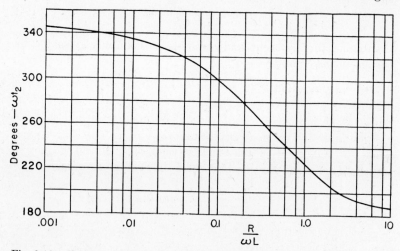

Fig. 6-16. Variation of cut-out angle ωt_2 with $R/\omega L$ for half-wave rectifier with series inductor filter.

ening of the conduction angle as the inductance is increased. As a further illustration of this behavior, the current wave forms for several values of $R/\omega L$ are plotted in Fig. 6-17. These wave forms are plotted for constant R, so that they show the effect of changing ωL.

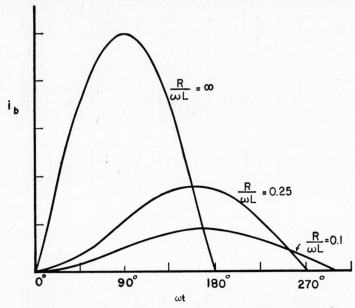

Fig. 6-17. Effect of changes in value of filter inductance on the wave form of current in half-wave rectifier with series inductor filter. (Load resistance R is constant.)

The d-c output may be obtained from Eq. 6-51 by averaging over the interval 0 to ωt_2. After integration and some manipulation, this becomes

$$I_{\text{d-c}} = \frac{E_m}{2\pi R}\,(1 - \cos \omega t_2), \qquad (6\text{-}54)$$

and the d-c voltage reduces to

$$E_{\text{d-c}} = \frac{E_m}{2\pi}\,(1 - \cos \omega t_2). \qquad (6\text{-}55)$$

A curve showing the variation of $E_{\text{d-c}}/E_m$ is drawn in Fig. 6-18 in terms of the parameter $R/\omega L$. Note that since the curve is plotted in terms of $R/\omega L$, the heavily loaded condition is with small $R/\omega L$,

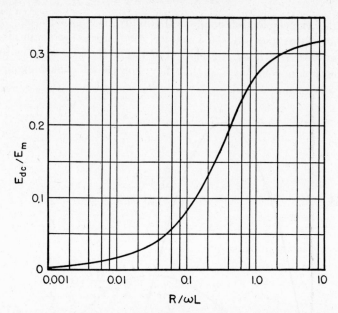

Fig. 6-18. Variation of $E_{d\text{-}c}/E_m$ with $R/\omega L$ for a half-wave rectifier with inductive filter.

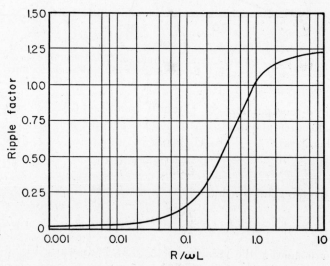

Fig. 6-19. Variation of ripple factor with $R/\omega L$ for the half-wave rectifier with inductor filter.

and the lightly loaded with large $R/\omega L$.   The highest voltage occurs with light loads, as would be expected.   Much lower voltages will be obtained from an inductive filter than from a capacitive filter for a given E_m.

Consideration of the curves of Fig. 6-17 shows that no excessive peak currents are to be expected with inductance in the circuit, since inductance prevents rapid changes in current.

The ripple produced in the load current may be investigated by calculating the effective value of the current and using the ripple Eq 6-23.   A curve of the ripple factor vs $R/\omega L$ is given in Fig. 6-19.   The largest ripple occurs with the circuit lightly loaded, or with $R/\omega L$ large.   This is opposite to the effect of load on the ripple of the shunt-capacitor filter, which has its largest ripple at heavy current loads.

The capacitor filter therefore produces a higher d-c voltage than the series inductor filter at the expense of heavy peak tube currents and greater voltage changes between no load (large R) and full load (small R), or poor voltage regulation.   The series inductor filter reduces tube current peaks and has better voltage regulation but requires a high a-c input voltage.   Neither circuit is capable of sufficiently low ripple for use as a source for radio receivers and transmitters without requiring excessively large capacitors and inductors.

6-7. The Full-Wave Rectifier with L-Section Filter

To meet the demand for lower ripple factors than are possible with the circuits already discussed, without excessively large values of either L or C, shunt capacitance and series inductance can be combined into an L-section filter as at (a), or a double section as at (b), Fig. 6-20, shown connected to a full-wave rectifier.   Combinations of L and C produce a lower ripple, with normal component values, than is possible with either L or C alone.

The method of analysis previously used becomes difficult when it is applied to the inductor input circuit because of lack of information concerning the points of cut-in and cutout for the diodes.   However, by use of information gained from the preceding analyses, the action of the circuit at light loads can be explained, and at heavy loads ordinary circuit analysis may be applied.

Obviously, for light loads when $R \cong \infty$, the capacitor will charge to the peak of the a-c voltage, and the output voltage will be E_m on open circuit. As a small current is taken by the load, or R is decreased, the diode switches the emf onto the circuit for an instant, and the capacitor charges on the peak of each cycle of applied voltage; the conduction angle of each diode is small, and the d-c voltage is lowered slightly owing to the average capacitor voltage being below the peak of the a-c wave. The current flowing is so low that the small energy stored in the inductor has almost no effect on the circuit except to lengthen the conduction time slightly. The circuit action is almost the same as with the capacitor-filter circuit. In

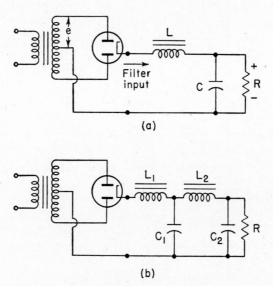

Fig. 6-20. Typical inductor-input (L-section) filters
connected to full-wave rectifiers.

general, the voltage follows the dashed portion of the load voltage curve of Fig. 6-21(b), decreasing rapidly with increasing load current, exactly as if two half-wave diodes were supplying a capacitor filter. For still larger load currents, the conduction angle lengthens owing to both the discharging effect on the capacitor and the presence of the inductor, and the average voltage is further decreased. At some value of current, I_k, the conduction angle of each diode is exactly 180°. Further increases in load current build up the stored energy in the inductance so that the current is maintained and the conduction angle increases to values over 180°.

With the full-wave rectifier, it is entirely possible to use sufficient inductance in L, Fig. 6-20(a), to obtain continuous current flow through the choke for values above I_k, where I_k may be appreciably smaller than the rated d-c load current. The two diodes act simply as synchronous switches to connect to the filter whichever trans-

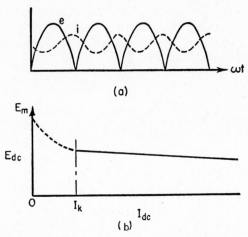

Fig. 6-21. (a) Voltage wave form applied to filters of Fig. 6-20; (b) E_{d-c} vs I_{d-c} for a single L-section filter.

former winding happens to be the more positive, and the current transfers smoothly from tube to tube. In effect, an emf composed of successive sinusoidal half waves as at (a), Fig. 6-21, is applied to the filter input with current of some such form as is shown by the dashed curve.

Therefore, with load currents above I_k and with diode voltage drop again neglected, an alternating emf of known harmonic content is continuously applied to a reactive and resistive circuit, and ordinary circuit analysis applies. The emf of (a), Fig. 6-21, is given by Eq. 6-17 as

$$e = \frac{2E_m}{\pi} - \frac{4E_m}{3\pi} \cos 2\omega t - \frac{4E_m}{15\pi} \cos 4\omega t - \frac{4E_m}{35\pi} \cos 6\omega t \cdots \cdot$$

The first term on the right is the d-c output voltage to be obtained under the specified conditions. The succeeding terms are the a-c harmonic emf's. The inductance of L will be so chosen as to have a high reactance at the second harmonic of the supply frequency, and will therefore have double this value of reactance at the fourth harmonic. Consequently, upon consideration of the voltage coefficients of the harmonics, the fourth-harmonic current in the circuit will be only 10 per cent of the second-harmonic current. The reactance of the capacitor C at the fourth harmonic is one-half of the second-harmonic value, so that any load voltage produced by flow of fourth-harmonic current will be only 5 per cent of the second-harmonic voltage. Therefore, as a simplifying assumption, currents due to the fourth and all higher harmonics will be neglected in the following analysis, and only the second harmonic will be considered. A design of a filter satisfactory for the lowest-order harmonic will thus be even more effective for the higher harmonics.

Since the capacitor C is intended to by-pass as much as possible of the alternating current around the load, it is desirable to choose C such that

$$\frac{1}{2\omega C} \ll R \tag{6-56}$$

is an allowable assumption. Under this condition, the input impedance of the filter circuit of Fig. 6-20(a) at the second-harmonic frequency 2ω is

$$Z = 2j\omega L - \frac{\dfrac{jR}{2\omega C}}{R - \dfrac{j}{2\omega C}}. \tag{6-57}$$

If the inequality of Eq. 6-56 is applied as a condition of circuit design, Eq. 6-57 becomes

$$Z = j\left(2\omega L - \frac{1}{2\omega C}\right). \tag{6-58}$$

For the full-wave rectifier, the rms value of the second-harmonic emf is

$$E_2 = \frac{4E_m}{3\pi\sqrt{2}},$$

and the magnitude of the alternating current flowing in the inductor L is

$$|I_L| = \frac{4E_m}{3\pi \sqrt{2} \left(2\omega L - \dfrac{1}{2\omega C}\right)} = \frac{8\omega C E_m}{3\pi \sqrt{2}\,(4\omega^2 LC - 1)}.$$

If I_C and I_R are, respectively, the alternating currents through the capacitor C and resistor R, then by inspection

$$|I_R| = \frac{1}{2\omega CR}\,|I_C|; \tag{6-59}$$

and since $I_C \cong I_L$ by reason of the assumption above,

$$|I_R| = \frac{4E_m}{3\pi \sqrt{2}\,R(4\omega^2 LC - 1)}. \tag{6-60}$$

The d-c load current may be obtained from the first term of the Fourier series as

$$I_{\text{d-c}} = \frac{2E_m}{\pi R}. \tag{6-61}$$

The ripple in the output current then is seen to be

$$\text{ripple} = \frac{\dfrac{4E_m}{3\pi \sqrt{2}\,R(4\omega^2 LC - 1)}}{\dfrac{2E_m}{\pi R}} = \frac{0.47}{4\omega^2 LC - 1}. \tag{6-62}$$

Ripple factor is plotted as a function of $\omega^2 LC$ in Fig. 6-22. It should be noted that as long as conduction of current is continuous in the inductance L, and $X_C \ll R$, the ripple factor is independent of the load current flowing. This is a valuable feature, since it permits the design of filters having given ripple factors that will operate over a considerable current range. The ripple factors obtainable may be seen as much smaller than are possible with reasonably sized inductors or capacitors in the circuits previously discussed. Obviously, for small ripple the condition of $4\omega^2 LC = 1$ should be avoided.

Frequently, a second section of filter is added, as in Fig. 6-20(b), to achieve still further reduction in ripple. The current I_L flows almost entirely through capacitor C_1, providing a voltage drop of

$$|E_{C1}| = \frac{4E_m}{3\pi \sqrt{2}\,(4\omega^2 L_1 C_1 - 1)}. \tag{6-63}$$

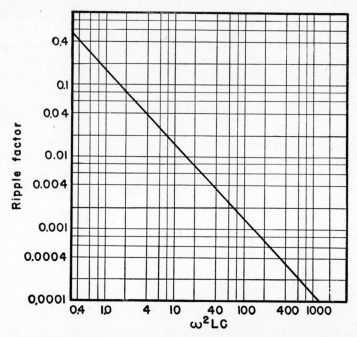

Fig. 6-22. Ripple factor vs $\omega^2 LC$ for a choke-input L-section filter with continuous current flow in the choke (full-wave rectifier).

Under the assumption that $X_C \ll R$ then I_2, the current in the second inductor L_2, is

$$|I_2| = \frac{\dfrac{4E_m}{3\pi \sqrt{2}\,(4\omega^2 L_1 C_1 - 1)}}{2\omega L_2 - 1/2\omega C_2}.$$

The currents in C_2 and R will also be related by Eq. 6-59, and the a-c component of load current will be

$$|I_{R2}| = \frac{4E_m}{3\pi \sqrt{2}\,R(4\omega^2 L_1 C_1 - 1)(4\omega^2 L_2 C_2 - 1)}. \qquad (6\text{-}64)$$

The ripple can then be calculated as

$$\text{ripple} = \frac{I_{R2}}{I_{\text{d-c}}} = \frac{0.47}{(4\omega^2 L_1 C_1 - 1)(4\omega^2 L_2 C_2 - 1)}. \qquad (6\text{-}65)$$

The equation for the ripple could be extended to include the effects of any number of sections, since each section reduces the ripple factor by $1/(4\omega^2 LC - 1)$.

The tube resistance and the resistances of the inductors, although neglected in this analysis, will reduce the d-c voltage available at the load. If the choke resistances are known and the diode resistance is approximated, allowance for the d-c resistance drops may be made and E_m increased sufficiently to obtain the desired value of E_{d-c}. As long as the reactance of the inductors is large with respect to diode and inductor resistances, the ripple-factor value will not be affected.

To avoid the rise in voltage for no load or for currents less than I_k, Fig. 6-21(b), a fixed resistor, known as a *bleeder*, may be placed in shunt with the load. The value of the bleeder resistor should be such that it draws a current of approximately I_k amp. It is then impossible for the total rectifier load to drop below I_k in value, and the filter capacitors and load circuit are protected from the high voltages at light rectifier load. The change in voltage from no load to full load is then reduced, and the rectifier regulation is improved.

The inductors or *chokes* used have inductances of the order of 5 to 30 henrys, with air gaps in the magnetic structure to reduce magnetic saturation by the d-c current present. The capacitors are of the order of 2 to 40 or more microfarads, and may be of wax-impregnated or oil-filled paper or of electrolytic types. The latter are suitable for working voltages up to 400, occupy less space, and are cheaper than the paper capacitors. Oil-filled paper capacitors are used for the higher voltages.

6-8. Critical Value of Filter Input Inductance

The value of I_k, Fig. 6-21(b), is determined by the load current at which the current through the inductor just becomes continuous.

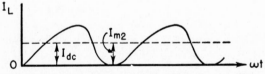

Fig. 6-23.　Current wave form through the filter inductance when $I_{d-c} = I_k$.

This means that the negative peak of the current curve just touches the zero axis, and the current wave form looks like that of Fig. 6-23 for a full-wave rectifier. With continuous current flow, the analysis of the preceding section is applicable. The current of Fig. 6-23 consists of the d-c value plus a-c harmonics, of which the second is of major importance. With higher harmonics neglected, for the current just to touch the zero axis requires that the peak of the second-harmonic wave just be equal to the $I_{\text{d-c}}$ value. By use of values from Eq. 6-17,

$$E_{\text{d-c}} = \frac{2E_m}{\pi}, \qquad E_2 = \frac{4E_m}{3\pi};$$

and since the resistance of the filter to direct current is R and the impedance to second-harmonic alternating current is given in Eq. 6-58, the direct current $I_{\text{d-c}}$ and peak second-harmonic current I_2 are, respectively,

$$I_{\text{d-c}} = \frac{2E_m}{\pi R} \qquad \text{and} \qquad I_2 = \frac{4E_m}{3\pi\left(2\omega L - \dfrac{1}{2\omega C}\right)}.$$

Equating these currents to find the conditions that determine I_k gives

$$R = 1.5\left(2\omega L - \frac{1}{2\omega C}\right). \tag{6-66}$$

This equation states that the current in the input choke becomes continuous, and that the output voltage levels off, at a *load having a resistance equal to* 1.5 *times the second-harmonic a-c impedance of the filter circuit*. This places the d-c value of I_k as

$$I_k = \frac{2E_m}{1.5\pi\left(2\omega L - \dfrac{1}{2\omega C}\right)} = \frac{0.424E_m}{2\omega L - \dfrac{1}{2\omega C}}, \tag{6-67}$$

ω being the angular velocity of the supply circuit. Although this has been derived by neglecting the resistance of the diodes, Schade (Ref. 5) has shown that Eq. 6-66 applies equally well for all usual values of diode resistance.

If the critical current I_k is reduced, then the range over which the load current can be varied without having $E_{\text{d-c}}$ rise can be increased, and a larger bleeder resistance can be used to reduce the power wasted in that circuit. The critical value I_k can be reduced by raising the a-c impedance of the filter circuit, since this operation permits R to be increased for the critical current.

The capacitor reactance is already small for low ripple and for low impedance in the load circuit, so that increasing the circuit impedance means increasing the input inductance. However, this may require the use of an inductor larger than would be needed merely to give the required filtering or ripple. This problem can be solved by use of a *swinging choke.* Such an inductor takes advantage of the variation of inductance of an iron-core reactor due to saturation by the d-c load current, and is designed to have an inductance at full load just large enough for the filtering required. At lighter current loads, the value of inductance rises, thereby increasing the a-c circuit impedance and reducing the value of current I_k at which discontinuous current flow begins in the inductor and the d-c voltage begins to climb.

It is usually true that

$$2\omega L \gg \frac{1}{2\omega C},$$

and under this assumption the critical value of inductance can be determined for the full-wave rectifier from Eq. 6-66 as

$$L_k = \frac{R}{3\omega} = \frac{R}{1131} \tag{6-68}$$

for a supply at 60 cycles.

A value of inductance at least equal to the critical value should

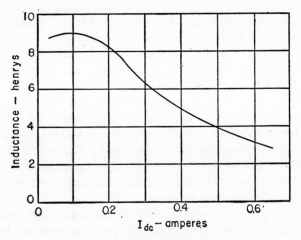

Fig. 6-24.   Variation of inductance of an iron-core reactor
with current.

always be in the circuit and will thus assure continuous current flow in the inductor and normal $E_{\text{d-c}}$.   By taking advantage of the variation of inductance of an iron-core reactor with direct current flowing, an approximately correct value of I_k can be obtained over a wide range of loads.   The inductance of a typical choke, plotted against $I_{\text{d-c}}$ flowing, is shown in Fig. 6-24.

6-9. The Full-Wave Rectifier with π-Section Filter

Frequently, a capacitor is placed across the input terminals of the L-section filter to form the π-section filter of Fig. 6-25.   Quantitatively, the circuit may be analyzed only with great difficulty, owing to the discontinuous current flow and lack of knowledge of cut-in and cutout angles for the diodes as switches.   However, the

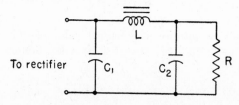

Fig. 6-25.   The π-section filter.

operation of the circuit may be understood from the discussion of the simple capacitor filter.   Capacitor C_1 draws a charging-current pulse twice each cycle and charges to E_m, the peak of the a-c applied voltage, before being disconnected from the source by the diodes as switches.   The capacitor then discharges through the inductance L and load R until its voltage falls to the point where a diode again connects the source.   The discharge current of C_1 is the d-c value plus harmonics and is therefore difficult to evaluate.

The use of an input capacitor results in a voltage higher at light loads (high R) than that obtainable from the L-section filter, since the voltage maintained by the capacitor C_1 approaches E_m.   At heavy current loads, this effect is reduced because the average capacitor voltage will be much below E_m.

Since in this circuit current flows through the diode only for a short interval in each half cycle, the peak currents are high.   In fact, during the first cycle of charging after the rectifier is turned on, the capacitor represents practically a short circuit on the rectifier, and the charging current for a large capacitor may be sufficient to damage the cathode in certain types of gas rectifiers.

Although the input capacitor materially reduces the ripple, the high-peak tube currents and the poor voltage regulation limit the use of the circuit to those installations where space or cost is a major factor, or higher voltage must be obtained from a given transformer than is possible with an *L*-section filter.

6-10. Voltage Doublers

In some applications, particularly where weight or cost will not permit the use of a transformer, it is desirable to obtain d-c voltages higher than can be obtained from the half-wave circuit discussed. The voltage-doubler circuit of Fig. 6-26 may then be used. In this circuit, with the upper a-c terminal assumed positive, diode T_2 passes

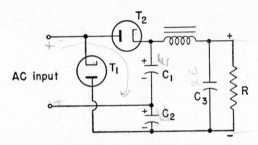

Fig. 6-26.   Voltage-doubling rectifier circuit.

current and charges capacitor C_1 to approximately the peak of the a-c voltage wave. During the next half cycle, the a-c polarity reverses, and diode T_1 carries current and charges capacitor C_2 to the peak of the a-c voltage. Capacitors C_1 and C_2 are effectively in series for the output circuit and, with polarities as marked, produce an output voltage which, at no load, approximates twice the peak value of the applied a-c voltage, provided that a symmetrical input wave form is used. Otherwise the circuit gives a voltage which approximates the sum of the positive and negative peaks.

The diodes conduct high-peak currents for very short times, so that capacitors C_1 and C_2 must be large in order to store enough energy to supply the output circuit during nonconduction periods of the diodes. Consequently, the regulation of the circuit is quite poor.

Other circuits of similar nature are used for tripling and quadrupling the input voltage.

6-11. Choice of Tubes

Certain factors must be considered when designing rectifier circuits and choosing tubes to operate in them. Some of these factors are as follows:

Peak Inverse Voltage. A diode is insulated to stand only a limited voltage without insulation breakdown. The P.I.V. of the circuit is the highest voltage applied to the tube during a cycle and must be less than the rated maximum inverse voltage of the tube.

Peak Tube Current. A cathode may be damaged if attempts are made to obtain currents greater than the emitted values. A circuit design should be checked to determine that I_m is well below the rated maximum current of the diode.

Average Tube Current. The life of the tube is largely set by the average current drain through gradual loss of the cathode emitting material. The heat generated in the tube is also a function of the average current, which should be within rating to ensure that the tube will not be overheated and thereby cause liberation of gas from the electrodes and permanent tube damage.

Filament Supply. Some rectifier diodes use filaments; others indirectly heated cathodes. Since the cathode of a rectifier is frequently operated at full d-c potential above ground, the insulation in the filament transformer or between cathode and heater must be adequate. In certain circuits, such as voltage doublers, the cathodes of the several diodes are not at the same d-c potential; consequently, tubes with a common cathode connection cannot be used.

PROBLEMS

6-1. The circuit shown in Fig. 6-27 is used with an applied voltage

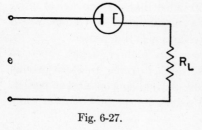

Fig. 6-27.

$$e = E_c(1 + m \cos \omega_m t) \cos \omega_c t.$$

Using the linear diode approximation, find the value of voltage across R_L averaged over one cycle of $\omega_c t$. This is the principle of the linear diode detector of radio waves, where ω_c and ω_m are carrier and modulation angular velocities, respectively.

It should be assumed that $\omega_c \gg \omega_m$, as is ordinarily true in radio operation.

6-2. A certain diode has a volt-ampere relation which can be expressed as

$$i = 0.259V^{1.37}$$

where i is in milliamperes and V is in volts.

(a) Compute r_p at $V = 1, 4, 7, 10$, and 30 v.

(b) Find r_b at the same points and explain the difference between the values for r_p and r_b.

(c) Plot the volt-ampere curve over the range used and check r_p and r_b values graphically.

6-3. A diode having a volt-ampere characteristic expressed by

$$i = 0.378V^{1.56} \qquad \text{ma}$$

is operated in series with a load resistor of 2500 ohms.

(a) Plot the static diode characteristic.

(b) Find the equation for the dynamic characteristic of the diode and load resistor.

(c) Plot the curve for (b) on the same sheet as (a).

(d) How much current flows through the load resistor if 22.5 v d-c is applied to the combination.

6-4. A 200-v d-c source is connected by a switch to the diode of Problem 6-3, making the anode positive. Find the current which will flow if the resistance of the load is 500, 1000, or 3000 ohms.

6-5. A half-wave rectifier uses a diode with $r_p = r_b = 250$ ohms. If the applied voltage is 320 rms, 60 cycles, and the load is 1750 ohms, find:

(a) $I_{\text{d-c}}$.

(b) $E_{\text{d-c}}$.

(c) I_{rms} in load.

(d) Rectification efficiency.

(e) Tube power loss.

6-6. A full-wave rectifier uses a 5Y3G tube with identical diodes of average $r_p = 225$ ohms $= r_b$. The rectifier is to supply a load of 3000 ohms at 300 v d-c. Find:

(a) E_{rms} of the transformer required.

(b) $I_{\text{d-c}}$.

(c) D-c power output.

(d) Peak tube current.

(e) Tube power loss.

(f) Power output of transformer.

6-7. For a current having a wave form shown in Fig. 6-28(a) find the d-c value, the ripple, and the d-c and a-c power losses if this current flows through a 2000-ohm resistance.

6-8. Find the form factor, ripple, and d-c current represented by a current wave form such as in Fig. 6-28(b).

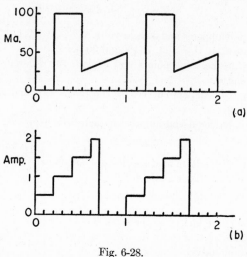

(a)

(b)

Fig. 6-28.

6-9. Find the value of load R required for maximum d-c power output from a full-wave rectifier using a 5Z3 tube rated at: P.I.V. = 1550 v, I_m per diode = 675 ma, I_{av} per diode = 112 ma.

(a) Under the above conditions find the efficiency of rectification, if $r_p = r_b = 120$ ohms.

(b) Plot a curve of rectification efficiency against the ratio R/r_p.

6-10. Starting with Eq. 6-51 for the current pulse in a half-wave rectifier with inductor filter, develop Eq. 6-55 for the d-c voltage on the load.

6-11. A shunt-capacitor filter on a half-wave rectifier with resistance load has the following readings taken: $I_{d-c} = 237$ ma, $E_{d-c} = 455$ v, $I_{rms} = 321$ ma. Find:

(a) Ripple.

(b) Efficiency of rectification, neglecting tube loss.

6-12. A half-wave rectifier having $r_b = r_p = 175$ ohms is used to charge a battery of 120 v (assumed constant) and 2.1 ohms internal resistance. The a-c supply voltage is 120 v rms. Find:

(a) Average rate at which battery is charged.

(b) Peak plate current.

(c) Total input power to circuit.

(d) Efficiency of the battery charging operation.

6-13. A half-wave rectifier operates into a shunt-capacitance filter of 12 μf under the following conditions: supply voltage 250 rms, frequency 60 cycles, and load resistance 7500 ohms. Find the ripple factor, angles of cut-in and cutout of the diode, and diode peak current.

6-14. A certain filter circuit has inductance in series with a resistance load.

(a) If the choke has an inductance of 10 henrys and the load is supplied 300 v and 0.100 amp, direct current, from a 60-cycle full-wave rectifier, find the ripple, using wave form considerations.

(b) Find the ripple if the inductor is removed.

6-15. Design an L-section filter for a 60-cycle full-wave rectifier to produce a ripple of 0.004, with $E_{d-c} = 300$ v, $I_{d-c} = 250$ ma.

(a) If only a 4 μf capacitor is available.

(b) If critical L_k is to be used, specify both L_k and C.

6-16. A double L-section filter is used on the output of the rectifier in Problem 6-6 with supply at 60 cycles. Capacitors C_1 and C_2 are to be equal and may be in sizes of 8, 12, 20, 30 or 40 μf, but for economic reasons not more than one unit can be used in each position. Design the filter, using the nearest possible value to critical inductance, and obtain a ripple factor of 0.001.

6-17. A 5Z3 rectifier has two diodes with a common cathode connection and is rated at P.I.V. $= 1550$ v, I_m per diode $= 675$ ma, and average I per diode $= 112$ ma. Find the maximum d-c power, current, and voltage simultaneously possible from this rectifier in a full-wave circuit without exceeding any rating.

6-18. An L-section filter is supplied by a half-wave circuit using a diode with an r_b value of 100 ohms. The filter inductance is constant at 15 h and has a resistance of 110 ohms; the filter capacitor is 8 μf. The transformer supplies 750 v rms to the circuit and the load has a resistance of 1400 ohms. Find the ripple factor and the value of E_{d-c} on the load.

6-19. Analyze the performance of a series-inductor filter supplied by a full-wave rectifier. Neglect tube resistance and

(a) Obtain expression for E_{d-c}.

(b) Obtain variation of angle ωt_2.

(c) Plot a current wave form for $R/\omega L = 0.25$, with $E_m = 300$ v and $R = 3000$ ohms.

6-20. (a) Plot a current wave form for the shunt-capacitor circuit for $\omega RC = 10$, with $E_m = 300$ v and $R = 1000$ ohms.

(b) For the same voltage and load, plot a current wave form for a series inductor filter for $R/\omega L = 0.15$.

6-21. For a half-wave rectifier with shunt-capacitor filter and with a supply voltage of 350 v rms, 60 c, plot the wave forms of output voltage for $C = 8$ μf, and load resistances of 500 and of 3000 ohms.

6-22. For the circuit of Problem 6-21, plot the current wave forms through the tube, and through the capacitor.

6-23. In a full-wave circuit, with tube resistance negligible, supplying a resistance load through an L-section filter, the applied rms voltage per side of the transformer is 300; f is 60 cycles; and $L = 10$ h, $C = 4$ μf. The average current rating of each diode is 225 ma. Find:

(a) The value of E_{d-c}.

(b) The maximum permissible value of R to prevent E_{d-c} from climbing.

(c) The resistance and wattage rating of a bleeder resistor to use.

6-24. (a) Find the value of ripple to be expected at full load from the circuit of Problem 6-23.

(b) Plot the variation in inductance required of a swinging choke used as L from full load to 10 per cent full load.

6-25. Prove that Eq. 6-37 can be obtained from the integrals given.

REFERENCES

1. Waidelich, D. L., "Diode Rectifying Circuits with Capacitance Filters," *Trans AIEE*, **60**, 1161 (1941).

2. Dellenbaugh, F. S., Jr., and Quimby, R. S., "The Important First Choke in High-Voltage Rectifier Circuits," *QST*, **16**, 14, February (1932); **16**, 27, March (1932); **16**, 33, April (1932).

3. Ryder, J. D., "Ferro-Inductance as a Variable Electric Circuit Element," *Trans AIEE*, **64**, 671 (1945).

4. Schade, O. H., "Analysis of Rectifier Operation," *Proc. IRE*, **31**, 341 (1943).

5. Waidelich, D. L., "Analysis of Full Wave Rectifier and Capacitive Input Filter," *Electronics*, **20**, 120, September (1947).

6. ———, "The Full-Wave Voltage-Doubling Rectifier Circuit," *Proc. IRE*, **29**, 554 (1941).

7. Waidelich, D. L., and Taskin, H. A. T., "Analyses of the Voltage-Tripling and -Quadrupling Rectifier Circuits," *Proc. IRE*, **33**, 449 (1945).

8. Schade, O. H., "Radio-Frequency-Operated High-Voltage Supplies for Cathode-Ray Tubes," *Proc. IRE*, **31**, 158 (1943).

9. Mautner, R. S., and Schade, O. H., "Television High Voltage R-F Supplies," *RCA Rev.*, **8**, 43 (1947).

CHAPTER 7

THE VACUUM TRIODE

The addition of the grid to the vacuum diode by De Forest in 1906 is regarded as the basic invention of modern electronics, if not one of the great inventions of all time. The grid made possible the electric field *control* of large amounts of power, and supplied a new basic principle which has been developed into the whole electronic industry. Modern radio devices, amplifiers, industrial controls, and television all depend on the control of an electric current by a potential applied to a small wire-mesh structure interposed in the electron stream between the cathode and anode of a diode. By reason of the three active elements the tube becomes a triode.

7-1. Energy Distribution of Emitted Electrons

In consideration of the motion of electrons emitted from a plane cathode in a vacuum tube, only outward or x-directed velocities are of interest, since velocity components in other directions will not contribute to the flow away from the surface. When only outward-directed components are considered, the distribution of energy among the electrons may be plotted in terms of energy of the electrons at some particular temperature, as is done in Fig. 7-1 for a temperature of 2600°K. A certain fraction of the electrons have sufficient energy to move away from the cathode and reach a point of -0.5 v potential, this fraction being represented by the ratio of the area under the curve, to the right of 0.5 on the energy axis, to the whole area under the curve. It can be seen that by varying a retarding potential on a plane set up in front of the cathode, the number of electrons reaching the plane can be controlled and varied.

Since the energy distribution is not a linear function, it is reasonable to suspect that any device depending on this distribution for

its operation will likewise not be a linear device.   That this is true
of the triode vacuum tube will be discovered in this chapter.

In Chapter 5 it was found that a potential minimum was established in front of the cathode by the space charge and that this
potential minimum, acting as a velocity or energy filter for the
emitted electrons, was able to control the current flowing.   If the

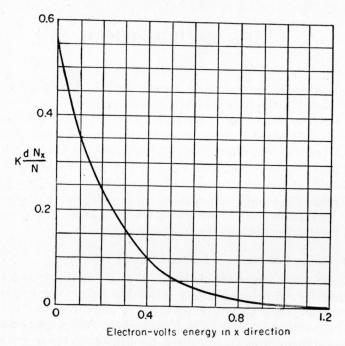

Fig. 7-1.   Maxwellian distribution of energy among electrons
emitted from a source at 2600°K, having positive-x-directed velocities.

electrons all had the same velocity, a potential minimum would
either stop the flow, or permit all the electrons to pass and reach
the anode, and a vacuum tube would have a step-shaped volt-ampere
characteristic.   It can now be seen that the actual smooth variation
of current versus potential is possible because of the manner in which
the energies of the emitted electrons vary, as in Fig. 7-1.

7-2. Function of the Grid

The space charge establishes a potential minimum near the cathode and in turn sets up a repelling field at the cathode surface which permits only the highest-energy electrons to leave the cathode. As the anode potential is raised, the depth of the potential minimum changes, the retarding potential is reduced, and lower-energy electrons are emitted and join the electron stream to the anode resulting in a greater current flow. When the anode potential falls, opposite effects occur, and the current is reduced. The current is controlled by the automatic raising or lowering of the space charge potential barrier by change in the anode potential, as illustrated in Fig. 7-2.

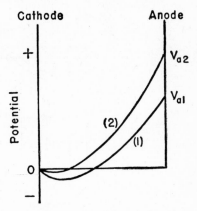

Fig. 7-2. Potential variations between electrodes in a diode with space charge.

If the anode potential were kept constant but the potential minimum were raised or lowered at will, the field at the cathode surface would be varied in just the same manner as by change of anode potential. If a grid of wire mesh is placed in the region near the cathode, the field at the cathode surface can be varied (see Fig. 7-3). The grid wires establish a potential in the space which is determined by the voltage between grid and cathode. The openings between the grid wires permit the electrons to have relatively free transit. Since the grid is not a solid metal sheet but does have large openings between the wires, it does not establish an equipotential surface. However, the fact that the *average* potential in the grid plane can be influenced over a considerable range results in a variation of the field at the cathode surface and permits control of the emitted electron current.

The rise of potential to the anode is called e_b, and it can be seen that the field strength at the cathode is a function of e_b, as in the diode. If the grid potential is given as e_c, the field strength at the

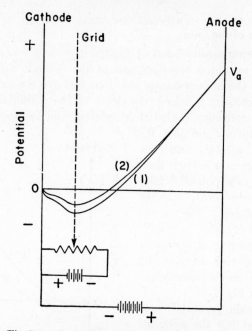

Fig. 7-3. Potential variations between electrodes
in a triode with space charge.

cathode surface is also a function of e_c. The grid is much closer to
the cathode than is the anode and, consequently, one volt on the
grid produces a larger electric field at the cathode surface than does
one volt on the anode; that is, a one-volt change in the potential
between the grid and cathode is more effective on the field strength
at the cathode than a one-volt change in anode potential.

The ratio of effectiveness of a potential change at the grid to the
same potential change at the anode is known as the *amplification
factor* of the triode, and is represented by the symbol μ. Since the
anode current is controlled by the electric field near the cathode
surface, the field and the current variations produced by a one-volt
change on the grid are μ times as effective on the current as a one-volt
change on the anode.

There is, obviously, some sort of a functional relationship between
the anode current i_b and e_b, the cathode-anode voltage rise. The
same functional relationship must also apply between anode current

and grid voltage if the grid-cathode voltage is written as μe_c to allow for the greater effectiveness of potentials on the grid. It is then possible to write for the anode current i_b

$$i_b = f(\mu e_c + e_b). \qquad (7\text{-}1)$$

This relationship will be of considerable use in the study of the triode.

Since, for the purpose of this analysis, the grid is assumed as having negative potentials that are constant during the flight time of one electron, no current will flow in the grid circuit, and the control of the plate current will be by pure electric-field means. If the potential of the grid changed during the time of flight of one electron, more electrons might be moving in the space between grid and anode than between cathode and grid, resulting in a net induced current in the grid circuit. This phenomenon will be discussed under Section 7-12, *Transit-Time Effects.*

Actually, since the grid has an appreciable physical area in the electron stream, a few electrons will be so directed and will have sufficient energy to overcome the negative grid field and

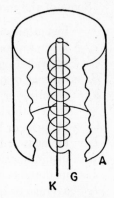

Fig. 7-4. Typical triode structure.

thus reach the grid. For tubes with grids normally negative at all times, this current is so small that it may be neglected entirely. Some tubes are designed for operation with grids at a positive potential, and, with these tubes, special methods of analysis are available to account for the grid current.

7-3. Vacuum-Tube Nomenclature

Since vacuum-tube circuits are in general quite complicated and involve many different voltages and currents, it is necessary to adopt a system of designating symbols if tube circuits are to be understood. The Institute of Radio Engineers has adopted certain standard symbols for electronic tubes, and, as far as possible, these symbols will be used in this book.

Voltages are measured *with respect to the cathode as zero, or reference potential.* In the symbols used, small, or lower-case, letters are employed for varying or instantaneous quantities, and capital letters denote rms or d-c values. Since the triode contains three elements—

a grid, a cathode, and a plate or anode—frequent use is made of the letters g, k, and p, as subscripts on quantities referring to the various circuits, although rigid consistency in the use of these letters is not to be expected. Also, in the early days of radio broadcasting, batteries supplying filament, plate, and grid circuits were referred to as A, B, and C, respectively, and certain of these letters have been retained as designating subscripts.

Some of the more common symbols are:

e_c = instantaneous total voltage rise from cathode to grid.

e_g = instantaneous value of a-c component of the voltage rise from cathode to grid.

E_c = average or quiescent value of voltage rise from cathode to grid.

E_g = effective or rms value of a-c component of the voltage rise from cathode to grid.

E_f = filament or heater terminal voltage.

I_f = filament or heater current.

i_b = instantaneous total anode current.

i_p = instantaneous value of a-c component of anode current.

I_b = average or quiescent value of anode current.

I_{bs} = average value of anode current with signal present. In this text this symbol will only be used when it is wished to emphasize the point that I_b and I_{bs} are different, as in nonlinear operation of the tube.

I_p = effective or rms value of a-c component of anode current.

e_b = instantaneous total voltage rise from cathode to anode.

e_p = instantaneous value of a-c component of voltage rise from cathode to anode.

E_b = average or quiescent value of anode voltage rise from cathode to anode.

E_p = effective or rms value of a-c component of anode voltage.

E_{bb} = anode-circuit supply voltage rise from cathode.

E_{cc} = grid-circuit supply voltage rise from cathode.

e_s = instantaneous value of a-c input voltage to the grid circuit.

E_s = effective or rms value of a-c grid-circuit input voltage.

Other symbols will be introduced and defined as needed.

Certain types of tubes may have more than one grid, and for these a system of numerical subscripts is used, as e_{c1}, e_{c2}, and so forth, the number indicating the particular grid meant, with the

grid nearest the cathode being counted as grid 1. If no subscript
is given, then only one grid is implied, or the grid used for control of
anode current by the signal is meant.

The grid-circuit bias voltage, E_{cc}, is made negative to the grid
for usual circuits. When a numerical value is introduced into
equations involving E_{cc}, the negative sign should also be introduced
if appropriate to the situation.

A typical triode circuit diagram is shown in Fig. 7-5. It is customary, for purposes of analysis, to assume that the grid input signal
e_s is sinusoidal and has an rms value E_s. The rise of potential e_c
actually appearing between cathode and grid is then the sum of the

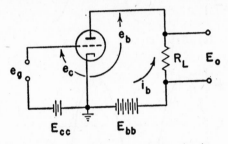

Fig. 7-5.   Basic triode amplifier circuit.

d-c bias voltage, E_{cc}, and an instantaneous alternating value e_g,
which in Fig. 7-5 is equal to e_s, although this is not always the case.
The total instantaneous voltage rise from cathode to grid e_c is then

$$e_c = E_{cc} + e_g. \tag{7-2}$$

If e_g or e_s is sinusoidal, then the variation of e_c with time is plotted
in (a) of Fig. 7-6.

If $e_g = 0$, the grid voltage is equal to E_{cc} and is steady. The
anode current is likewise steady or constant, and the tube is said to
be in a *quiescent* condition. The anode current then has the value
I_b. As a result of variation of the grid-cathode voltage by the
component e_g, the current in the anode circuit will also vary with an
instantaneous total value of i_b. This is composed of the steady
d-c value I_b, to which is added the instantaneous value of the a-c
component i_p, or

$$i_b = I_b + i_p. \tag{7-3}$$

Under some conditions of operation the average value of current in the anode circuit will be different with signal, and it is then given the symbol I_{bs}.

The current and grid voltage phase relations will be as shown in Fig. 7-6(a) and (b), as can be demonstrated by considering that

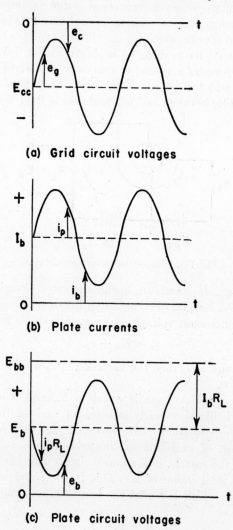

(a) Grid circuit voltages

(b) Plate currents

(c) Plate circuit voltages

Fig. 7-6. Currents and voltages in a triode circuit.

when the grid voltage swings positive (becomes less negative), the plate current increases and is, therefore, also in its positive half cycle. The plate current is in phase with the grid-cathode voltage.

When the anode current has only the quiescent value I_b, the anode-cathode voltage, or the tube voltage, is E_b, and is obtained by considering the $I_b R_L$ voltage drop in the load resistor, or

$$E_b = E_{bb} - I_b R_L. \tag{7-4}$$

Owing to variation of the anode current when e_c varies, the a-c component of anode current produces an alternating drop in the load, and the instantaneous tube voltage is

$$e_b = E_{bb} - (I_b + i_p)R_L \tag{7-5}$$

$$= E_b - i_p R_L, \tag{7-6}$$

from which the load-voltage rise (cathode reference) appears as

$$e_0 = -i_p R_L = e_b - E_b, \tag{7-7}$$

and these relations are plotted in Fig. 7-6(c). Since the anode current increases on positive grid voltage, the load voltage magnitude also increases, and as a result the tube voltage decreases as plotted, since the sum of the load and tube voltages is constant and equal to E_{bb}. Therefore the variation of tube voltage e_b is out of phase with the grid voltage, and this relationship accounts for the position of the curve in Fig. 7-6(c).

7-4. Graphical Characteristics

If a triode is arranged to have a constant value of anode voltage and the grid voltage is caused to vary, the depth of the potential minimum in front of the cathode varies. From the curve of Fig. 7-1 it may be reasoned that this variation causes the current through the tube to vary, owing to the differences in energy of emission of the various emitted electrons, the grid acting as a velocity filter, passing only electrons having velocities above a certain minimum which is determined by the grid voltage.

Since the vacuum tube is, in general, a nonlinear circuit device, the most convenient means available for expressing its operating characteristics is in the form of graphs, or families of curves, showing the actual performance of the tube, or its volt-ampere relations. Figure 7-7 constitutes one set of such curves. Note that each curve is drawn for a different value of anode voltage. Curve e_{b1} is for the lowest value of voltage; each of the other curves is for progressively higher values. Also indicated is the fact that for positive values of e_c, a current i_c flows to the grid. The total emission from the cathode is limited, and at high values of anode current the grid subtracts sufficient electrons from the stream so that the anode current not only levels off owing to saturation effects but may actually begin to fall at high, positive grid-voltage values.

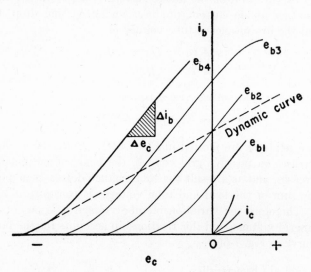

Fig. 7-7.   Grid voltage-plate characteristics of a triode.

The curves are seen to be nonlinear, although a considerable region exists over which the *slopes* are practically constant, and assumptions of linearity might be made with small loss of accuracy. These curves are called *transfer* or *grid* characteristics, since they relate current in the anode circuit to voltage in the grid circuit.

The curves of Fig. 7-7 are taken without load impedance in the external anode circuit and, consequently, are called *static* characteristics, as was a similar curve for the diode. The static curve is not useful in predicting actual triode performance in a circuit such as that of Fig. 7-5 because in that circuit the anode supply voltage is kept constant and the tube voltage varies, contrary to conditions assumed for Fig. 7-7. To predict the actual performance in a circuit it is necessary to draw a *dynamic* curve by plotting the variation of i_b with changes in e_c, for a constant E_{bb}. A dynamic curve for a particular value of R_L is drawn as the dashed curve of Fig. 7-7. Note that the slope of the dynamic curve will always be less than the static curve, and the dynamic curve will also be more nearly linear.

Use of the dynamic transfer curve allows graphical determination of the wave form of anode current for a given wave form of e_g. The value of e_c is given by

$$e_c = E_{cc} + e_g, \tag{7-8}$$

where
$$e_g = E_m \sin \omega t. \tag{7-9}$$

Reference to Fig. 7-8 shows that this voltage may be plotted on the e_c axis with the value E_{cc} as a time axis, this bias voltage being negative as is usual. By projection to a dynamic curve drawn for a particular E_{bb} and a certain R_L, the wave form of anode current may be plotted horizontally against time. This wave form may or may

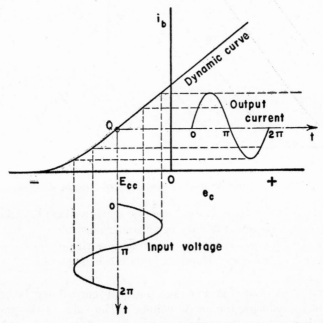

Fig. 7-8. Graphical determination of anode-current wave form from the dynamic transfer curve.

not be similar to the grid-voltage wave form, depending on whether the dynamic curve is linear or not. The point marked Q is called the *operating point*, or *quiescent point*, since operating swings of voltage and current occur about it as an origin.

The dynamic curve predicts the performance of the tube for a certain R_L and E_{bb}; if either is changed, a new curve must be plotted. Since it is a curve, this is a laborious process. As a result, although the dynamic curve is frequently used as a starting point in theoretical analyses of vacuum-tube operation, it is rarely employed for solution of practical design and operating problems.

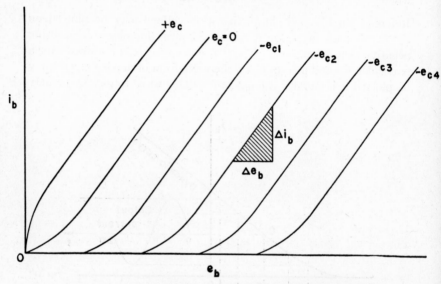

Fig. 7-9.   Plate voltage-plate current characteristics of a triode.

If the grid voltage e_c is fixed and the anode voltage is varied, the anode current is found to vary in a manner illustrated by the curves of Fig. 7-9, the subscripts on e_c increasing with progressively more negative grid voltage. These curves are called the *plate* characteristics.

For a given value of grid voltage, the anode current may be brought to zero by reducing the anode voltage. The value of the grid bias which just reduces the current to zero for a given anode voltage is called the *cutoff* bias.

A third type of triode characteristic may be obtained if the anode current is held constant by simultaneous variation of e_b and e_c. The results are plotted in Fig. 7-10 and are called the *constant-current* characteristics. The constant-current curves do not give any additional information over that obtainable from the plate and grid characteristics, although they are found useful for analysis of transmitting-tube performance.

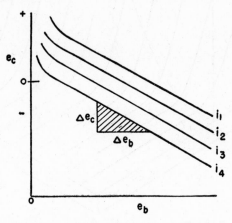

Fig. 7-10.   Grid voltage-plate voltage or constant-current characteristics of a triode.

All three types of curves are means of projecting on a plane the information concerning tube operation which is actually represented by a surface. The performance of a tube is given in terms of three variables i_b, e_b, and e_c; and since these are interrelated they can be completely represented only by a surface in three-dimensional space, as in Fig. 7-11.

By passing planes parallel to the i_b,e_c axes, a set of intersections with this surface are obtained as shown for various anode voltages. These respective intersections when drawn on the i_b,e_c plane represent the grid voltage-plate current or transfer characteristics previously discussed.

Intersections of planes parallel to the i_b,e_b axes with the surface may be obtained for various grid-voltage values. The intersection for one such plane, drawn at -25 grid volts, is indicated by the dashed lines of Fig. 7-11. These intersections when projected onto

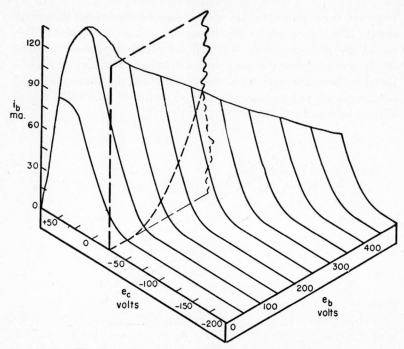

Fig. 7-11. The vacuum triode characteristic surface.

the i_b, e_b plane represent the curves previously referred to as the plate family.

Likewise, if planes are passed through the figure parallel to the e_b, e_c plane, at selected values of i_b, then the constant-current family of curves is obtained by projection of the intersections onto the e_b, e_c plane.

The curves of Figs. 7-7, 7-9, and 7-10 are merely convenient forms of representation of the actual tube operating surface. As such they are widely employed for design and analysis of tube performance, as will be shown in later chapters.

7-5. Triode Coefficients

Since vacuum tubes are employed largely in circuits having varying voltages and currents, their actions under dynamic or varying conditions must be studied. In the curves of Fig. 7-7, the absolute value of current i_b at a certain value of e_c and e_b is not of as much importance as the *change* of i_b that may be produced by a given *change* in e_c. Since for a certain value of e_b such a change in i_b would take place along one of the curves of Fig. 7-7, the slope of the curve, or *rate of change* of i_b with respect to e_c, is the really important matter. The slope may be given by

$$\text{slope} = \frac{\partial i_b}{\partial e_c}\bigg]_{e_b=k}. \qquad (7\text{-}10)$$

Here the partial derivative is used to indicate that the third variable, e_b, is held constant or the change is made along the transfer curve.

The dimensions of the derivative may be noted as current over voltage, or conductance, but the current is measured in the anode circuit and the voltage in the grid circuit, so that a transfer conductance is implied. The derivative in Eq. 7-10 is given the symbol g_m, or

$$g_m = \frac{\partial i_b}{\partial e_c}, \qquad (7\text{-}11)$$

and g_m is called the *grid-plate transconductance*, or the *mutual conductance*. In tubes having several grids, the transconductance between the control grid and the anode is meant unless denoted otherwise by numerical subscripts. The transconductance is an important figure of merit for a vacuum tube because it gives an indication of the magnitude of current change possible to produce per volt of grid-potential change. The units of conductance are, of course, mhos, but for convenience in avoiding decimals, it is customary to state the values of g_m in micromhos, or 10^{-6} mhos. Vacuum triodes are manufactured with values of g_m ranging from a few hundred to above 40,000 micromhos.

Because the slope of the transfer curves of Fig. 7-7 is not constant for all values of e_c, the value of g_m is not in general a constant but varies with the point on the curves at which the tube operation takes place. At moderate values of current the variation of slope and of value of g_m is not great, and g_m is frequently assumed as constant over small ranges of current to simplify certain types of vacuum-tube circuit analysis.

The curves of Fig. 7-9 indicate the variations of anode current to be expected with changes of anode potential. For a fixed e_c value, changes of anode current occur along curves of Fig. 7-9, and the value of the rate of change of current with respect to anode voltage, or the slope of the curve, is of interest. The slope of the current-voltage curve is defined as

$$\text{slope} = \frac{\partial i_b}{\partial e_b}\bigg]_{e_c=k}, \tag{7-12}$$

the partial derivative again being used to imply that e_c is held constant. The derivative is dimensionally a conductance, and since both current and voltage are measured in the plate or anode circuit, the derivative is given the name *plate conductance* and the symbol g_p, or

$$g_p = \frac{\partial i_b}{\partial e_b}. \tag{7-13}$$

Frequently it is more convenient to use the reciprocal of g_p. This quantity is given the name *plate resistance* of the tube and the symbol r_p, or

$$r_p = \frac{\partial e_b}{\partial i_b}. \tag{7-14}$$

The slope of the curves of Fig. 7-9 is not constant; thus r_p is in general a variable, depending on the operating position on the curves. As for g_m, r_p may be assumed constant over a considerable region with only small error.

The factor $g_m = \partial i_b/\partial e_c$ measures the effectiveness of the grid voltage in controlling the plate current. Likewise, $g_p = \partial i_b/\partial e_b$ measures the effectiveness of the plate voltage in changing the plate current. A factor μ was defined in Section 7-2 as the ratio of the effect of the grid voltage to the effect of the plate voltage on the electric field near the cathode, or on the current flowing. Therefore, from Eqs. 7-11 and 7-13, it can be seen that by definition

$$\mu = \frac{g_m}{g_p} = \frac{\partial i_b/\partial e_c}{\partial i_b/\partial e_b} = -\frac{\partial e_b}{\partial e_c}. \tag{7-15}$$

The partial derivative implies that for determination of μ, i_b must be held constant. The term μ is given the name of *amplification factor*, and the derivative, being voltage over voltage, is dimensionless. As the name *amplification factor* implies, μ is to a considerable extent an indication of the possible amplification of voltage obtainable from a tube.

The negative sign in Eq. 7-15 indicates that in order to hold i_b

constant as required for the partial derivative the changes of e_b and e_c must be made in opposite directions.

Equation 7-15 is more frequently written as

$$\mu = g_m r_p, \tag{7-16}$$

which relates the three tube coefficients at the point of operation and shows that they are interdependent. This factor imposes limitations in the design of some tube types. The coefficient g_m is most affected by the size of tube and cathode, whereas μ and r_p are largely controlled by location of the grid and spacing of the grid wires. Therefore, for a given cathode design, μ and r_p may be expected to increase or decrease together as the grid design is changed.

The three tube coefficients μ, g_m, and r_p are all slopes on the three-dimensional surface of Fig. 7-11. They are also variables over a range of operating conditions, although in certain regions the variation is small and the coefficients may be considered constants. The amount and type of variation are illustrated for a small receiving triode, type 6J5 in Fig. 7-12.

Grids are ordinarily made as wire-wound helices; and a closely

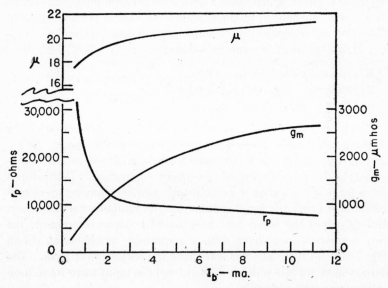

Fig. 7-12. Variation of μ, g_m, and r_p vs plate current for a 6J5 triode. This tube is rated at: $\mu = 20$, $r_p = 7700$ ohms, $g_m = 2600$ μmhos at $I_b = 9$ ma.

wound grid, or a grid close to the cathode, will have greater effect on the cathode field and a higher μ than open-wound grids or grids relatively far from the cathode. Means of calculating these effects are available for design purposes (Refs. 1 and 2) but are usually so involved that much design work is carried out by experiment.

7-6. Wave-Form Distortion in Vacuum-Tube Circuits

One of the most important applications of the vacuum tube is in the amplification of speech and music. These sounds consist of complex wave forms of acoustic pressure which must be converted by the microphone to electric wave forms, transmitted along a wire or through space, passed by the receiving amplifiers, and reconverted to sound wave forms by the loudspeaker. The ideal—to hear the music or speech exactly as it sounded in the studio—requires that the wave form of sound pressure produced by the loudspeaker be identical with that reaching the microphone. If at any point in the chain an alteration of the wave form occurs, the sounds will not be heard as they were originally produced, and the loudspeaker output will be said to be *distorted*. Phenomena in a circuit device or network which cause a difference between input and output wave forms are said to produce distortion. Three possible types of distortion are recognized in vacuum-tube circuits. These are classified according to their cause as follows:

1. Frequency distortion.
2. Nonlinear (amplitude) distortion.
3. Phase or delay distortion.

Frequency distortion is produced by unequal amplification of the different component frequencies present in a given signal. At (a) in Fig. 7-13, a certain input wave form is analyzed into a fundamental and a second-harmonic-frequency component. If this input wave form is applied to a vacuum-tube amplifier having an output which is n times the input voltage for the fundamental frequency, and $2n$ times the input for the second-harmonic component, the two components will have output amplitudes as shown at (b) in Fig. 7-13, and their sum will constitute the output wave form. The output wave form is widely different from the input wave form, indicating frequency distortion.

The presence of frequency distortion is usually indicated by plot-

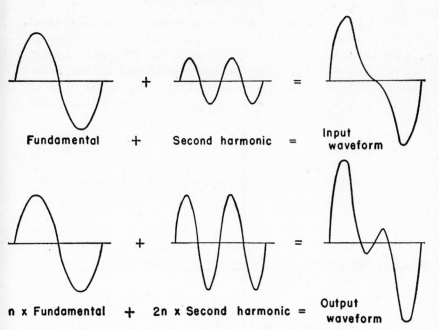

Fig. 7-13.   Frequency distortion: (a) above; (b) below.

ting a curve of vacuum-tube output voltage against frequency for a constant-amplitude sinusoidal input. The ideal curve, with zero frequency distortion, is a straight horizontal line, as shown in Fig. 7-14. For comparison, the curve obtained for a form of voice-frequency amplifier is shown as the dashed line.

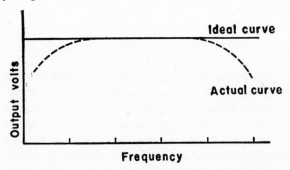

Fig. 7-14.   Usual form of the amplifier gain-frequency curve.

Nonlinear, or amplitude, distortion is produced if the input-output amplitude curve of the tube and circuit is not linear or if different amplitudes of input voltage are not all amplified the same amount. For a vacuum tube, if the dynamic transfer characteristic is not linear over the operating range, nonlinear distortion will occur, as shown in Fig. 7-15. It can be seen that although the grid input

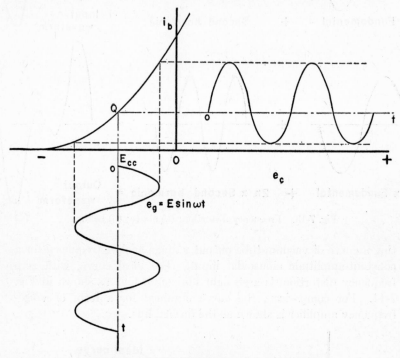

Fig. 7-15. Nonlinear distortion in a vacuum tube.

voltage was sinusoidal, the output current contains even harmonics which were generated by the nonlinear action of the tube.

A special form of nonlinear distortion is known as *intermodulation*. For a single input frequency a nonlinear characteristic introduces harmonics, or produces frequencies in the output which were not present in the input. If two or more frequencies are simultaneously present in the input, then, besides harmonics, frequencies which are the sums and differences of all the input frequencies will be present in the output. These sum and difference frequencies bear no harmonic relationship to the original frequencies and are treated by the ear as noise, which is usually objectionable.

Nonlinear distortion is usually caused by the vacuum tube. Its effects can be minimized by operation over suitably linear portions of the dynamic characteristic and by use of special circuits.

The above discussion is based on a steady-state situation. The response of circuits to transients may be different than their response to steady-state conditions, and the presence of transient input voltages may cause other and unrelated transient output conditions. Although transient response is not given much attention in amplifiers for audio use, transient response of amplifiers for television and pulse transmission must be carefully studied.

Phase or *delay distortion* occurs if the phase relation between the various frequency components making up the sound wave is not the same in the output as in the input. If, in (a) of Fig. 7-16, an input wave form of fundamental and second harmonic is again chosen, and the time of transmission of the second harmonic is different from the time of the fundamental, the output wave form may be

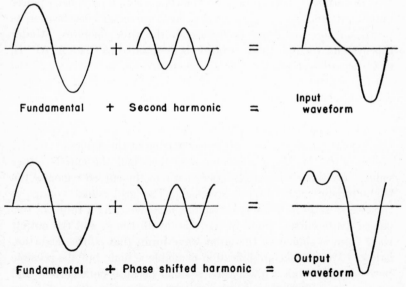

Fig. 7-16.   Phase distortion: (a) above; (b) below.

appreciably altered, as in (b) of Fig. 7-16, and this alteration constitutes phase distortion.

If the phase angle θ by which the various frequencies are shifted is proportional to frequency, the phase of all the components is shifted by the same *time interval*, and the whole wave shifts as a unit, giving no phase distortion. The important criterion in connection with phase distortion is the relative change of θ with respect to ω, or that $d\theta/d\omega$ be a constant for zero distortion.

Phase distortion is due to the presence of reactive elements in the tube and circuits, and may be reduced by elimination of, or compensation for, these reactances. The human ear shows a considerable tolerance for phase distortion, and this distortion is usually neglected in amplifiers designed for audible output, except for the feedback amplifier, where phase performance may be a limiting factor on operation. In amplifiers for use with television and other systems, where the ear is not the final receiver, the elimination of the effects of phase distortion becomes an important matter.

7-7. Amplifier Classification

Vacuum-tube operation may be classified according to the function performed, as oscillators, modulators, voltage amplifiers, power amplifiers, and so on, but another and universal classification is based on the conditions under which the tube operates. Under this system, vacuum-tube operation is designated as Class A, AB, B, or C, according to the voltage and current conditions existing in the circuit. Operation under Class A, B, and C conditions is graphically illustrated in Fig. 7-17, where the dynamic transfer characteristic of a tube is used in explanation.

Under Class A operation, the grid-bias voltage (E_{cc}) is set so that operation occurs over the linear portion of the dynamic transfer curve, or E_{cc} is chosen somewhat less than half the cutoff-voltage value. By this choice of E_{cc}, operation into the curved region of the characteristic near cutoff is avoided. The grid signal voltage is then selected so that the grid remains negative. As a result of this choice, plate current flows in the tube at all times, and the output wave form is similar to the input wave form; that is, the distortion is low. The voltage amplification available is high, but the possible power output from a given tube is small because both current and voltage are restricted to relatively small variations. The efficiency of conversion of d-c power to a-c signal power is quite poor, having a maximum theoretical value of 50 per cent, but in practice being in the range of 2 to 20 per cent. Class A smplifiers are used where linearity, or freedom from distortion, and high voltage amplification are desired with low power output; these amplifiers constitute the form of operation for possibly 90 per cent of all vacuum tubes in service.

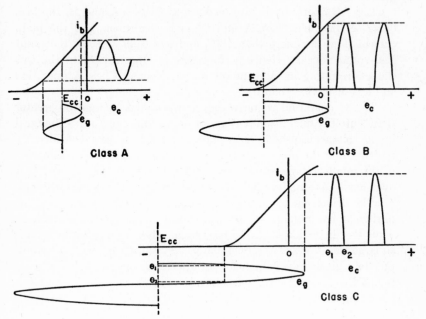

Fig. 7-17.   Vacuum-tube operation under Class A, B, and C conditions.

For Class B operation, the grid-bias voltage is set at approximately the cutoff value. The grid-signal voltage may be large enough to drive the grid positive at times. The plate current flows for one-half the time, or 180° of the input grid-voltage cycle, and the pulses of output current closely approach in form the wave form of the positive half cycles of grid input voltage. Since the negative half cycles are completely absent, the distortion is high. The voltage input required is larger than for Class A, and the voltage amplification is reduced. The power output is higher than is obtainable under Class A operation with a given tube, and the plate-conversion efficiency is also higher.   The maximum theoretical value of efficiency is 78 per cent, and practical circuits achieve efficiencies of 50 to 60 per cent.   The attractive feature of Class B operation is the possibility of large power output from a small tube.   Circuits have been devised that will remove most of the distortion produced, making well-designed Class B amplifiers feasible for good-quality speech or music reproduction.

Class AB operation is intermediate to Classes A and B, the bias being set between Class A and Class B conditions, and the plate current flows for more than 180°, and less than 360°, of the input grid-voltage cycle.   Hence performance is intermediate to the two classes, resulting in more power output than in Class A operation and less distortion than in Class B operation.

Class C operation requires that the grid-bias voltage be greater than cutoff value, usually two or more times cutoff.   The grid input voltage is usually very large, driving the grid considerably positive, and the plate current flows through an angle less than 180° of the input-voltage cycle.   The pulses of output current may flow over angles as small as 50° to 100° of the cycle; and since the grid may be driven up to plate-current saturation, these pulses bear no particular resemblance to the wave form of the grid input voltage. Thus the distortion is exceedingly high.   The voltage input used is so large that voltage amplification is very small, but the power output for a given tube is higher than in Class B operation.   The maximum theoretical power efficiency is 100 per cent, with practical operating conditions usually achieving 70 to 85 per cent.   Since the distortion is so very high, Class C operation is used for high power output and then only at radio frequencies, where the distortion products can be removed by simple filter circuits.

A general-purpose tube may be operated under any of the classifications, depending on the results desired.   However, certain specialized types have been developed, which will be more satisfactory when operating under the conditions for which they were designed. These types include highly linear, low-plate-resistance tubes for Class A power amplification, and so-called *zero bias* tubes for Class B use which operate at cutoff with zero grid bias and rated anode voltage, eliminating the complications of a bias-voltage source.   Other tubes are designed especially for Class C service in radio transmitters where power outputs of many kilowatts are required.

7-8. Vacuum-Tube Amplifiers

In electronic practice, a small signal voltage from a microphone, antenna, or other pickup device is built up to a large voltage by cascading of successive tubes, each with its own associated circuit. The first tubes in the chain handle driving signals of small voltage; the last tube will be given a signal at quite a large voltage and may be required to supply considerable power in its output circuit.

In such a cascaded vacuum-tube amplifier, the load or output voltage of the first tube becomes the signal voltage of the second tube, and so on. Means must be provided to introduce the a-c voltage drop across the load into the grid-cathode circuit of the following tube, and at the same time to block the d-c plate-supply voltage from reaching the second tube grid and altering its bias voltage. Coupling circuits to perform these functions may consist of resistors to provide the load voltage drop and capacitors to block out the d-c voltages, as in resistance-capacitance coupled stages; inductors and capacitors as in impedance or choke-coupled amplifiers; and transformers.

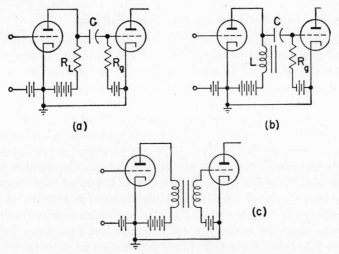

Fig. 7-18. Amplifier coupling circuits.

Observation of the typical coupling circuits of Fig. 7-18 shows that in addition to the coupling resistor or inductance, a resistor R_g called the *grid leak* is connected between grid and cathode of the second tube. If this resistor were not present, the grid would be isolated to direct current, and no path would exist through which an operating bias voltage could be supplied to the grid. Also, a few electrons strike the grid even though it is negative, and these would build up a negative charge and potential on the grid if a path were not provided over which they can *leak* off. The resistance of the grid leak should be high enough that it does not seriously reduce the value of R_L as the load impedance for the first tube, and low enough that a charge cannot be built up on the grid by the few electrons reaching it. As a result, desirable values of R_g are usually between 100,000 and 1,000,000 ohms.

In a cascaded voltage amplifier, the over-all gain or amplification, given as a voltage ratio, is the product of the individual stage gains. The gain is usually computed by working with each tube separately.

It should be understood that while batteries may be frequently shown as d-c power sources in amplifier circuits for simplicity, in actual practice they would usually be replaced with rectifiers and filters for operation from a-c lines.

7-9. Graphic Tube-Circuit Analysis—the Load Line

Since coupling circuits involve reactive elements and the tube is in general a nonlinear device, there is definite possibility of all types of distortion being introduced. Means must be developed for analysis of tube circuits to determine general performance, gain, and the extent of any distortion developed.

For usual tubes the dynamic characteristic of Fig. 7-8 has some curvature, or is nonlinear. When a large a-c voltage is applied to the input of a tube, operation will be over a considerable portion of this curve and the nonlinearity must be considered. Graphical methods have been developed which, through use of the *actual* tube characteristic curves, permit prediction of performance and design of tube circuits, even though operating in the nonlinear region, as are those circuits discussed in Chapter 10. The method applies equally well to all tube types, but triode curves will be used for illustration

Equation 7-1 stated the functional relation existing between current, grid voltage, and plate voltage in the tube. This relation was

$$i_b = f(\mu e_c + e_b). \qquad (7\text{-}17)$$

Referring to Fig. 7-19, the voltages present in the resistive *load* circuit are

$$e_b = E_{bb} - i_b R_L$$

or
$$i_b = \frac{E_{bb}}{R_L} - \frac{e_b}{R_L}. \qquad (7\text{-}18)$$

Equations 7-17 and 7-18 are both expressions involving the same current. Simultaneous solution of these two equations should give a value for i_b, but owing to the general form of Eq. 7-17 such an analytical solution is not possible. However, the equation is graphically represented by the plate family of curves of Fig. 7-9, and a simultaneous graphical solution of the two equations is possible by plotting Eq. 7-18 on the plate characteristics.

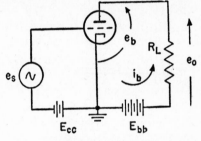

Fig. 7-19. Basic triode amplifier with plate load.

If Eq. 7-18 is compared with the $y = b + mx$ form for a straight line it may be noted that the equation represents a line with y intercept $= E_{bb}/R_L$, and x intercept $= E_{bb}$, with slope of $-1/R_L$. Use of this line, simultaneously, or superimposed on Fig. 7-9 will predict tube performance for the given load.

Drawing such a line on the plate characteristics of a triode gives the *d-c load line* of Fig. 7-20. This line determines the *current* and *voltage* conditions under which the tube operates with the resistive load selected. In the figure the line is drawn for $E_{bb} = 300$ v, $R_L = 4000$ ohms, so that the y intercept $= 300/4000 = 0.075$ amp, and the x intercept $= E_{bb} = 300$ v. A straight line drawn between these intercepts will have a slope of the proper amount and is the true d-c load line. If the E_{cc} bias applied to the tube be set at -20 v, the Q point, or the point of operation with the tube at rest or with no a-c signal, will fall at the intersection fixed by the d-c load line and the characteristic curve for $e_c = -20$ v. This intersection indicates a current $I_b = 37$ ma, and a tube voltage $= E_b = 152$ v, thus

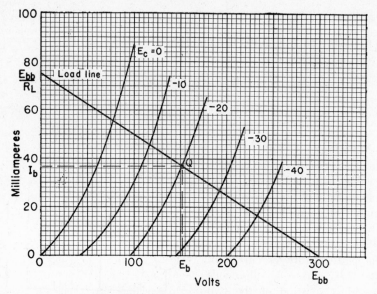

Fig. 7-20.   The use of the d-c load line.

determining the operating conditions at the quiescent point.   It is
then obvious that the load voltage is 148 v.

If a branch composed of C and R_2 in series is added as part of an
R-C coupling network, the circuit becomes that of Fig. 7-21.   This
is representative of a large class of actual tube circuits wherein the
d-c and a-c current paths are not identical.   *The d-c load line continues to fix the Q point and the d-c operating values,* but an additional

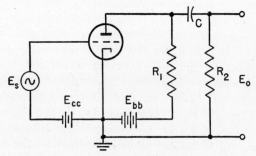

Fig. 7-21.   *R-C* coupling circuit added to the
simple circuit of Fig. 7-19.

load line is needed to indicate the path of operation with an a-c signal present. If the d-c load value remains at 4000 ohms, but if $R_1 = R_2 = 4000$ ohms, and the reactance of C is negligible, the a-c load value is 2000 ohms.

For zero a-c grid voltage the tube is under quiescent conditions, or at the Q point fixed by the d-c load line. Thus the Q point is also on the a-c load line. A line passed through the Q point with a

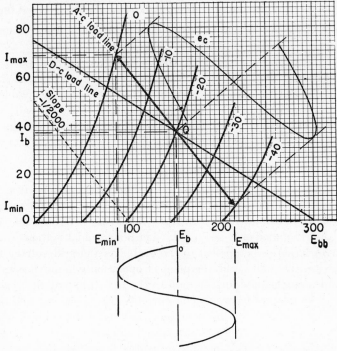

Fig. 7-22. General method of drawing a-c and d-c load lines.

slope determined as $-1/R_{\text{a-c}}$ (or having a slope of $-1/2000$ for the circuit of Fig. 7-21) will thus be the a-c load line shown in Fig. 7-22.

A line drawn with x intercept $= 100$ v, and y intercept $= i$ $= 100/R_{\text{a-c}}$ will fix the proper slope as shown by the dashed line in the corner of Fig. 7-22. The a-c load line may then be drawn parallel and through the Q point. All points on the a-c load line represent simultaneous solutions of Eq. 7-1 and Eq. 7-18 for *varying* grid voltages.

General rules for setting up the load lines may be stated as follows:

1. Draw a d-c load line on the plate characteristics with y intercept E_{bb}/R_L, and slope equal to the negative reciprocal of the external d-c plate load resistance, or with x intercept E_{bb}.
2. On this d-c load line, locate the Q point.
3. Through the Q point draw an a-c load line with a slope equal to the negative reciprocal of the a-c load resistance.
4. Determine the a-c operation of the tube on the a-c load line.

Note that the voltage intercept of the d-c line always occurs at a value equal to the plate supply voltage E_{bb}.

For the circuit of Fig. 7-19, the d-c and a-c current paths are identical, and the d-c and a-c load lines coincide. In Fig. 7-21, if R_1 be replaced by a very large inductive reactance of negligible resistance, the d-c load line will have a slope of $-1/0$ or infinity, and the line will be vertical. The a-c load line will pass through the Q point on this line with appropriate slope.

7-10. Performance Calculations from the Load Line

Complete a-c and d-c operating data may be obtained from the load lines set up in the preceding section. As an example, assume the load lines of Fig. 7-22, with $E_{bb} = 300$ v, $R_1 = R_2 = 4000$ ohms, with the reactance of C neglected. Let a sinusoidal voltage of 20 v peak, 14.1 rms v, be applied to the grid. As the grid voltage rises on the positive half cycle, the point of operation will move from the Q point along the a-c load line up to the $e_c = 0$ line at the positive peak, with instantaneous anode current $I_{max} = 69$ ma, and tube voltage $E_{min} = 89$ v. On the negative half cycle the point of operation will move down the load line, reaching $e_c = -40$ v at the negative maximum. At this instant I_{min} will be 6 ma, and $E_{max} = 215$ v. The point of operation thus slides back and forth along the a-c load line during a cycle of input voltage.

The wave forms of output current and voltage may be plotted as shown. If the intersections of the grid-voltage lines are not equally spaced along the a-c load line, amplitude distortion will be evident.

The a-c output voltage E_o may be readily obtained by noting that $E_{max} - E_{min}$ expresses the double peak value; thus

$$E_o = \frac{E_{max} - E_{min}}{2\sqrt{2}} = \frac{215 - 89}{2\sqrt{2}} = 45.5 \text{ v rms.}$$

Since $\sqrt{2}$ is the relation between peak and rms values only for a sine wave, the result will be in error if the amplitude distortion is large.

The fundamental rms component of a-c plate current is also given by

$$I_p = \frac{I_{max} - I_{min}}{2\sqrt{2}} = \frac{69 - 6}{2\sqrt{2}} = 22.3 \text{ ma rms.}$$

The *magnitude of the voltage gain* of the amplifier is then given by the ratio of output to input voltage, or

$$|\text{Gain}| = |A| = \left|\frac{E_o}{E_s}\right| = \frac{45.5}{14.1} = 3.2.$$

Thus the load line allows considerable operating information to be obtained. Its further use will be studied in Chapter 10.

7-11. The Series or Voltage-Source Equivalent Circuit

In the preceding section the performance of a tube was discussed using a graphical method starting from a curve family representing Eq. 7-1:

$$i_b = f(\mu e_c + e_b). \tag{7-19}$$

This method is most suited to large input signals if accuracy is to be achieved.

However, if a *small signal* is applied to the tube input, operation will be over only a short length of the dynamic curve, and a sufficiently small section of any curve may be considered a straight line. Such a linear assumption applied to the above equation leads to a very useful analytical method of determining tube performance.

Assuming linearity of the tube characteristics in the neighborhood of a given E_b, I_b operating point implies that μ, g_m, and r_p are constants, since they are related to the slopes of the curves at the point. Equation 7-19 may then be written under this assumption as

$$i_b = k_1(\mu e_c + e_b) + C, \tag{7-20}$$

where C is the intercept of this portion of the curve extended as a straight line. If e_c is maintained constant and the derivative taken,

$$\frac{\partial i_b}{\partial e_b} = k_1 = g_p,$$

from which k_1 is seen to be the slope at the point E_b, I_b, or is equal to the plate conductance at that point. This would also be the value of k_1 if Eq. 7-20 is looked on as the first two terms of a Taylor's series expansion of Eq. 7-19 around the operating point E_b, I_b.

The relation between total anode current and the tube voltages then becomes

$$i_b = g_p(\mu e_c + e_b) + C. \tag{7-21}$$

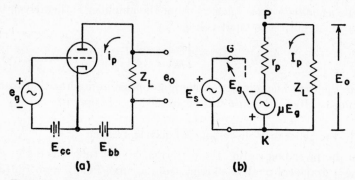

Fig. 7-23. Derivation of the series or voltage-source equivalent circuit of the triode.

The currents and voltages were defined in Section 7-3 for a circuit such as at (a), Fig. 7-23, as

$$i_b = I_b + i_p, \tag{7-22a}$$

$$e_c = E_{cc} + e_g, \tag{7-22b}$$

$$e_b = E_b + e_o, \tag{7-22c}$$

where e_o was the instantaneous load voltage rise. Use of these values in Eq. 7-21, and substitution of the reciprocal of the plate resistance for the plate conductance, leads to

$$i_p + I_b = \frac{1}{r_p}(\mu E_{cc} + E_b + C r_p) + \frac{1}{r_p}(\mu e_g + e_o). \tag{7-22}$$

The first term on the right is composed entirely of constant voltages which fix the operating point. This term must equal I_b, the constant term on the other side of the equation. Consequently,

$$i_p + I_b = I_b + \frac{1}{r_p}(\mu e_g + e_o),$$

from which $\qquad i_p r_p = \mu e_g + e_o,$ $\qquad\qquad$ (7-23)

as an equation expressing a relation between the *varying* components of voltage in the circuit, all d-c values being eliminated.

If the varying voltages and currents in the circuit are assumed sinusoidal, the above equation may be written in effective values. It may be noted that e_o was defined as the load voltage rise, and it may be replaced with an effective value E_o also considered as a *rise* from cathode. Hence

$$I_p r_p = \mu E_g + E_o,$$
$$-\mu E_g + I_p r_p = E_o. \qquad (7\text{-}24)$$

It is now convenient to consider the companion circuit at Fig. 7-23(b). The rise in voltage through the tube from cathode to plate may be written

$$-\mu E_g + I_p r_p.$$

Since this must be equal to the rise in voltage E_o taken from cathode to plate through the load path,

$$-\mu E_g + I_p r_p = E_o. \qquad (7\text{-}25)$$

It is apparent that Eq. 7-25, describing the action of the assumed circuit at (b), is identical with Eq. 7-24, which was derived from the a-c operation of a triode in a circuit of the type of (a), Fig. 7-23. Thus Eq. 7-24 applies to the circuit of (b), wherein a generator of emf opposite in phase to the cathode-grid rise of voltage E_g acts in series with a resistor r_p, the plate resistance of the tube. Hence a triode may be considered as *equivalent for linear a-c operation* to the circuit as shown between K and P and K and G.

Figure 7-23(b) shows that when E_o is considered as a rise in voltage from cathode toward anode, consistent with the indicated current and with the use of the cathode as reference, then

$$E_o = -I_p Z_L, \qquad\qquad (7\text{-}26)$$

so that $\qquad\qquad -\mu E_g + I_p r_p = -I_p Z_L$

from which $\qquad\qquad I_p = \dfrac{\mu E_g}{r_p + Z_L}. \qquad\qquad (7\text{-}27)$

Equation 7-27 can be seen to apply to the current and circuit of Fig. 7-23(b). The voltage E_g is measured as a *rise* directly from cathode K to grid G of the tube.

Equation 7-27, which is based on the assumption of a linear relation between current and voltage, or that μ, g_m, and r_p are constants in the region of operation, is one of the most important relations in the study of electron tubes.

This equation shows that a vacuum tube operating in the linear region, or for small signals under Class A conditions, may be replaced with an *equivalent voltage-source series circuit*, as shown in Fig. 7-23(b). Since all d-c quantities were eliminated in the operation which resulted in Eq. 7-23, *the equivalent circuit applies for alternating or variable quantities only, and does not even exist for direct current.* The d-c voltages and currents serve only to determine the operating point and the particular values of μ, r_p, and g_m, and to supply the energy needed.

A definite procedure should be followed in setting up the equivalent circuit. Assuming that the signal voltage is positive in the direction shown in Fig. 7-23 at the instant of observation, the equivalent generator μE_g should be given reversed signs to account for the reversal of phase with respect to the grid-cathode voltage, as noted for Eq. 7-24. The current I_p in the anode circuit is then set up in a direction consistent with the polarity of the μE_g generator, or out of the positive terminal. Circuit equations may then be written in the usual manner for the solution of the vacuum-tube-equivalent network as an ordinary a-c circuit.

An important consideration in a vacuum-tube circuit is the *gain* or amplification of voltage obtainable. The amplification or gain is defined *as the ratio of output-voltage rise to input-signal-voltage rise*, or

$$\text{gain} = A = \frac{E_o}{E_s}. \tag{7-28}$$

The current I_p flowing in the equivalent circuit of Fig. 7-23 is given by the mesh equation as

$$I_p = \frac{\mu E_g}{r_p + Z_L}. \tag{7-29}$$

The output voltage E_o is given as a rise in voltage by

$$E_o = -I_p Z_L = -\frac{\mu E_g Z_L}{r_p + Z_L}. \tag{7-30}$$

Hence, from Eq. 7-28 the gain is

$$A = \frac{E_o}{E_s} = \frac{E_o}{E_g} = \frac{-\mu Z_L}{r_p + Z_L}. \tag{7-31}$$

The amplification A will, in general, be a complex number. There will be a phase reversal inherent in the tube for all frequencies, owing to the negative phase of the equivalent generator μE_g. This phase reversal is indicated by the minus sign in front of the right side of the equation. The angle then found with the complex gain represents the phase shift in addition to the tube reversal.

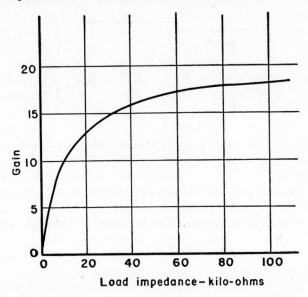

Fig. 7-24. Variation of gain with load impedance. Type 6J5 tube, $\mu = 20$, $E_{bb} = 250$ v, $E_{cc} = -8$ v.

Equation 7-31 shows that the amplification is a function of Z_L. If Z_L is made large enough, the gain may approach, but not exceed, the value of μ. Figure 7-24 shows the variation of amplification for a typical triode as the load impedance is varied. For this tube with μ of 20, a gain of 15 is about all that is normally expected, owing to the asymptotic curve shape. Also, since the load is frequently a resistance, the d-c voltage drop therein becomes large for high R_L, thereby lowering E_b and raising r_p, so that the full theoretical gain cannot be reached.

7-12. The Parallel or Current-Source Equivalent Circuit

Frequently the load circuit of a vacuum tube is split into a number of parallel-connected branches. For analysis of tubes operated in

this manner, a second form of equivalent circuit is more convenient.

The voltage-source equivalent circuit of Fig. 7-23, being a linear
a-c network, may be transformed to the circuit of Fig. 7-25 by the
use of Norton's theorem (Ref. 8). The circuit of Fig. 7-25 is called

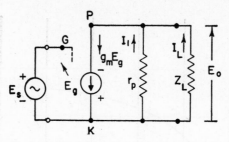

Fig. 7-25. Parallel or current-source equivalent circuit for the vacuum tube.

a *current-source equivalent circuit* and employs a generator of constant
current whose current output at all times is equal to that of the emf
generator of Fig. 7-23 with a short circuit at its terminals, or

$$I_{sc} = \frac{\mu E_g}{r_p} = g_m E_g. \tag{7-32}$$

This constant-current source is shunted by a resistance equal to the
internal resistance r_p of the emf generator. The source current
divides between the r_p and load branches, and the load branch
current I_L produces a drop across Z_L which is the tube output voltage.

Writing a current summation at point P, Fig. 7-25 gives

$$-g_m E_g + I_1 + I_L = 0,$$

$$-g_m E_g - E_o(g_p + Y_L) = 0,$$

from which the load-voltage rise E_o is

$$E_o = -g_m E_g \left(\frac{1}{g_p} + \frac{1}{Y_L}\right) = \frac{-\mu E_g Z_L}{r_p + Z_L}. \tag{7-33}$$

Since $E_o = -I_L Z_L$, then

$$I_L = \frac{\mu E_g}{r_p + Z_L}. \tag{7-34}$$

Since the values of load current and voltage computed from Fig. 7-25 are identical with Eqs. 7-29 and 7-30 for the same quantities calculated from the voltage-source circuit, the current-source circuit is equivalent to the voltage-source circuit.

This current-source circuit will be found to be extremely useful in vacuum-tube circuit analysis for small signals.

7-13. Input Admittance of the Grid Circuit

Up to this point nothing has been said concerning conditions in the input or grid-cathode circuit of the triode, nor has anything been said about the internal capacities of the tube. These capacities must exist, as is seen by the observation that the grid, cathode, and anode have area and are exposed to each other and separated by a dielectric (vacuum). The capacities present may be considered as

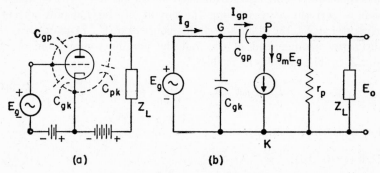

Fig. 7-26.   (a) Triode circuit including capacities; (b) current-source equivalent circuit for (a), with C_{pk} included in Z_L.

three, namely, C_{gk}, the capacity between grid and cathode; C_{gp}, the capacity between grid and plate; and C_{pk}, the capacity between plate and cathode. These three capacities are represented in (a), Fig. 7-26, and are usually small, of the order of a few micromicrofarads.

Under Class A and negative-grid conditions it might appear from Fig. 7-26 that the admittance into which the grid generator E_g operates is wholly due to these capacities. Actually, this is not true, since the admittance is composed of a capacity of value different from that to be expected from circuit observation, at times shunted by a resistance. The fact that the input capacity is larger than the geometric tube capacity is called the *Miller effect*.

An analysis of the input circuit of a tube in the circuit of Fig. 7-26 can be made under the assumption of a negative grid, and of linear operation. Upon selection of the current-source equivalent circuit, the output capacity C_{pk} may be considered as part of the load Z_L, since the capacity and the load are directly in parallel. The circuit is then as indicated in Fig. 7-26(b). The alternating current flowing to the grid I_g can be written by the superposition theorem as

$$I_g = I_g' + I_g'', \tag{7-35}$$

where I_g' is the current in the grid circuit due to generator E_g alone, and I_g'' is the current due to the generator of constant current $g_m E_g$. According to the superposition theorem, the component of current due to the generator E_g is the current flowing in the network when all other source emf's are removed from the circuit. If this operation is performed by opening the circuit of the constant-current generator $g_m E_g$, the resultant circuit consists of C_{gk} in parallel with the series arrangement of C_{gp} and the parallel combination of r_p and Z_L. The current I_g' is then

$$I_g' = j\omega C_{gk} E_g + \cfrac{E_g}{\cfrac{r_p Z_L}{r_p + Z_L} - \cfrac{j}{\omega C_{gp}}}. \tag{7-36}$$

For most circuits and tubes

$$\frac{r_p Z_L}{r_p + Z_L} \ll \frac{j}{\omega C_{gp}}, \tag{7-37}$$

so that Eq. 7-36 may be reduced to

$$I_g' = j\omega(C_{gk} + C_{gp})E_g. \tag{7-38}$$

If the generator E_g is short-circuited, it becomes possible to write for the current I_g'' in the grid circuit, owing to the plate-circuit constant-current source:

$$I_g'' = -j\omega C_{gp} E_o, \tag{7-39}$$

where E_o is the voltage rise across the load circuit. The load voltage is due to the current $g_m E_g$ flowing through r_p, Z_L, and C_{gp} in parallel, with generator E_g short-circuited. With the condition of Eq. 7-37 used again, the load voltage E_o is

$$E_o = -g_m E_g \left(\frac{r_p Z_L}{r_p + Z_L} \right). \tag{7-40}$$

Then

$$I_g = I_g' + I_g'' = j\omega(C_{gk} + C_{gp})E_g + j\omega C_{gp}g_m \left(\frac{r_p Z_L}{r_p + Z_L}\right) E_g.$$

The admittance of a circuit is defined as the ratio of the current input to the voltage input, so that

$$Y_g = \frac{I_g}{E_g} = j\omega \left[C_{gk} + C_{gp}\left(1 + g_m \frac{r_p Z_L}{r_p + Z_L}\right)\right]. \quad (7\text{-}41)$$

Equation 7-41 is the expression for the input or grid-circuit admittance of a vacuum tube under the assumptions.

The input admittance can be seen as the sum of the grid-cathode capacity and the grid-plate capacity multiplied by a factor usually much greater than unity. If the parallel plate-circuit impedance is defined as

$$Z' = \frac{r_p Z_L}{r_p + Z_L}, \quad (7\text{-}42)$$

Z' will, in general, be a complex number, or

$$Z' = R' \pm jX'. \quad (7\text{-}43)$$

Substituting this in Eq. 7-41 results in

$$Y_g = -g_m\omega C_{gp}(\pm X') + j\omega[C_{gk} + C_{gp}(1 + g_m R')]. \quad (7\text{-}44)$$

If the reactance in Eq. 7-43 is capacitive, the real term of Eq. 7-44 is positive, and vice versa. In Fig. 7-27 the admittance of such a parallel input circuit may be written

$$Y = \frac{1}{R_{in}} + j\omega C_{in}; \quad (7\text{-}45)$$

and by comparing Eqs. 7-45 and 7-44, it can be seen that

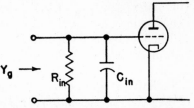

Fig. 7-27.   Input circuit of a triode.

$$R_{in} = -\frac{1}{g_m\omega C_{gp}(\pm X')}, \quad (7\text{-}46)$$

$$C_{in} = C_{gk} + C_{gp}(1 + g_m R'). \quad (7\text{-}47)$$

Three possible cases arise from the signs in Eq. 7-46:

1. The load reactance may be inductive; X' then has a plus sign, and R_{in} becomes a negative resistance.

2. The load reactance may be zero (load essentially resistive), and R_{in} is infinite, or represents an open circuit.

3. The load reactance may be capacitive; X' has a minus sign, and R_{in} becomes a positive resistance.

The input capacitance C_{in} is the same for all three cases.

Presence of a negative resistance in the grid circuit indicates that power is being generated in the circuit, rather than dissipated as in a positive resistance. Actually, when R_{in} is negative, with inductive load, the current I_g'' has a phase relation with respect to E_g such that power is being received in the grid circuit from the plate circuit through C_{gp}. Whenever the power fed back per cycle is equal to, or greater than, the grid-circuit losses per cycle, the net circuit resistance appears zero or negative, and the tube is no longer an amplifier but becomes an oscillator.

When the load is resistive (with C_{pk} considered as included in Z_L), the input circuit is capacitive, but has a magnitude considerably larger than C_{gk}. For capacitive loads, the input resistance is positive and the grid circuit absorbs power from the source of signal.

Since ω appears in the denominator of R_{in}, the magnitude of R_{in} is a function of frequency as well as of the capacity C_{gp}. Tubes for operation at high frequencies must then have small values of C_{gp} if the input resistance is to be kept high. In actual circuits, the input of a tube may be supplied by a very high-impedance source (the antenna circuit or plate circuit of another tube, etc.). If R_{in} is not high with respect to the source impedance, the source voltage will be lowered and the amplifier gain be seriously reduced.

A more rigorous and complex analysis, in which C_{pk} is not combined with the load and in which no assumption is made regarding the relative magnitudes of the reactance of C_{gp} and the impedance of the parallel combination of r_p and Z_L (Eq. 7-37), leads to a modified result for Case 1. The input resistance R_{in} then is found to be

$$R_{in} = \frac{(R_L^2 + \omega^2 L_L^2)\left[\left(\dfrac{1}{r_p} + \dfrac{R_L}{R_L^2 + \omega^2 L_L^2}\right)^2 + \omega^2\left(C_{gp} + C_{pk} - \dfrac{L_L}{R_L^2 + \omega^2 L_L^2}\right)^2\right]}{\omega^2\{R_L C_{gp}^2 + g_m C_{gp}[A(R_L^2 + \omega^2 L_L^2) - L_L]\}},$$

(7-48)

where
$$A = C_{gp}\left(\frac{\mu + 1}{\mu}\right) + C_{pk}.$$

Although the expression is extremely complex, it can be seen that actually R_{in} is not negative for all values of inductive load, as implied by Case 1 above. The denominator of Eq. 7-48, and thus R_{in}, will be negative only if

$$L_L > \frac{R_L C_{gp}}{g_m} + (R_L^2 + \omega^2 L_L^2)A. \qquad (7\text{-}49)$$

Equating the denominator of Eq. 7-48 to zero leads to a quadratic, and thus two limiting values of L_L, with R_{in} taking on negative values between.   These limiting values of load inductance are obtained from

$$L_L = \frac{1 \pm \sqrt{1 - \dfrac{4\omega^2 A R_L}{g_m}(C_{gp} + Ag_m R_L)}}{2\omega^2 A}. \qquad (7\text{-}50)$$

If R_L is very large, the solution for the limiting values of L may be imaginary, and there is then no value of load inductance which will give a negative input resistance.

7-14. Transit-Time Effects

The grid in a Class A triode is usually maintained negative, and it may be assumed that no electrons strike the grid.   A little thought, however, will show that electrons approaching a negative grid will induce an instantaneous electron current flowing from negative to positive in the grid source, or the electrons will supply energy to the grid circuit as they are decelerated.   Likewise, electrons moving away from the negative grid will induce an instantaneous electron current from positive to negative in the source, or the electrons will take energy from the grid as they are repelled by it.   However, if a number of electrons are approaching a grid from one side, and simultaneously an equal number are going away from the grid on the other side, the induced-current effects cancel and the net energy interchange is zero.

At ordinary audio frequencies and the lower radio frequencies, the time of transit of a single electron between cathode and anode is usually very short with respect to the time of a cycle of grid voltage. Thus, for each incremental change in grid voltage during a cycle there is a practically instantaneous readjustment of space charge and electron flow.   At all times, equal numbers of electrons are approaching and leaving the grid, and no alternating current is induced in the grid circuit.

As operation enters the higher-frequency regions, the time of transit of the electron is no longer short with respect to a cycle of grid voltage. As a result, electrons may be leaving the cathode at an increased rate owing to a positive change of grid voltage, whereas in the grid-anode space, the electron density is lower owing to the preceding more negative value of the grid voltage. A net induced current then flows in the grid circuit, and it can be seen that this current may have a very arbitrary phase relation with respect to the a-c grid voltage, since its angle of lag depends on the relation of time of transit to time of a cycle. However, in general the induced current will have a component in phase, or 180° out of phase, with the a-c grid voltage. If a component of current is in phase with the grid voltage, energy is supplied by the grid circuit to the electron stream. Flow of an in-phase component of alternating

Fig. 7-28.   Large power tube for very-high-frequency use, with low transit time.
(Courtesy General Electric Co.)

current in the grid circuit implies a conductance component in the grid admittance. Such a conductance is independent of, and in addition to, the grid conductance discussed in the preceding section.

Since grid-voltage sources are usually of high impedance, the shunting of the impedance, introduced by transit-time conductance, results in a lowering of the voltage applied to the grid and decreased amplification at the higher frequencies. Also, since many grid sources are parallel-resonant circuits, shunting them with a conductance reduces the resonant impedance and broadens the resonant response curve, giving reduced selectivity. For these reasons, tubes intended for very high-frequency service are made in a manner intended to reduce the transit time. This is frequently accomplished by very close spacing of the electrodes, so that transit distances are of the order of only a few thousandths of an inch. The first tubes of this class were called *acorn* tubes because of their shape. Other types suited to extremely high frequencies are known as the *lighthouse* and *pencil* tubes.

7-15. The Decibel and VU

Since the outputs of most amplifiers are ultimately received by the human ear, certain properties of the ear are important in amplifier design. The ear is observed experimentally to obey the Weber-Fechner law, which states, "The change in stimulus necessary to produce a perceptible change in response is proportional to the stimulus already existing." The energy required to produce a just perceptible whisper in an open field is very small, whereas the energy required to produce speech just audible above the roar of an airplane motor is very great. The ear hears sound intensities on a proportional, or logarithmic, scale and not on a linear one. Therefore, it is convenient to have a system of sound-intensity measurement based on logarithmic ratios, so that sound levels can be measured according to the stimulus they will produce on the ear.

Of equal importance are the exponential relations existing in the attenuation of power along telephone lines. Use of a logarithmic unit here allows losses or gains to be directly added or subtracted, making frequent exponential calculations unnecessary. The telephone industry has proposed and has popularized such a logarithmic unit, named the *bel* for Alexander Graham Bell. The bel is defined as the logarithm to the base 10 of a power ratio, or

$$\text{number of bels} = \log \frac{P_2}{P_1}. \tag{7-51}$$

A unit one-tenth as large approximates the power change required to produce a just detectable change in sound intensity. This smaller unit is called the *decibel*, abbreviated db, and is defined as

$$\text{db} = 10 \log \frac{P_2}{P_1}. \tag{7-52}$$

If the output of an amplifier under one condition is 3.5 w and under a second condition is 7 w,

$$10 \log \frac{7}{3.5} = 3.01 \text{ db.}$$

A change in power of 2 to 1 has resulted in a change of 3.01 db in power level. Since 1 db is about the minimum change in level detectable by the ear, doubling the power produces a change in sound only three times greater than the minimum detectable change.

The output of a microphone is 0.003 w, but after the current passes through a length of cable, only 0.0006 w is available:

$$10 \log \frac{0.0006}{0.003} = -10 \log 5 = -7.0 \text{ db.}$$

The negative sign indicates that a power loss of 7 db has taken place in the cable.

Although the unit thus described is a power ratio and not an absolute power measurement, it can be used for absolute measurements if a certain reference, or zero, level for P_1 is adopted beforehand and known or stated. A variety of various reference values have been used; one which has become common in the broadcasting industry is 0.001 w. Consequently, the amplifier above with 7 w output is

$$10 \log \frac{7}{0.001} = 38.45 \text{ db}$$

above zero level. The microphone output at the end of the cable of 0.0006 w is at

$$10 \log \frac{0.0006}{0.001} = -10 \log \frac{0.001}{0.0006} = -2.2 \text{ db,}$$

or 2.2 db below zero level.

In the broadcast field when 0.001 w is employed as the zero reference, it is common practice to state absolute power in terms of *volume units*, or VU, where 10 db above 0.001 w equals 10 VU. In other words,

$$VU = 10 \log \frac{P}{0.001}, \qquad (7\text{-}53)$$

where P is the amount of power measured. The VU is employed for measurement of speech and music, and implies the use of a special instrument of specified dynamic characteristics, or a particular response to the voice frequencies involved.

If input and output of an amplifier are measured across the same resistance values, then by the definition of power

$$10 \log \frac{E_2^2}{E_1^2} = 20 \log \frac{E_2}{E_1} \text{ db.} \qquad (7\text{-}54)$$

If the grid-cathode circuit of a tube represents an open circuit, and the output voltage E_o is supplied to a circuit also drawing no power (as a grid-cathode circuit of a second tube), the db gain of a voltage-amplifier stage is also sometimes defined by Eq. 7-54.

7-16. Measurement of the Triode Coefficients

The values of μ, g_m, and r_p may be determined by measuring the slopes of the respective characteristic curves at the desired operating points, but owing to the curvature, this method lacks accuracy. Another method is to measure the changes in plate current produced by small changes in plate potential or by small changes in grid potential. This method does not give accurate values except in the region where the coefficients are relatively constant, since it uses finite rather than infinitesimal

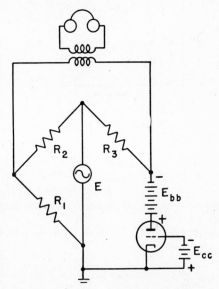

Fig. 7-29.   Bridge circuit for measurement of r_p.

changes. Bridge methods have been developed which, if used with small applied a-c potentials, can yield accurate and consistent results.

The Wheatstone bridge of Fig. 7-29 is suitable for measurement of r_p. The circuit may be balanced for no sound in the headphones by adjustment of R_1 and R_2, and then, by application of Wheatstone balance conditions,

$$\frac{r_p}{R_1} = \frac{R_3}{R_2},$$

(7-55)

and then

$$r_p = \frac{R_1 R_3}{R_2}.$$

(7-56)

The measurement may be made at any operating point by adjustment of E_{cc} and E_{bb}. Any audible frequency may be used, provided it is low enough that the tube capacities may continue to be neglected.

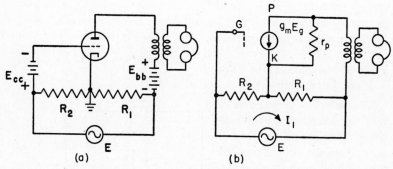

Fig. 7-30.   (a) Miller bridge for measurement of μ; (b) current-source equivalent circuit for (a).

The bridge of Fig. 7-30 may be used to measure the value of μ by balancing for no sound in the detector by adjustment of R_1 or R_2. For zero voltage across the headphones,

$$g_m E_g r_p = I_1 R_1;$$

also,

$$E_g = I_1 R_2.$$

Then

$$\mu = g_m r_p = \frac{R_1}{R_2}.$$

(7-57)

A third bridge circuit for use in the direct measurement of g_m is drawn in Fig. 7-31. For balance, or zero sound, in the headphones,

$$g_m E_g \left(\frac{r_p R_3}{r_p + R_3} \right) = I_1 R_1.$$

Also,

$$E_g = I_1 R_2,$$

so that

$$g_m = \frac{R_1(r_p + R_3)}{r_p R_2 R_3}. \tag{7-58}$$

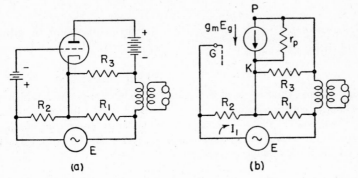

Fig. 7-31.   (a) Bridge circuit for measurement of g_m; (b) current-source equivalent circuit for (a).

Now, it is desirable that the measurement be independent of the other tube coefficients, so by choosing $R_3 \ll r_p$, which for most tubes can be satisfied if R_3 is a few hundred ohms, Eq. 7-58 reduces to

$$g_m = \frac{R_1}{R_2 R_3}. \tag{7-59}$$

A transformer is shown for coupling the headphones into the circuit to avoid having the direct plate-current component flow through the headphones. Another, and usually more satisfactory, detector is obtained by connecting a cathode-ray oscillograph across the transformer secondary, replacing the headphones. This method allows very low frequencies to be used and increases the precision of balance because of the oscillograph amplifiers. Grounding of the circuits at some suitable point is advisable.

PROBLEMS

7-1. (a) Using the plate characteristics for the 6J5 tube in the Appendix, plot the static transfer characteristic for $E_b = 200$ v.

(b) In the same way, plot the dynamic characteristic for $E_{bb} = 200$ v, the load resistor being 25,000 ohms.

7-2. The following data are taken on a certain triode:

i_b (ma)	e_c (v)	e_b (v)
3.0	−3	200
4.0	−3	225
4.0	−2	185
4.6	−2	200

Find, independently, the value of μ, g_m, and r_p.

7-3. If the function of Eq. 7-1 is expanded, it yields

$$i_b = k_0 + k_1(\mu e_c + e_b) + k_2(\mu e_c + e_b)^2 + \cdots .$$

Using the first three terms of the series, find values for k_1 and k_2 which will produce an equation fitting the $E_c = -4$ curve for the 6J5 characteristics in the Appendix. Plot your curve with the actual curve for comparison.

7-4. For a certain triode, the function of Eq. 7-1 may be expanded as the expression for i_b in amperes:

$$i_b = 65 \times 10^{-6}(17e_c + e_b) + 0.33 \times 10^{-6}(17e_c + e_b)^2.$$

If the operating point is at $e_c = -10$ v and $e_b = 200$ v, find:

(a) The value of i_b.

(b) The plate resistance r_p.

(c) The mutual conductance g_m.

7-5. A triode has a characteristic given by

$$i_b = 7.6 \times 10^{-3}(20e_c + e_b)^{1.61} \quad \text{ma.}$$

When operated at $e_b = 250$ v, and $e_c = -8$ v, find:

(a) The plate resistance.

(b) The value of g_m.

(c) The grid voltage change required to change the plate current by 1 ma positive, at the above operating point.

7-6. (a) If the dynamic grid transfer characteristic can be expressed as an equation of the form

$$i_b = a_0 + a_1 e_g + a_2 e_g^2,$$

show that a small input voltage $e_g = E \sin \omega t$ will produce an output current

$$i_b = a_0 + \frac{a_2 E^2}{2} + a_1 E \sin \omega t - \frac{a_2 E^2}{2} \cos 2\omega t.$$

(b) What kind of distortion is this?

(c) Find the expression for the output current if $e_g = E_1 \sin \omega t + E_3 \sin 3.5 \, \omega t$. Point out the various distortion terms in the expression.

7-7. Two tubes having the following coefficients are connected in parallel:

$$\mu = 7 \qquad g_m = 1500 \ \mu\text{mhos}.$$

$$\mu = 20 \qquad g_m = 3200 \ \mu\text{mhos}.$$

Find the equivalent μ, g_m, and r_p for the combination.

7-8. A triode has $g_m = 2100 \ \mu\text{mhos}$ and $r_p = 7000$ ohms.

(a) Find the plate-current change produced by variation of the grid voltage from -4 to -1 v, at $E_b = 200$ v.

(b) Find the anode voltage which will restore the plate current to its former value.

7-9. For a particular triode, Eq. 7-1 may be approximated as

$$i_b = 0.0027(10e_c + e_b)^2,$$

where i_b is in milliamperes. If $e_b = 180$ v and $E_{cc} = -12$ v, and if $e_g = 3$ v peak sine wave, find the average, maximum, and minimum values of plate current. Also determine the amplitude of the second-harmonic current.

7-10. (a) For series loads of 5000, 10,000, and 25,000 ohms, determine graphically the values of E_b and I_b for a 6J5 tube operated with $E_{bb} = 300$ v, $E_{cc} = -6$ v. (Characteristics in the Appendix.)

(b) If a grid voltage of 4 v peak is applied, find the value of I_p for each of the above loads.

7-11. (a) What load resistance will place the Q point at $I_b = 6$ ma, $E_{cc} = -8$ v, for a plate supply voltage $E_{bb} = 325$ v, with a 6J5 tube?

(b) Calculate the gain of the tube operated as in (a).

7-12. A 2A3 tube (characteristics in the Appendix) is operated in the circuit of Fig. 7-21 with $R_1 = 3000$ ohms, $R_2 = 1500$ ohms, and $C = 2.0 \ \mu\text{f}$. The grid is supplied with a sine wave input of 30 v peak, 1000 cycles, and $E_{cc} = -40$ v, $E_{bb} = 350$ v.

(a) Find the a-c output voltage and the d-c power lost in the tube.

(b) What are the peak and rms plate current values?

7-13. (a) In the circuit of Fig. 7-21, R_1 is replaced by an inductor of very large L and 500 ohms d-c resistance. If the tube is a 2A3, $R_2 = 2000$ ohms, $E_{cc} = -40$ v, find the plate supply voltage required for $I_b = 60$ ma.

(b) If the grid signal is a 20-volt rms sine wave, find the a-c output voltage and the gain.

7-14. A 6SF5 triode is used in the circuit of Fig. 7-34, with $E_{cc} = -1.5$ v, $I_b = 0.6$ ma. The resistance of the inductor may be neglected. If the grid signal is 1 v peak, find gain and rms output voltage at 2000 cycles.

7-15. (a) Draw the voltage-source equivalent circuits for the circuits of Fig. 7-32.

(b) Indicate assumed loop currents and polarity of all voltages and voltage drops produced by the varying signal components.

7-16. Draw the current-source equivalent circuits for the circuits of Fig. 7-32.

7-17. By use of equivalent circuits find the gain or ratio E_0/E of the circuit of (f), Fig. 7-32.

7-18. Find the expression for the angle between the signal voltage E and the current through E, for (b), Fig. 7-32.

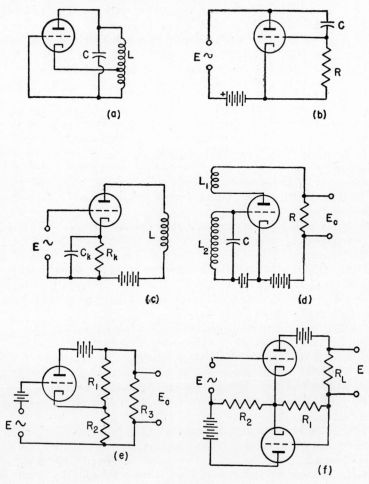

Fig. 7-32.

7-19. For a 6C4 triode having $\mu = 17$, $g_m = 2200$ μmhos, a driving signal of 5 v rms, and a load of $20,000 + j20,000$ ohms, find:

(a) The value of I_p.

(b) The a-c output voltage.

(c) The gain of the amplifier.

(d) The a-c power output.

7-20. Find the gain, E_0/E, for the circuit of (j), Fig. 7-32.

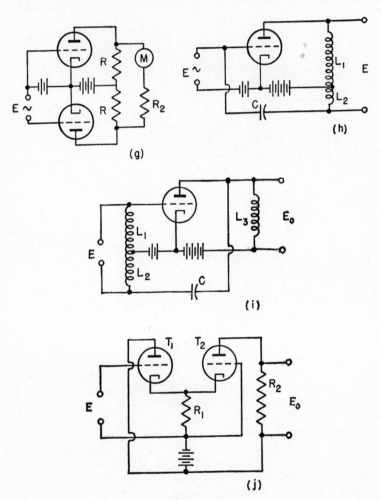

Fig. 7-32. (*continued*)

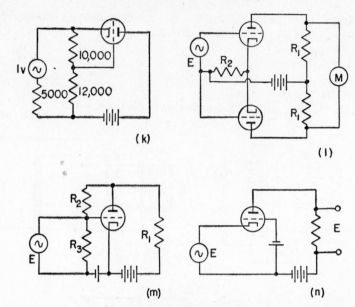

Fig. 7-32. (*continued*)

7-21. By use of the current-source equivalent circuit for (g), Fig. 7-32, if $R = 10,000$ ohms, $\mu = 10$, and $r_p = 7000$ ohms, find the current flowing through the meter M of resistance $R_2 = 100$ ohms, if $E = 1.0$ v. Assume identical tubes.

7-22. In (e), Fig. 7-32, let $R_1 = 10,000$, $R_2 = 3000$, $R_3 = 5000$, $r_p = 10,000$, $g_m = 2500$ micromhos. Find the voltage E_0, and the current through the tube, if $E = 2.0$ v.

7-23. Find the value of a-c plate current in the circuit of (k), Fig. 7-32, if $\mu = 20$, $r_p = 7000$ ohms.

7-24. If E is short-circuited, the meter M of (l), Fig. 7-32, reads zero, with identical tubes of $\mu = 22$, $g_m = 1600$, $R_1 = 15,000$ ohms, $R_2 = 2000$ ohms. Find the reading of meter M if $E = 1.0$ v rms, 60 cycles.

7-25. In Fig. 7-34, if $\mu = 17$ and $r_p = 30,000$ ohms, what input voltage E_s will be required to produce an output of $E_0 = 2$ v rms, 100 cycles?

7-26. One unit of a 6AT6 triode has $\mu = 70$, $r_p = 58,000$ ohms, $C_{gp} = 2.0$ $\mu\mu$f, $C_{gk} = 2.2$ $\mu\mu$f, $C_{pk} = 0.8$ $\mu\mu$f. Calculate the input capacitance and resistance if the load has a value of $40,000 + j40,000$ ohms at 25,000 cycles.

7-27. (a) The 6AT6 tube of Problem 7-26 has a plate-circuit load consisting of a 100 μh inductance at a frequency of 10^6 cycles. Compute the value of R_{in} and C_{in}.

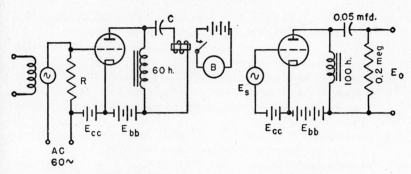

Fig. 7-33.   Fig. 7-34.

(b) Repeat at a frequency of 10^8 cycles. Would this tube grid circuit constitute a suitable load for a radio-receiver antenna circuit having 10,000 ohms impedance at this frequency?

7-28. A certain microphone of 200 ohms impedance has an output at −60 db below a 1-mw zero reference. The microphone serves as input to an amplifier which is to have an output level of +32 db into a load of 12 ohms.

(a) Find the microphone output voltage.

(b) Find the gain required of the amplifier in decibels.

(c) Compute the amplifier power output, load current, and voltage.

(d) The power output is to be reduced by 60 per cent. What will be the amplifier-output decibel level?

7-29. The loss on a certain radio-frequency transmission line is 2.3 db per 100 ft. How long can a line be made which will have an efficiency of 75 per cent?

7-30. A generator with output of 0.0025 w supplies power to the input circuit of an amplifier which in turn supplies power to a 2000-ohm load. If the power level in the load is to be +16 VU, what power gain in decibels is required of the amplifier?

7-31. A radio receiver has an input impedance which is 230 ohms resistive. The signal picked up by the antenna and applied to this input is 500 μv. The electrical output to the loudspeaker is to be at +26 db level (6 mw reference). Find:

(a) Input power level in decibels.

(b) Decibels gain in the receiver.

(c) Output power in watts.

REFERENCES

1. Dow, W. G., *Fundamentals of Engineering Electronics*, John Wiley & Sons, Inc., New York, 1937.

2. Vogdes, F. B., and Elder, F. R., "Formulas for the Amplification Constant for Three-Element Tubes," *Phys. Rev.*, **24**, 683 (1924).

3. Chaffee, E. L., *Theory of Thermionic Vacuum Tubes*, McGraw-Hill Book Company, Inc., New York, 1933.

4. *Standards on Electronics*, Institute of Radio Engineers, New York, 1938.

5. *American Standards for Graphical Symbols for Electronic Devices*, American Standard Z32.10—1944, American Standards Association, New York.

6. *Coordination of Electrical Graphical Symbols*, American Standard Z32.11 —1944, American Standards Association, New York.

7. *Standards on Abbreviations, Graphical Symbols, Letter Symbols, and Mathematical Signs*, Institute of Radio Engineers, New York, 1948.

8. Ryder, J. D., *Networks, Lines, and Fields*, Prentice-Hall, Inc., New York, 1949.

9. Miller, J. M., "Dependence of Input Impedance of a Three-Electrode Vacuum Tube upon the Load in the Plate Circuit," *Sci. Paper* 351, National Bureau of Standards, Washington, D.C.

10. Thompson, B. J., and Rose, G. M., "Vacuum Tubes of Small Dimensions for Use at Extremely High Frequencies," *Proc. IRE*, **21**, 1707 (1933).

11. McArthur, E. D., "Disk-Seal Tubes," *Electronics*, **18**, 98, February (1945).

12. Rose, G. M., Power, D. W., and Harris, W. A., "Pencil-Type UHF Triodes," *RCA Rev.*, **10**, 321 (1949).

CHAPTER 8

MULTI-ELEMENT TUBES

Once the basic invention, the addition of the grid to the diode, was evolved, it would seem that progress in development of the vacuum tube should have been rapid, but such was not the case. Other inventions and techniques had to be developed, and it was twenty years before it occurred to Dr. A. W. Hull that if one grid was desirable, two might be better—and the tetrode, or screen-grid tube, was born. This second signpost on the road was sufficient. A third grid was added, making the pentode, and now special-purpose tubes with as many as six grids are in use. On the surface, multigrid tubes may appear complex, but after it is realized that methods of analysis are the same as those for the triode, the application of multigrid tubes becomes simple.

8-1. Difficulties with the Triode

In the development of the input admittance of a triode, it was pointed out that the value of the negative resistance which might appear in the grid circuit was an inverse function of frequency. The shunt resistance component was stated as

$$R_{\text{in}} = -\frac{1}{g_m \omega C_{gp}(\pm X')} \tag{8-1}$$

and, if X' was positive, represented a positive feedback of energy from the plate to the grid circuit, resulting in instability and oscillation of the circuit. As long as the low frequencies used made ω small, the value of R_{in} shunted across the grid circuit was large enough to be neglected. As the frequency of operation of radio receivers approached 1,000,000 cycles, the instability and oscillation introduced by the negative input resistance precluded reasonable amplification of the signals at incoming, or radio, frequencies. Attempts to obtain increased receiver sensitivity by amplification of the signal before rectification were met with squeals and howls as evidence of self-oscillation induced by the positive energy feedback.

Equation 8-1 shows that the internal grid-plate capacity C_{gp} is at the root of the trouble. As a cure, the Hazeltine and other neutralizing circuits were developed; these introduced into the grid circuit a current equal to the current flowing through C_{gp}, but of opposite phase. Since no net energy was fed back to the grid or input circuit, R_{in} appeared of high value, the circuit was stable, and amplification at signal frequencies became possible. However, the adjustment of the neutralizing circuits was critical; in some cases it varied with frequency, and was upset upon replacement of the tubes—all conditions not conducive to mass production or mass use of radio receivers and equipment.

8-2. The Tetrode

Since the capacity C_{gp} was so obviously the cause of the feedback, the work of Hull and others centered on elimination of the cause rather than a cure. At (a), Fig. 8-1, the grid-plate capacity C_{gp} serves to couple grid and plate circuits. If C_{gp} is broken into two capacities in series, as at (b), Fig. 8-1, and the junction of the two capacities is short-circuited to cathode or ground, then flow of current from anode to grid inside the tube is impossible because the anode and grid circuits are connected at only one point. Insertion of a metal sheet into the grid-anode space would be an ideal means of breaking C_{gp} into two capacitances, but it would also stop the electron flow. Therefore a wire-mesh grid is used at this point to establish essentially a plane of zero a-c potential in the space while still permitting passage of electrons to the anode through the holes in the mesh.

The tube then has four elements, or is a *tetrode*. The second grid is called a *screen* or *shield* grid because its function is to act as an electrostatic shield, or screen, between anode and control grid. In addition to a screen between control grid and anode, a shield outside the anode is usually provided to reduce stray external capacitances to the anode, and if the tube has a glass envelope, the whole tube is enclosed in a grounded metal shield. By such means, the capacitance between grid and plate can be reduced from a value of 2 to 7 micromicrofarads ($\mu\mu$f) for a triode to 0.01 $\mu\mu$f or less, for a comparable tetrode.

Introduction of a grounded, or cathode-potential, shield grid in the control grid-anode space results in almost zero accelerating field at the cathode surface set up by the plate voltage, because the anode is almost entirely electrostatically shielded from the cathode, and so electric flux lines starting from the anode end on the screen instead of reaching to the cathode. The anode current is, there-

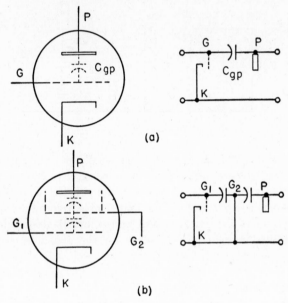

Fig. 8-1. Grid-plate capacities in (a) triode and (b) tetrode.

fore, practically zero. To overcome this situation, a positive d-c potential is applied to the screen; and since the screen is relatively close to the cathode, a voltage somewhat less than anode supply potential may be used and still obtain high accelerating forces on the electrons. However, the requirement that the screen be at cathode potential for alternating current must still be fulfilled. This may be met satisfactorily if a capacitor of low reactance is connected directly between screen and cathode. At some frequencies, a rather large capacitor may be required if its reactance is to be sufficiently small. A reactance of a few hundred ohms may usually be tolerated.

The screen potential may be obtained from the anode supply by a potentiometer arrangement, as in Fig. 8-2. By increasing the value of R_1, resistor R_2 may be omitted, and the proper screen potential will be obtained because of the voltage drop in R_1 produced by the

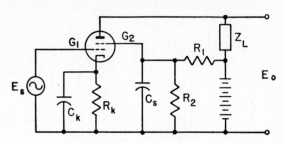

Fig. 8-2. Typical tetrode circuit.

screen current. The latter method is usually preferred because the screen potential becomes more or less self-adjusting to compensate for improper adjustments elsewhere in the circuit.

The screen current will be an appreciable fraction (possibly 20 to 40 per cent) of the anode current under normal conditions. Since the anode and screen are competing for the available electrons in the space current, and the space current is largely determined by screen potential, the division of current between the two will be determined by the relative ratio of screen area to anode area, and the screen and anode potentials. If the anode potential is removed, the total space current will be only slightly reduced but will now flow entirely to the screen. Since the screen is of small area and cannot readily dissipate the energy conveyed to it by the electrons, it may be overheated or even melted. For this reason, the anode potential should never be removed from a tetrode without also removing the screen potential. The use of the series-resistor method of obtaining screen potential is helpful in such a case in preventing screen damage because an increased screen current causes reduced screen potential.

Plate characteristics of a typical tetrode are shown in Fig. 8-3. They are taken for a value of screen voltage of 125, and would vary considerably for other screen potentials. It should be noted that for values of anode voltage somewhat above the screen potential, the curves are smooth, regular, and approximately linear. When the anode voltage falls below screen potential, the curves become nonlinear and with slopes indicating negative plate resistances at certain points. Therefore linear operation can be obtained only when the anode voltage is at all instants above the screen-voltage value.

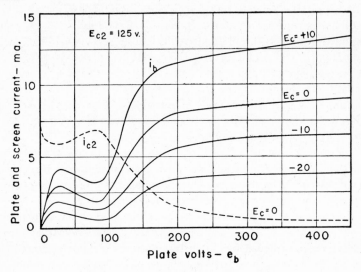

Fig. 8-3.   Plate characteristics of a tetrode.

Observation of the curves in the quasi-linear region shows that the slopes are quite small, indicating a small plate conductance or a high plate resistance. If the screening effect were perfect, the anode potential would have no effect on anode current. If the plate current were independent of plate voltage, the value of r_p would be infinite. Since the screening is not perfect, the plate resistance is finite and, for a typical tetrode, is of the order of 400,000 to 1,000,000 ohms.

Since the effect of the control grid on the electron stream has not been altered, the value of g_m is of the same order of magnitude as for a typical triode, 1000 to 2000 μmhos. However, since

$$\mu = g_m r_p$$

and r_p is large, μ is also large, and may have values of 200 to 500.

Since C_{gp} was reduced to a small value due only to stray capacities, very much smaller than C_{gp} of the triode, stable amplification at radio-signal frequencies became possible through introduction of the tetrode in 1928.

8-3. Difficulties with the Tetrode

Although the tetrode made stable radio-frequency amplification possible, its range of output voltage is severely limited by the large nonlinear region in the plate characteristics. The value of e_b varies throughout a cycle, and at the instant of current maximum, e_b is at its lowest point owing to the load voltage drop (resistive load assumed). If this minimum value of e_b is below the screen voltage, the tube is operating into the nonlinear region of the plate characteristics, and severe distortion occurs. This distortion prevents operation with large output voltages.

The nonlinear region of the tetrode is caused by the phenomenon of *secondary emission*, which was discussed in detail in Chapter 4. The electron stream from the cathode is accelerated by the positive potential on the screen grid and attains a high velocity. After passing through the interstices in the screen, the electrons continue to the anode and strike with high energy. Some of this impact energy is given to electrons in surface atoms, causing electrons to be emitted from the anode surface. These electrons are the secondary electrons. If the anode is instantaneously the most positive electrode in the space, the secondary electrons return immediately to the anode, and no effects are noted. If, however, the anode potential is instantaneously below the screen voltage, the secondary electrons are attracted from the anode to the more positive screen. The accelerating field acting on the secondary electrons at this instant is indicated by the slope of the potential curve in Fig. 8-4(a). During a cycle the anode potential point will move up and down on the anode line A, and at times the anode potential will be above that of the screen (G_2), and at times below it as shown.

At the time illustrated the primary stream of electrons is passing to the anode, but the secondary electrons are attracted to the more positive screen grid and constitute a current away from the anode. The net anode current is then less than the primary current, or the anode current is reduced by the secondary-emission current that flows at any time in an output cycle at which the anode voltage drops below the fixed screen voltage. Since the number of secondaries emitted may approach, or even exceed, the number of primary electrons, the net anode current may be seriously reduced, and under certain conditions may actually reverse in direction of flow.

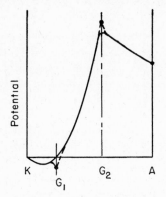 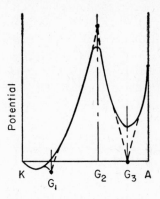

Fig. 8-4. (a) Potential distribution in a tetrode (anode potential below that of the screen); (b) potential distribution in a pentode, with the suppressor at cathode potential.

The secondary electron emission, therefore, accounts for the non-linearity of the tetrode characteristics at values of anode voltage below the screen potential.

The tetrode, though once widely used, has been largely superseded by the pentode because of improved performance.

8-4. The Pentode

The cure for the difficulties inherent in the tetrode lay in elimination of the effect of secondary emission, and this was achieved about 1930, by the addition of a third grid, resulting in a five-element tube, or *pentode*. This additional grid, called a *suppressor*, was placed between screen and anode, and normally connected to the cathode. The primary electron stream from the cathode has sufficient energy to override the retarding field introduced by the cathode-connected suppressor grid, and to reach the anode. The secondary electrons are always emitted with low energy, and even at low anode voltage they are still faced with a repelling field owing to the suppressor.

They then return immediately to the anode with no resultant effect on the anode current.

The repelling field which the secondary electrons face is apparent by the slope of the potential curve in (b), Fig. 8-4. This repelling field will always be present irrespective of the screen-anode potential relationship, since the suppressor, at cathode potential, will always be at a potential below that of the anode.

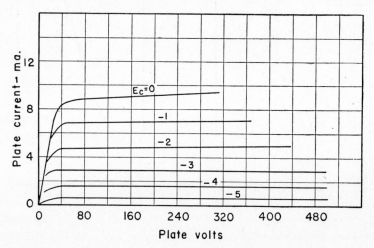

Fig. 8-5. Plate characteristics of a voltage-amplifier pentode. Screen volts = 100.

The characteristics of an amplifier pentode are shown in Fig. 8-5. Note that the nonlinear region existing in the tetrode when the anode potential is below that of the screen has been almost entirely eliminated by the addition of the suppressor grid. Owing to the additional grid-anode screening made possible by the suppressor, the value of C_{gp} for a pentode designed for radio-frequency amplifier service is further reduced to values approximating 0.004 $\mu\mu$f. The low slope of the plate characteristics of Fig. 8-5 indicates a very high plate resistance, with r_p for typical amplifier pentodes usually above 1 megohm. At the same time, since g_m is relatively unaffected, the value of μ is also high, reaching 2000 in some tube types.

Circuit connections for a pentode are indicated in Fig. 8-6. The value of C_s is again required to represent a low reactance, and resistor

R_s is chosen so that with normal rated screen current flowing, the voltage drop in R_s will ensure the proper value of voltage on the

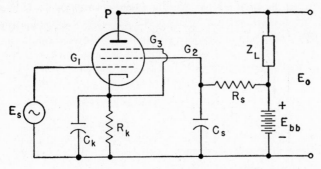

Fig. 8-6. Connections for a pentode tube. G_1 = control grid;
G_2 = screen grid; G_3 = suppressor grid.

screen. The suppressor is ordinarily connected directly to cathode, and in some types of tubes this connection is made internally. For special circuit functions, voltages may be applied to the suppressor for various forms of control of the electron stream.

In the construction of a pentode, the three grids are arranged concentrically about the cathode, and all are enclosed by the metal anode, or plate. The construction is totally shielded by the anode and also by additional screens.

8-5. The Equivalent Circuit of a Pentode

In the characteristics of Fig. 8-5, a large linear region may be seen. In this region, μ, g_m, and r_p may be assumed constants with small error, and under this assumption an equivalent circuit of the type derived for the triode in Chapter 7 can easily be obtained.

If an attempt is made to use a resistance load that is large with respect to r_p, an excessively high value of E_{bb} will be required, since the load must have a value of several megohms. If resonant load circuits are used, it is difficult to obtain resonant impedances of the order of magnitude of r_p. Because of these difficulties, the plate loads usually employed are of the order of 100,000 to 250,000 ohms. Thus a tube with r_p greater than 1 megohm will operate much as a constant-current source, the current being determined almost entirely by the generator resistance and being nearly independent of the load impedance.

In the current-source form of equivalent circuit, r_p and Z_L are directly in parallel. If, then, $r_p \gg Z_L$, as is usually the case, the current may be assumed as flowing entirely through the Z_L branch, with r_p dropped from the circuit. This leads to a form of approximate equivalent circuit for the pentode, as drawn in Fig. 8-7. This circuit is based on the assumption of small signals, and $r_p \gg Z_L$.

The gain for a pentode may then be obtained as

$$E_o = -g_m E_g Z_L,$$

$$\text{gain} = \frac{E_o}{E_s} = \frac{E_o}{E_g} = -g_m Z_L, \quad (8\text{-}2)$$

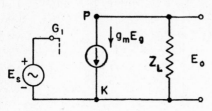

Fig. 8-7. Current-source equivalent circuit for a high-r_p pentode.

a result having an advantage in simplicity over that for a triode.

With g_m that of the 6AK5 pentode (5100 μmhos) and a load of 25,000 ohms, a gain of 127 per stage can be realized. Because of the excellent screening and low value of C_{gp}, such gains can be realized up to frequencies of several megacycles. Frequencies up to several hundred megacycles can be amplified with gains reduced somewhat by the effects of C_{gk} and C_{pk}. For this reason, pentodes have largely superseded tetrodes and triodes as voltage amplifiers at radio frequencies.

An additional factor in favor of the pentode is the decreased input admittance. Since C_{gp} is so small (0.02 $\mu\mu$f for the 6AK5), the input conductance is nearly zero, and the input susceptance is almost entirely that due to C_{gk} alone. Although C_{pk} may be larger than is usual for a triode owing to the capacitance between anode and screen, its effect can be reduced by lowering of the load impedance, with the gain still maintained relatively high because of the large values of μ and g_m obtainable in a pentode.

8-6. The Beam Tube

Although the pentode is excellent for the amplification of small signals, it develops several minor difficulties when employed for amplification of very large signals. The screen grid, being highly positive and located directly in the electron stream, intercepts considerable numbers of electrons, with resultant high screen currents and loss of power in the screen. Also, the rounded shoulders of the

i_b-e_b curves at low anode voltages result in nonlinear response and distortion for large voltage outputs. Some secondary emission from the anode is still taking place and the rounded portions of the curves are the remnants of the twisted tetrode curves in this region. The suppressor grid is, of course, full of holes to permit the primary electron stream to pass to the anode. Hence it cannot be a perfect equipotential plane and some of the secondary electrons from the anode take advantage of the holes to reach the screen.

Both difficulties have been reduced in a modified form of tube. The screen-grid wires are wound with the same pitch as the control

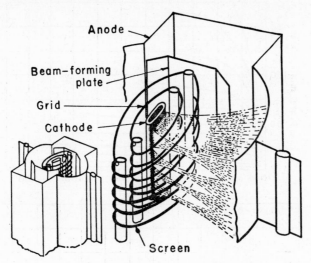

Anode

Beam—forming plate

Grid

Cathode

Screen

Fig. 8-8.　Internal structure of a beam tube.

grid, and in assembly they are accurately aligned behind the control-grid wires or in their shadow. The number of electrons captured by the screen is reduced in this way. In addition, the electron stream is concentrated into thin slices, or beams, passing between the wires of the two grids, and the stream is further condensed and concentrated by cathode-connected beam-forming plates, as shown in Fig. 8-8. The high electron density achieved in the region between the screen and anode depresses the potential at some point in this space to a value such that a low-potential plane similar to that of the suppressor in the pentode is produced.

The negative charge of the electrons in the space is brought into play to eliminate the suppressor grid and to produce suppressor-grid action which is nearly perfect, since the low-potential plane set up by the space charge need have no holes. Because of the formation of the electrons into beams, such a tube is called a *beam* tube. Although the construction of the tube makes it a tetrode, its characteristics and performance are more like those of a pentode.

Figure 8-9 shows the plate characteristics of a 6L6 beam tube,

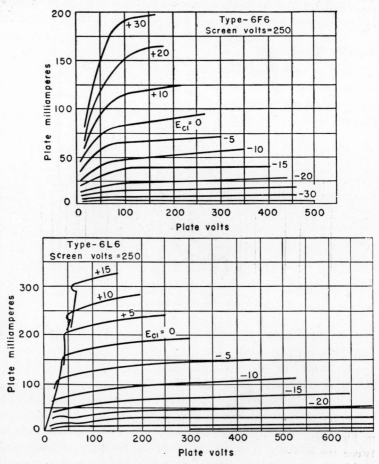

Fig. 8-9.   (a) Plate characteristics of the 6F6 power pentode; (b) plate characteristics of the 6L6 beam-power tetrode.

with those of a 6F6 pentode designed for similar service included
for comparison.   The beam tube has advantages over the pentode
when large power outputs are desired, since a lower grid-signal
voltage is required for a given power output.   This implies an increased value of g_m; in fact, the g_m of a beam tube may be appreciably
larger than that of a comparable pentode.

The current-source equivalent circuit is most suitable when an
equivalent is required for analysis of performance.   However, the
plate resistance of the beam tube is usually low enough and the load
high enough that r_p cannot always be neglected with respect to Z_L.

8-7. The Variable-Mu Tube

The gain of a pentode amplifier has been shown to be given by $g_m Z_L$.
As the point of operation on the dynamic grid characteristic is moved
down the curve toward cutoff, the slope, or value of g_m, becomes
less, reaching zero at cutoff [see Fig. 8-10(a)].   Shifting of the point

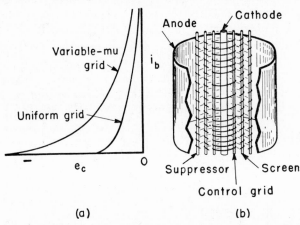

Fig. 8-10.   (a) Grid characteristic of a variable-mu and of
a uniform-spaced grid tube; (b) variable-mu tube grid construction.

of operation or quiescent point by change of bias voltage E_{cc} provides a means of varying the gain of the amplifier in order to obtain
desired output from both weak and strong signals.   However, owing
to the abrupt curvature at the bottom of the characteristic for the
ordinary triode or pentode, considerable distortion results if a large

signal is applied to the tube when the bias is set to bring the quiescent point into a region of low slope, as it would be to give the low gain needed for amplification of a large signal.

To avoid distortion and still provide the convenient means of gain control by bias adjustment, the *variable-mu*, or remote-cutoff, pentode was designed, and is used for most radio-frequency amplifiers where some large signals may be encountered. The special characteristics result in a dynamic grid characteristic such as is shown at (a), Fig. 8-10, with a much smoother variation of slope and g_m resulting in decreased nonlinear distortion for signals of several volts amplitude. The tube provides a region of considerable linearity at low slope (g_m) and thus can handle larger signals at low gain per stage than is possible with variable bias on an ordinary fixed-mu pentode.

The result is obtained by use of a specially wound grid as shown at (b), Fig. 8-10. The control-grid wires are wound with coarse spacing at the middle, varying to close spacing at the ends. When low negative grid bias is applied to the tube, the tube has some high value of g_m, or of μ, obtained as an average of the effects of the coarsely and finely spaced portions of the grid. As the bias is increased negatively, the closely spaced portions of the grid set up electric fields which cut off the plate current, and the g_m or μ takes a lower value, as an average of the effects of the remaining coarser-spaced portions of the grid. By this means, the gain can be smoothly varied by adjustment of the bias either manually or by automatic volume control (AVC) circuits. The transconductance for a typical remote-cutoff pentode may be 2000 μmhos at -3 v E_{cc}, giving a theoretical gain of 200 with a load of 100,000 ohms. At a grid bias of -35 v, the g_m is reduced to 10 μmhos and the gain to unity.

8-8. The Magic-Eye Tube

Certain electron-ray tubes designed for visual indication have been named *magic-eye* tubes because of their similarity in appearance to the iris of the eye. They provide visual indication, by means of a fluorescent target, of the effects of a change in a controlling voltage. Common uses are as tuning indicators in radio receivers, bridge-balance indicators, remote-position indicators, or wherever an approximate indicator without mechanical movement is desired.

As indicated in Fig. 8-11, a target made in the form of a shallow cone is coated internally with a fluorescent material similar to that used in cathode-ray tubes, and which gives a greenish glow when struck by electrons. A portion of an indirectly heated cathode enters the bottom of the cone and furnishes a supply of electrons, which are attracted to the target by a positive potential on the latter. When the electrons strike, they produce a glow on the fluorescent coating of the target, resulting in a ring of greenish light. A ray-control electrode is mounted at one side of the cathode between cathode and target. If this electrode is at target potential, it has

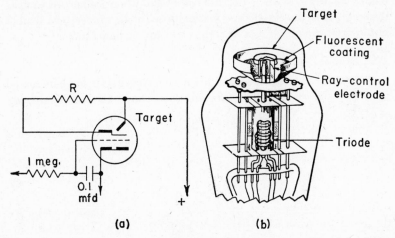

(a) (b)

Fig. 8-11. (a) Circuit for the magic-eye tube; (b) construction of magic-eye electron-ray tube.

no effect on the electrons; but when its potential is reduced below that of the target, an electric field is set up which repels electrons, and they are unable to reach that portion of the target behind the electrode. The ray-control electrode, in effect, then casts an electronic shadow on the target, the size of the shadow angle varying from zero, when the ray-control electrode is near target potential, to about 100°, when the ray-control electrode is 80 to 100 v negative with respect to the target electrode.

To provide the ray-control voltage, an amplifier tube is usually provided internally in the magic-eye tube, or as a separate unit, and connected as in Fig. 8-11(a). A highly negative voltage on the amplifier grid causes only a small amplifier plate current to flow.

As a result of this small current, the voltage drop in R is small, the potential of the ray-control electrode is practically that of the target, and the shadow angle is small or the eye is closed. Reduction of negative grid voltage allows more plate current in the amplifier tube; the drop in R is greater; the ray-control electrode voltage is then considerably below target voltage and the shadow angle is large, or the eye is open.

The grid of the built-in triode may be either sharp cutoff for closing the eye on a small change in voltage or remote cutoff for more gradual change of the shadow. For indicator use, where some precision is desired, the sharp cutoff type is usually selected, whereas the remote cutoff is more suitable as a radio-receiver tuning indicator.

8-9. Special-Purpose Tubes

As radio equipment has been improved, the circuits have increased in complexity and electron-tube functions have become highly spe-

Fig. 8-12. Special high-frequency forms. In descending order are the miniature, the acorn, the lighthouse, and at lower left, the doorknob.

cialized. This trend has led to development of special tubes to handle specific functions. Among these special tubes are frequency converters having five or more grids designed for efficient frequency changing in certain types of receivers. The grids perform the usual functions of control, screen, and suppressor, but the tubes may be complicated by several control, or screen, grids, although still having pentode characteristics.

A class of multiple-unit tubes for special purposes has grown up at the insistence of equipment designers. These are combinations of two or more of the basic tube types in the same envelope (to save space and wiring), designed with a view to reducing costs. The combinations may be diode-triodes, double diode-triodes, diode-pentodes, triode-pentodes, double triodes, and any others a designer believes will be convenient. Since the combination in no way changes the characteristics of the individual types, and the performance of a multiple-unit tube may be analyzed as that of its separate types each acting individually, there appears no need for further consideration of the multiplicity of types "wished upon" the engineer. In the absence of exigencies of space and cost, a better engineering design can usually be obtained with tubes in individual envelopes. One exception to this general statement may be noted in the use of the double triode. In certain types of balanced circuits where equal capacities to ground and short leads are important, the double triode with separate cathodes performs a useful service.

PROBLEMS

8-1. A 6AT6 triode and a 6BA6 pentode have the following characteristics at a normal operating point:

6AT6

$$\mu = 70$$
$$g_m = 1200 \ \mu\text{mhos}$$
$$r_p = 58{,}000 \text{ ohms}$$
$$I_b = 1.0 \text{ ma}$$
$$C_{gk} = 2.3 \ \mu\mu\text{f}$$
$$C_{gp} = 2.1 \ \mu\mu\text{f}$$
$$C_{pk} = 1.1 \ \mu\mu\text{f}$$
$$E_{bb} = 250 \text{ v}$$
$$E_{cc} = -3 \text{ v}$$

6BA6

$$g_m = 4400 \ \mu\text{mhos}$$
$$r_p = 1.5 \text{ megohms}$$
$$I_b = 5.5 \text{ ma}$$
$$C_{gk} = 5.5 \ \mu\mu\text{f}$$
$$C_{gp} = 0.0035 \ \mu\mu\text{f}$$
$$C_{pk} = 5.0 \ \mu\mu\text{f}$$
$$E_{bb} = 250 \text{ v}$$
$$E_{c1} = -3 \text{ v}$$
$$E_{c2} = 100 \text{ v}$$
$$I_{c2} = 4.2 \text{ ma}$$

Plot curves of input resistance and capacitance for both tubes over a range of 1 to 100 megacycles, using a logarithmic frequency scale. The plate load is constant at $2500 + j2500$ ohms for all frequencies.

8-2. A 6BA6 pentode tube is used in the circuit of Fig. 8-6.

(a) Calculate values of R_s, C_s, R_k, and C_k which will give satisfactory operation over the frequency range 500 to 1500 kc. The tube is to operate at the rated values of Problem 8-1.

(b) If the load consists of a resonant circuit having an impedance of 125,000 ohms, resistive, at $f = 1.1 \times 10^6$ c, find the gain.

8-3. If the screen supply circuit of Fig. 8-2 is to be used with a 6BA6 pentode at rated values, find suitable values for C_s, R_1, and R_2, if the total resistance of R_1 and R_2 is to be 25,000 ohms, and the frequency range of interest is 50 to 10,000 c.

8-4. A type 6BA6 pentode is operated as an amplifier with a load $R = 22,000$ ohms, $g_m = 1600$ μmhos, $r_p = 0.75$ megohms, and capacitance values as given in Problem 8-1. Calculate the input capacitance of this tube at a frequency of 150 megacycles.

8-5. A pentode has an amplification factor of 750 and a g_m of 2000 μmhos. The load voltage is to be 25 v rms with an alternating plate current of 0.4 ma.

(a) What signal voltage is required?

(b) What error is introduced in (a) by use of the approximate equivalent circuit (r_p assumed infinite)?

REFERENCES

1. Hull, A. W., and Williams, N. H., "Characteristics of Shielded-Grid Pliotrons," *Phys. Rev.*, **27**, 432 (1926).
2. Ballantine, S., and Snow, H. A., "Reduction of Distortion and Cross-Talk in Radio Receivers by Means of Variable-Mu Tetrodes," *Proc. IRE*, **18**, 2102 (1930).
3. Schade, O. H., "Beam Power Tubes," *Proc. IRE*, **26**, 137 (1938).

CHAPTER 9

SMALL-SIGNAL AMPLIFIERS; FEEDBACK

In Chapter 7 two methods of analysis of vacuum tube circuits were developed, *the equivalent circuit* restricted to small grid-voltage swings, and the *graphical method*, not so limited but more suited to circuits with large grid voltages. In this chapter it is proposed to discuss circuits with small signals, using the equivalent circuit method, the graphical method being applied in Chapter 10. While a great many circuits have been developed for specific applications certain fundamentals underly all, and it is these basic methods which are discussed here.

It is assumed that the amplitudes of the signal voltages are sufficiently small that the dynamic characteristics of the tube may be considered linear, and μ, g_m, and r_p constants, thus justifying the use of the equivalent circuit.

Primary considerations in amplifier analysis and design vary according to application. They may include gain, frequency response over narrow or wide frequency bands, phase shift or delay, response to transient voltages, low noise or erratic current generation, desirable values of input or output impedance, and others.

9-1. Fundamental Amplifier Types

A triode has three active internal elements: the cathode, the control grid, and the anode or plate. Multi-element tubes have additional grids, but their functioning can be described in terms of the same three elements, and they operate in the same basic circuits.

Three major types of amplifier circuits have been developed, differing by reason of the element connections to input and output circuits, and the tube element selected for the common terminal or ground.

The circuit of greatest use is the *grid input-plate output amplifier* wherein the input voltage appears between grid and cathode, the output between anode and cathode, with the cathode common. A second type of considerable importance is the *cathode follower* in which the input appears in the grid lead, the output in the cathode lead, and with the anode grounded for alternating voltages and common to input and output. A third type of recent importance is the *grounded-grid* circuit, which introduces the signal in the cathode lead with the output in the anode lead, the grid being the common and grounded terminal.

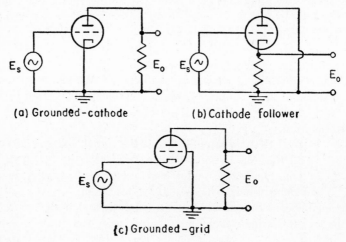

(a) Grounded-cathode   (b) Cathode follower

(c) Grounded-grid

Fig. 9-1.   Basic amplifier circuits.

The common terminal is taken as the reference point for a-c voltage measurement and it is usually also placed at ground potential. The reasons for grounding usually include a desire for electric-field shielding and isolation between input and output circuits.

All the various coupling circuits may be used with any of the three basic amplifiers. Differences in performance which are then encountered are due to the differing input and output impedances of the vacuum tube, when connected in these three fundamental ways. The circuits will usually be studied in terms of resistance loads and R-C coupling but are not so limited.

9-2. The Grid-Input Plate-Output Amplifier; R-C Coupling

The internal tube capacities and reactances present in coupling networks, are the causes of frequency and delay distortion which may be present in amplifier circuits. Gain-frequency curves for amplifiers are usually plotted on semilogarithmic scales with frequency on the log scale, since the ear hears logarithmically by octaves. Such a curve indicates frequency distortion in regions in which it is not a horizontal straight line. Delay distortion is present if constant delay for all frequencies is not obtained.

A typical *R-C* coupled amplifier appears in Fig. 9-2, and the gain-frequency performance will be found to appear as in Fig. 9-3, with distortion inevitably appearing at the frequency extremes. Defi-

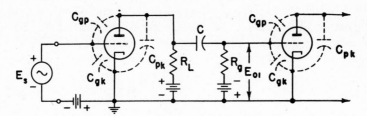

Fig. 9-2.   Two-stage, resistance-capacity coupled amplifier, showing tube capacities.

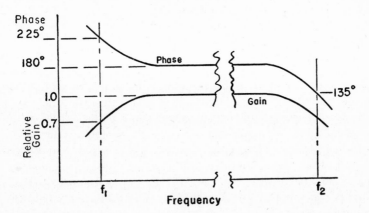

Fig. 9-3.   Typical form of gain-frequency and phase angle-frequency plots.

nition of the frequencies f_1 and f_2 will appear in the following sections, it being sufficient to point out here that they represent frequencies at which the voltage gain is 0.707 of its midrange value, or the output power has one-half of its midrange value.

Consideration of the amplifier circuit of Fig. 9-2 will show that the circuit is quite complex, and while the tube may be replaced with its equivalent circuit for design and analysis of gain-frequency and delay-frequency performance, simplification of the circuit would be desirable.

The input capacity of the second tube has been determined as

$$C_{\text{in}} = C_{gk} + C_{gp}(1 + g_m R')$$

which may be considerably larger than C_{gk} alone. If E_s has zero internal impedance, shunting of the first tube by C_{in} will have no effect on the grid-cathode voltage, and C_{in} of the first tube may be neglected. However, C_{in} of the second tube cannot be neglected because it appears in shunt with resistors having values possibly comparable with the reactance of C_{in}. The circuit of the triode am-

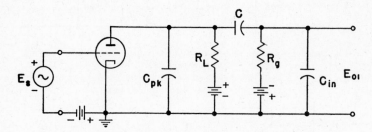

Fig. 9-4.   Circuit of the first stage of the amplifier of Fig. 9-2.

plifier to be analyzed then becomes that of Fig. 9-4, which is redrawn in the voltage-source and current-source equivalent forms at (a), Fig. 9-5. These circuits have either five or six meshes, and solution by usual mesh equations would involve considerable labor.

It has been mentioned that C_{in} and C_{pk} are small capacitances, so that at low frequencies they will have high reactances, possibly so high compared with R_L and R_g that they may be considered open circuits and dropped from the circuit. The equivalent circuits then become as at (b), Fig. 9-5. By use of the voltage-source form of (b), the current I_p may be found as

$$I_p = \frac{\mu E_g}{r_p + Z_L}, \tag{9-1}$$

where Z_L is defined as *the impedance of all components in the external anode circuit through which alternating current flows*, or

$$Z_{L_{lo}} = \frac{R_L(R_g - j/\omega C)}{R_L + R_g - j/\omega C}. \tag{9-2}$$

Then the output voltage rise from cathode to anode may be written

$$E_p = -I_p Z_L = -\frac{\mu E_g Z_L}{r_p + Z_L}, \tag{9-3}$$

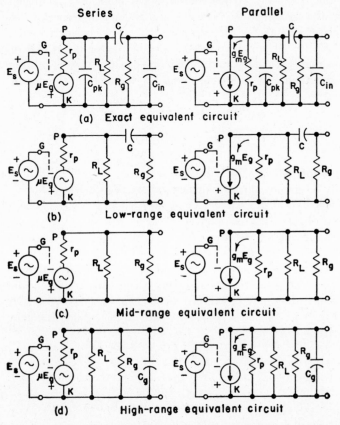

Fig. 9-5. Simplification of triode-amplifier equivalent circuits by designation of frequency ranges.

and by use of the potential division factor introduced by the voltage divider consisting of the capacitor C and grid leak R_g, the output voltage E_o is

$$E_o = - \frac{\mu E_g Z_L}{r_p + Z_L} \times \frac{R_g}{R_g - j/\omega C}, \qquad (9\text{-}4)$$

from which the over-all amplification is

$$A_{\text{lo}} = \frac{E_o}{E_s} = \frac{E_o}{E_g} = \frac{-\mu Z_L}{r_p + Z_L} \times \frac{R_g}{R_g - j/\omega C}. \qquad (9\text{-}5)$$

This expression may be called the *low-frequency gain*.

If the frequency is now raised, some point will be reached at which the reactance X_c becomes negligible with respect to the resistance R_g. In some cases this point may be considered reached if $X_c < R_g/10$. Then the potential division factor of Eq. 9-5 reduces approximately to unity, and the circuits become those of (c), Fig. 9-5. The gain then may be written from Eq. 9-5 or from the circuit as

$$A_{\text{mid}} = \frac{E_o}{E_s} = \frac{E_o}{E_g} = \frac{-\mu Z_L}{r_p + Z_L}, \qquad (9\text{-}6)$$

where

$$Z_{L \text{ mid}} = \frac{R_L R_g}{R_L + R_g}. \qquad (9\text{-}7)$$

Equation 9-6 is called the *mid-frequency amplification* and may usually be employed for frequencies above that at which $X_c = R_g/10$ and below that at which $X_{c_g} = 10 R_g R_L/(R_g + R_L)$. The phase angle of the gain in this range is 180°.

If the frequency is raised still further, a point will be reached at which the reactances of C_{pk} and C_{in} are no longer high with respect to the circuit resistances R_L and R_g in parallel. Since, with capacitor C neglected, C_{pk} and C_{in} and any stray wiring capacity will be directly in parallel, they may be lumped as one capacitance, C_g, as shown at (d), Fig. 9-5. Since the load paths are all in parallel, the gain may be written

$$A_{\text{hi}} = \frac{E_o}{E_s} = \frac{E_o}{E_g} = \frac{-\mu Z_L}{r_p + Z_L}, \qquad (9\text{-}8)$$

if Z_L is taken as

$$Z_{L \text{ hi}} = \frac{R_L R_g}{R_g + R_L + j\omega C_g R_L R_g}. \qquad (9\text{-}9)$$

Equations 9-8 and 9-9 define the *high-frequency gain* and may be used for all frequencies higher than those suitable for use of Eq. 9-7.

In general, the gain of a resistance-coupled amplifier may always be expressed by Eq. 9-5 if proper meaning is given to the quantity Z_L. The potential-division factor automatically becomes unity at the higher frequencies, and the equation then reduces to the form of Eqs. 9-6 and 9-8.

As an example of the use of the current-source form of equivalent circuit, the gain may be computed for the mid-frequency range. The current equation for (c), Fig. 9-6, is

$$g_m E_g = -E_o \left(\frac{1}{r_p} + \frac{1}{R_L} + \frac{1}{R_g} \right),$$

from which
$$A_{\mathrm{mid}} = \frac{-g_m r_p R_L R_g}{R_L R_g + r_p R_g + r_p R_L}$$

$$= \frac{-\mu \dfrac{R_L R_g}{R_L + R_g}}{r_p + \dfrac{R_L R_g}{R_L + R_g}} = \frac{-g_m Z_L}{1 + Z_L/r_p}. \tag{9-10}$$

This result is of the form of Eq. 9-6 modified by Eq. 9-7, as was to be expected. If a pentode is used it is probable that the term Z_L/r_p in Eq. 9-10 will be found negligible and dropped from consideration. Thus for pentodes the current-source circuits should be used in this analysis, as was pointed out in Chapter 8.

9-3. Variation of Gain and Phase-Shift with Frequency

Any variation of gain as a function of frequency is apparent as frequency distortion. Any variation of $d\phi/d\omega$ as a function of frequency is delay distortion. Both such types of distortion are matters of considerable importance in the design of amplifier circuits.

It may be noted that the low- and high-range expressions of the preceding section differ from the mid-frequency equation because of the introduction of the capacitive reactances. Since in the mid-frequency range there is no variation of gain with frequency, it is the capacitive reactances that cause changes of gain in the other ranges. Capacitance C, if not sufficiently large, will cause the gain and phase angle to vary at the lower frequencies, and the effect of C_g is to produce a variation at the high-frequency end of the range.

Since the amplitude and phase angle of the A_{mid} gain are independent of frequency, it is convenient to compare the variation of gain magnitude and phase angle at other frequencies with that in the middle range of frequencies considered as a standard. The desired information is then obtained in terms of ratios $A_{\mathrm{lo}}/A_{\mathrm{mid}}$, $A_{\mathrm{hi}}/A_{\mathrm{mid}}$, $\phi_{\mathrm{lo}}/\phi_{\mathrm{mid}}$, and $\phi_{\mathrm{hi}}/\phi_{\mathrm{mid}}$.

By use of the value of Z_L, the low-range gain may be written as

$$A_{\mathrm{lo}} = \frac{-\mu R_L R_g}{r_p \left(R_L + R_g - \dfrac{j}{\omega C} \right) + R_L \left(R_g - \dfrac{j}{\omega C} \right)}.$$

By taking the ratio of this to the midrange gain of Eqs. 9-6 and 9-7, after some labor there can be obtained the ratio

$$\frac{A_{\mathrm{lo}}}{A_{\mathrm{mid}}} = \frac{1}{1 - \dfrac{j}{\omega C} \left(\dfrac{1}{R_g + \dfrac{r_p R_L}{r_p + R_L}} \right)}. \qquad (9\text{-}11)$$

This is a useful expression, since the mid-frequency gain is easy to compute.

At some frequency f_1, the reactive term will become unity, and thus f_1 is defined as

$$f_1 = \frac{1}{2\pi C \left(R_g + \dfrac{r_p R_L}{r_p + R_L} \right)}. \qquad (9\text{-}12)$$

Substitution of this value in Eq. 9-11 gives

$$\frac{A_{\mathrm{lo}}}{A_{\mathrm{mid}}} = \frac{1}{1 - j\dfrac{f_1}{f}}. \qquad (9\text{-}13)$$

The phase angle of the A_{mid} gain is 180° and independent of frequency. The phase-shift ratio, which is then the phase shift of the amplifier at the low frequencies (exclusive of the 180° inherent in the circuit), is

$$\frac{\phi_{\mathrm{lo}}}{\phi_{\mathrm{mid}}} = \phi_{\mathrm{lo}} = \tan^{-1}\frac{f_1}{f}. \qquad (9\text{-}14)$$

Frequency f_1 is seen to be a constant for a particular amplifier, and is determined by the designer through his choice of tubes and circuit parameters. A physical meaning is obtainable for f_1 if it be noted that at $f = f_1$ the voltage gain A_{lo} is $1/\sqrt{2}$ of the midrange gain. Thus at $f = f_1$ the *power* output of the amplifier is one-half of the midrange power, or f_1 is spoken of as a *half-power frequency.*

Dimensionless curves for gain and phase shift are plotted in Fig. 9-6, where the variation of A_{lo}/A_{mid} and ϕ as a function of the frequency ratio is shown. Note that these curves are actually plotted in terms of the reciprocal value, f/f_1, in order that the ratio will increase with frequency. These curves then apply to any amplifier of the type under discussion. At some very low frequency (f/f_1 small) the gain is zero and the phase shift becomes $+90°$ (μE_g reference).

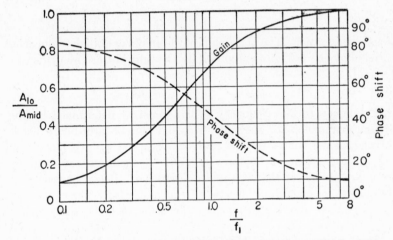

Fig. 9-6. Generalized gain and phase-shift curves of the R-C coupled amplifier in the low-frequency range.

Large values of C may be used to reduce the low-frequency drop in gain, but the requirements on C are stringent, since it must be able to withstand full anode-supply voltage with zero leakage current if the bias of the second tube is not to be disturbed. Cost frequently dictates the use of a value for C below the size that good design requires.

By a similar process involving the high-range gain of Eqs. 9-8 and 9-9, the ratio of the high-range gain to the mid-frequency gain can be reduced to

$$\frac{A_{hi}}{A_{mid}} = \frac{1}{1 + j\omega C_g \left(\dfrac{1}{\dfrac{1}{r_p} + \dfrac{1}{R_L} + \dfrac{1}{R_g}} \right)}. \qquad (9\text{-}15)$$

This equation shows that the susceptance of C_g is the factor causing the high-frequency amplification to vary and fall off with increasing frequency. Defining a frequency f_2 as that at which the reactive term above becomes unity gives

$$f_2 = \frac{1}{2\pi C_g}\left(\frac{1}{r_p} + \frac{1}{R_L} + \frac{1}{R_g}\right). \tag{9-16}$$

and then

$$\frac{A_{hi}}{A_{mid}} = \frac{1}{1 + j\dfrac{f}{f_2}} \tag{9-17}$$

for the gain ratio. The phase shift of the amplifier at high frequencies (excluding the 180° shift produced by the tube in this circuit) is

$$\frac{\phi_{hi}}{\phi_{mid}} = \phi_{hi} = -\tan^{-1}\frac{f}{f_2}. \tag{9-18}$$

Frequency f_2, like frequency f_1, is a constant determined by the design parameters of the amplifier, and can be arbitrarily fixed. Dimensionless curves for the ratio A_{hi}/A_{mid} and ϕ_{hi} are plotted in Fig. 9-7 as a function of the ratio f/f_2. Again these curves apply to any amplifier of the type under discussion. It can be seen that frequency f_2 is again a half-power frequency, with a phase angle of $-45°$. At a very high frequency the gain would be zero, with a phase shift of $-90°$.

Small values of C_g can be obtained by careful reduction in wiring

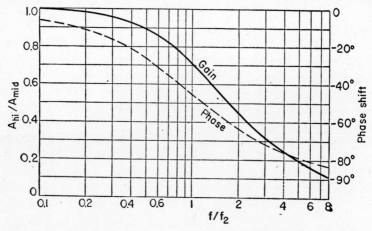

Fig. 9-7. Generalized gain and phase-shift curves of the R-C coupled amplifier in the high-frequency range.

capacitances and by using pentodes in preference to triodes. If C_g cannot be reduced, reduction of R_L and R_g can raise f_2 to higher values and extend the usable range of the amplifier, at some sacrifice in gain.

9-4. Transformer-Coupled Grid-Input Plate-Output Amplifier

A transformer may be used to couple two cascaded vacuum tubes and to separate the a-c signal from the d-c components in the cir-cuit. Analysis of a transformer-coupled amplifier of the grid-input plate-output type, as shown in Fig. 9-8, can be carried out by recourse to the equiva-lent circuits of Figs. 9-9 and 9-10. Fig. 9-9(b) shows the transformer equivalent circuit of (a) reduced to a unity turns-ratio basis, where $a = N_1/N_2$. Resistance R_1 is the primary winding resistance, which will be neglected with respect to r_p. Other

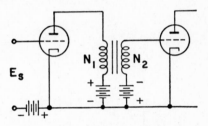

Fig. 9-8.　Transformer coupling of an amplifier.

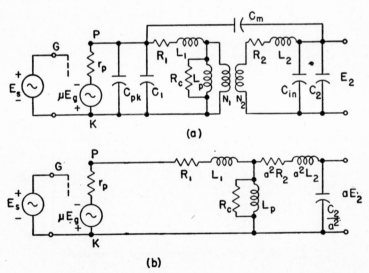

(a)

(b)

Fig. 9-9.　Equivalent circuits for a transformer-coupled amplifier: (a) normal, including capacities; (b) primary capacities neglected, all quanti-ties referred to primary.

quantities are the primary leakage inductance L_1, L_p, the primary inductance through which the magnetizing current flows, and a^2R_2 and a^2L_2, which are, respectively, the secondary resistance and leakage reactance when placed on the primary side. Resistance R_c is the equivalent core loss resistance which will also be neglected on the assumption of the use of good iron in the magnetic circuit.

Winding capacitances and tube capacitances are represented in Fig. 9-9(a), with the primary capacitances treated as negligible in (b). Thus C_2 is a representation of secondary winding capacitance, capaci-

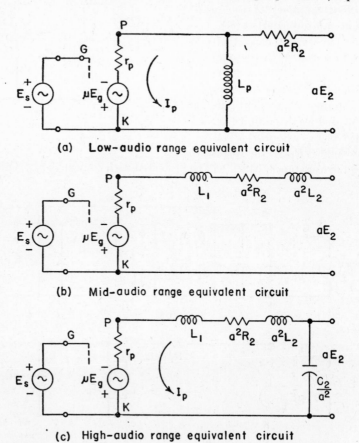

(a)   **Low-audio range equivalent circuit**

(b)   **Mid-audio range equivalent circuit**

(c)   **High-audio range equivalent circuit**

Fig. 9-10.   Equivalent circuits for the transformer-coupled amplifier, classified according to frequency ranges.

tance between windings, and C_{in}, the following tube input capacitance. This capacitance C_2 has considerable effect on transformer performance.

The performance may be considered by use of the three equivalent circuits of Fig. 9-10. At low frequencies the gain is

$$A_{lo} = \frac{\mu}{a} \times \frac{-1}{1 - j\left(\dfrac{r_p}{\omega L_p}\right)}. \qquad (9\text{-}19)$$

If the gain is not to fall off at low frequencies, L_p must be large and tubes of low r_p must be used.

As the frequency is raised ωL_p increases, and at some frequency at which $\omega L_p \gg r_p$ the gain becomes

$$A_{mid} = -\frac{\mu}{a} = -\mu \frac{n_2}{n_1}. \qquad (9\text{-}20)$$

The circuit has then been reduced to that of (b), Fig. 9-10, and I_p equals zero.

Further frequency increases bring the effect of C_2/a^2 into the circuit, and at frequencies where its effect can no longer be neglected, the circuit becomes that of (c) and the gain is

$$A_{hi} = \frac{\mu}{a} \times \frac{j}{\dfrac{\omega C_2}{a^2}(r_p + a^2 R_2) + j\left[\dfrac{\omega^2}{a^2}(L_1 + a^2 L_2)C_2 - 1\right]}. \qquad (9\text{-}21)$$

This equation shows that the gain will have a peak at a frequency at which the leakage reactances and the capacitance C_2/a^2 become series resonant. The voltage across the capacitance then rises and may exceed the value μ/a. This peak may be reduced by shunting the secondary with a resistor, at some loss in gain.

A typical gain-frequency curve for a transformer-coupled amplifier is shown in Fig. 9-11. The fall at low frequency is due to insufficient primary inductance L_p, and the high-frequency peak indicates resonance between the leakage inductance and the secondary capacitances. Increase of L_p to improve the low-frequency response will also increase the leakage and the capacitance, and thus lower the frequency at which the peak occurs. This has led to the use of expensive high-permeability steels to provide higher inductances without many turns.

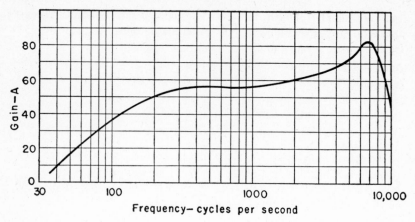

Fig. 9-11. Gain-frequency curve for a transformer-coupled amplifier. Tube type 6J5, $\mu = 20$, $r_p = 7700$ ohms, $N_2/N_1 = 3$.

Since low-r_p, and consequently low-μ, tubes must be used, greater over-all gain can be obtained with high-μ tubes in an R-C amplifier. Both cost and gain favor this and at present transformers are largely used only for coupling a tube to a loudspeaker or other load, where impedance matching is also a required function.

9-5. The Grounded-Grid Amplifier

The amplifier with input in the cathode-grid circuit and output between plate and grid is sometimes called a *grounded-grid amplifier.* The grounding of the grid is done largely to obtain electrostatic shielding inside the tube between the input and output circuits.

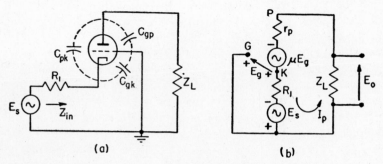

Fig. 9-12. Cathode input or grounded-grid amplifier. Circuit (b) neglects tube capacities.

At very high frequencies this shielding reduces the transfer of energy between output and input circuits, and prevents oscillation.

For small input signals at nominal frequencies the equivalent circuit may be drawn as at (b), Fig. 9-12, with the internal tube capacitances shown in the circuit at (a) neglected. Since the plate current flows through the signal source, the internal impedance of the source must be included as R_1. This impedance is frequently that of a resonant circuit, and therefore it is permissible to consider it as resistive.

Writing equations for the two meshes gives

$$\mu E_g + E_s - I_p(r_p + R_1 + Z_L) = 0, \qquad (9\text{-}22)$$

$$E_g - E_s + I_p R_1 = 0, \qquad (9\text{-}23)$$

and the plate current then is

$$I_p = \frac{(\mu + 1)E_s}{r_p + (\mu + 1)R_1 + Z_L}.$$

The load-voltage rise from ground to plate is

$$E_o = -I_p Z_L,$$

and since E_s represents a negative rise above common circuit terminal, the gain for the circuit can be written

$$A = \frac{E_o}{E_s} = \frac{(\mu + 1)Z_L}{r_p + (\mu + 1)R_1 + Z_L}. \qquad (9\text{-}24)$$

The output of the amplifier is in phase with the signal generator E_s, or there is no 180° phase shift in this circuit.

If the output load Z_L actually is made up of the coupling circuits of Section 9-2, or by a transformer as in Section 9-4, the methods of those sections may be applied for aiding the solution in terms of equivalent circuits useful in various frequency bands.

It can be seen that the signal E_s is in series with the equivalent generator μE_g. The input voltage thus adds to that of the equivalent generator. If Eq. 9-24 is compared with Eq. 7-31 for the grid input circuit it can be seen that the grounded-grid tube appears to have an amplification coefficient of $(\mu + 1)$ and an internal plate resistance of

$$r_p' = r_p + (\mu + 1)R_1.$$

Since current flows in the signal source, the impedance into which the source generator works is of importance. Neglecting the tube capacitances and considering $R_1 = 0$, this impedance is

$$Z_{\text{in}} = \frac{E_s}{I_p} = \frac{r_p + Z_L}{\mu + 1}. \tag{9-25}$$

This represents the total impedance of the plate circuit divided by $(\mu + 1)$, and the circuit can be considered a step-up impedance transformer. For a tube having $\mu = 20$, $r_p = 7000$ ohms, with a resistive load of 50,000 ohms, the input resistance is 2714 ohms. Since tubes designed for this circuit have very complete shielding between plate and cathode by the grid structure, the major effect of the tube capacitances is to add C_{gk}, in parallel with this input impedance. It can be seen that the circuit will be usable to quite high frequencies before the shunting effect of C_{gk} is appreciable.

It may be noted that in this circuit the input and output currents are identical, the tube appearing analogous to a pump which raises water from a low-pressure system to a high-pressure pipe line. The circuit is of value in transforming from a low-impedance source, as an antenna, to a load of high impedance.

9-6. The Grid Input-Cathode Output Amplifier, or Cathode Follower

The amplifier with input in the grid circuit and output in the cathode circuit, or with the plate common, is usually called a *cathode follower*. This name is applied because the cathode a-c potential or output is at all times practically equal to or follows the grid-signal voltage. The circuit and its equivalent in voltage-source form are drawn in Fig. 9-13.

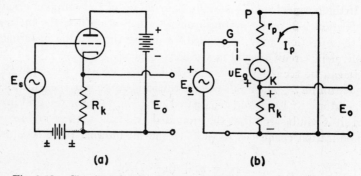

Fig. 9-13. Circuit and voltage-source equivalent for a cathode-output or cathode-follower amplifier.

Neglecting the tube capacitances, the grid-cathode voltage can be written as

$$E_g = E_s - I_p R_k, \qquad (9\text{-}26)$$

and the plate current can be written

$$I_p = \frac{\mu E_g}{r_p + R_k},$$

which by substitution of Eq. 9-26 leads to

$$I_p = \frac{\mu E_s}{r_p(1 + g_m R_k) + R_k}. \qquad (9\text{-}27)$$

The load voltage is $E_o = I_p R_k$, giving for the amplification

$$A = \frac{\mu R_k}{r_p + (\mu + 1)R_k}. \qquad (9\text{-}28)$$

Since the quantities in the denominator are all positive, the gain is always less than unity, approaching unity if $\mu R_k \gg (r_p + R_k)$.

The impedance which the cathode follower presents to its load circuit may be obtained by further consideration of (b), Fig. 9-13. Assume a generator of voltage E_o connected at the output terminals and a current I_1 flowing from the generator and through R_k from plus to minus. The impedance looking into the E_o terminals is then the ratio of E_o to I_1, with the internal source E_s short-circuited. Two mesh equations are

$$-E_g = E_o = (I_1 + I_p)R_k, \qquad (9\text{-}29)$$

$$\mu E_g = I_p r_p + (I_1 + I_p)R_k. \qquad (9\text{-}30)$$

Solving for I_p gives

$$I_p = \frac{-(\mu + 1)R_k I_1}{r_p + (\mu + 1)R_k},$$

and inserting this result in Eq. 9-29 and dividing by I_1 yields

$$Z_{\text{out}} = \frac{E_o}{I_1} = \frac{r_p R_k}{r_p + (\mu + 1)R_k} = \frac{\left(\dfrac{r_p}{\mu + 1}\right)R_k}{\dfrac{r_p}{\mu + 1} + R_k}. \qquad (9\text{-}31)$$

This is simply the relation due to two resistors in parallel, that is, to R_k in parallel with another resistor of value $r_p/(\mu + 1)$. This internal tube resistance becomes simply $1/g_m$ for a pentode where

$\mu \gg 1$. The result of Eq. 9-31 may be confirmed by rearrangement of Eq. 9-28 as

$$A = \frac{\dfrac{\mu}{\mu + 1} R_k}{\dfrac{r_p}{\mu + 1} + R_k} \tag{9-32}$$

which indicates that the tube has an internal resistance of $r_p/(\mu + 1)$, and also an effective amplification factor of $\mu/(\mu + 1)$.

For the case of a pentode $\mu \gg 1$, and Eq. 9-31 may be simplified to

$$Z_{\text{out}} = \frac{R_k}{1 + g_m R_k}. \tag{9-33}$$

When a pentode is used in this circuit the screen by-pass capacitor should connect to cathode and not to ground. This arrangement is necessary, since the screen must be held at zero a-c potential *with respect to cathode* for proper screening action in a pentode.

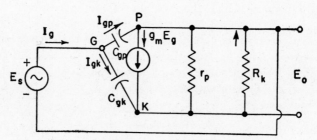

Fig. 9-14. Current-source equivalent circuit for the cathode follower, including capacities associated with the tube.

Another valuable property of the cathode-follower circuit is a reduced input admittance. From the circuit of Fig. 9-14, with the current-source equivalent circuit used for convenience, and with C_{pk}, which appears in shunt with R_k, neglected as a large reactance compared with R_k, it is possible to write

$$I_g = I_{gp} + I_{gk} \tag{9-34}$$

$$I_{gp} = j\omega C_{gp} E_s,$$

$$I_{gk} = j\omega C_{gk}(E_s - E_o).$$

Substitution in Eq. 9-34 and division by E_s to obtain the admittance of the grid circuit gives

$$Y_{\text{in}} = \frac{I_g}{E_s} = j\omega\left[C_{gp} + C_{gk}\left(1 - \frac{E_o}{E_s}\right)\right];$$

and since E_o/E_s is the gain A,

$$Y_{\text{in}} = \frac{I_g}{E_s} = j\omega[C_{gp} + C_{gk}(1 - A)].$$

With the load consisting of R_k, and with the effect of C_{pk} in shunt with R_k neglected, the gain A is real and positive, so that the input admittance is wholly due to a capacitance, or

$$C_{\text{in}} = C_{gp} + C_{gk}(1 - A). \tag{9-35}$$

Since the gain A is less than unity but ordinarily near it, the input capacitance is almost entirely reduced to that of C_{gp}. For wide frequency ranges this is an advantage.

Use of the gain expression and the assumption that $\mu \gg 1$ gives for the input capacitance

$$C_{\text{in}} = C_{gp} + C_{gk}\left(\frac{1}{1 + g_m R_k}\right).$$

A disadvantage present is that the capacitance between cathode and heater appears shunted across the load. In certain circuits involving R_k values of 50,000 ohms or more, this capacitance may cause introduction of some hum into the circuit, owing to the capacitance between a-c heater and cathode.

With the voltage gain always less than unity, the circuit *appears* to be of no value, whereas the opposite is true. It may be used as an impedance transformer to couple a very high-impedance source to a low-impedance load, and with one side of the output circuit at ground potential. In its impedance-transforming property it is the opposite of the grounded-grid circuit. Like the latter circuit, the output voltage is in phase with the input signal.

The current flowing in resistor R_k is

$$I_k = I_b + I_p,$$

and this causes a voltage drop of

$$E_k = R_k I_b + R_k I_p. \tag{9-36}$$

The second term on the right is the a-c output voltage E_o, already discussed. The first term on the right is a d-c voltage with negative toward the grid. This is exactly the polarity needed for a grid bias, so that if I_b and R_k can be selected properly, no additional bias source is needed. If the value of R_k is dictated by other considerations, the I_bR_k voltage may be either too large or too small to supply the value of E_{cc} needed. In such a case the circuit may be modified as in Fig. 9-15, wherein R_{k1} is chosen to provide the proper bias voltage, and $R_{k1} + R_{k2}$ represent the load.

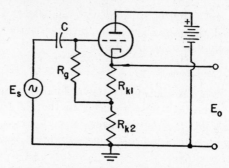

Fig. 9-15.   Modified cathode follower to
provide correct bias voltage.

Replacement of R_{k2} with a transformer provides a transformer-coupled circuit of improved performance. The low resistance which the tube represents shunts the transformer primary, and resonance and other undesirable effects are reduced.

9-7. Feedback in Amplifiers

For an ordinary amplifier, as in Fig. 9-16(a), of one or more stages, the gain has been defined as

$$A = \frac{E_o}{E_s}.$$

Frequently, fractions of the output voltage are introduced or fed back into the input circuit either intentionally or unintentionally.

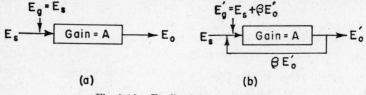

(a)   (b)

Fig. 9-16.   Feedback in an amplifier.

If intentionally, the feedback is achieved by special circuit arrangement; if unintentionally, it happens owing to magnetic- or electric-field coupling, or by reason of voltage drops across impedances common to both input and output circuits. An amplifier with feedback is shown diagrammatically at (b) in Fig. 9-16. The gain with feedback, A', is then defined as before:

$$A' = \frac{E_o{}'}{E_s}.$$

The input voltage $E_g{}'$ is given by

$$E_g{}' = E_s + \beta E_o{}', \tag{9-37}$$

so that the output voltage $E_o{}'$ is

$$E_o{}' = (E_s + \beta E_o{}')A,$$

where
$$\beta = \frac{\text{voltage fed back } \underline{/\theta_1}}{\text{output voltage } \underline{/\theta_2}}. \tag{9-38}$$

Then
$$A' = \frac{E_o{}'}{E_s} = \frac{A}{1 - A\beta}. \tag{9-39}$$

The effective gain A' is a function of β, the proportion of voltage fed back. In general, both A and β are complex.

It can be seen that if $|1 - A\beta|$ is less than unity, gain A' is greater than A before feedback was applied. The feedback is then said to be *positive* or the circuit is said to be *regenerative*. In general, positive feedback gives increased gain, decreased stability, and higher amplitude distortion. It is to be avoided for most applications.

If the denominator $|1 - A\beta|$ is greater than unity, gain A' is less than A before feedback was applied. The feedback is then said to be *negative* or *inverse* and the circuit is *degenerative*. Degenerative feedback reduces gain, increases stability, and reduces distortion.

For the case in which $A\beta = 1 + j0$ the gain becomes infinite, or the amplifier becomes an oscillator, having an output voltage totally independent of any external input voltage.

Negative feedback makes possible an engineering design of an amplifier which will perform as predicted, and eliminates experiment. Calibrated instruments may be designed to include vacuum tubes, and may retain their accuracy indefinitely, irrespective of supply voltage or tube variations.

Positive feedback, or regeneration, is present when the input conductance of the tube becomes negative with inductive load, as shown in Section 7-13. When the conductance is positive with capacitive load, negative feedback, or degeneration, takes place. In both cases the feedback occurs through the internal tube capacitance, C_{gp}.

9-8. Inverse-Feedback Effects

Because of the advantages listed above, negative or inverse feedback is very frequently employed. If the voltage fed back opposes or reduces the magnitude of the input voltage to the amplifier, the feedback is said to be *negative* or *inverse*. The term $A\beta$* is called the *feedback factor*, and is in general complex. Although it may change over a wide angle with frequency, an attempt is usually made to bring its angle to 0° or 180° over the frequency range in which a given amplifier is to be operated.

If $|A\beta|$ is made large with respect to unity, $|1 - A\beta| > 1$, and negative or inverse feedback occurs. Equation 9-39 then becomes

$$A' = - \frac{1}{\beta},   (9\text{-}40)$$

showing that the gain, while reduced, can be made entirely independent of original gain variations due to tubes, and supply voltages. Since β is usually fixed by resistors, and these can have very long time stability, the gain of an amplifier can be just as stable. The vacuum tube then becomes a predictable engineering device.

Equation 9-40 also shows that the gain can be made independent of the amplifier load impedance, provided that the load is not a factor determining the value of β.

An important point in connection with the above equation is that the amplification is an inverse function of β. Thus if β is allowed to vary with frequency, the amplification will vary in an inverse manner with frequency. If the circuit determining β is designed to reject some particular frequency range; the amplifier will respond to, and amplify, this frequency range. Such action is limited, of course, by the availability of sharply selective networks for use in the feedback circuit, but the principle is frequently employed in the design of selective amplifiers.

---

* In some of the literature, the feedback factor is given as $\mu\beta$, with μ being the over-all amplifier gain. To avoid confusion with the amplification factor, the term $A\beta$ is used here.

It is also apparent that if the amplification can be made to depend wholly or even partially on β, and if β is not a frequency function, any frequency distortion which may have been present in the amplifier will be reduced. Phase distortion also can be reduced by negative feedback.

The reduction of amplitude or nonlinear distortion possible by use of negative feedback is easily shown. If D is the amplitude-distortion component of voltage in the output of an amplifier, then, since the distortion increases with output or as the tube is driven over a wider range on the dynamic curve, the distortion D is some function of the output voltage E_o. Hence

$$D = f(E_o).$$

With feedback,

$$D' = f(E_o') + A\beta D', \tag{9-41}$$

where the last term is the percentage of the distortion ($\beta D'$) reamplified by a gain of A. Actually, there are additional terms present, since a percentage of $A\beta D'$ is again fed back and reamplified additional times; but since these involve β^2 and higher powers, they will be neglected as small. Consequently, Eq. 9-41 leads to

$$D' = \frac{f(E_o')}{1 - A\beta};$$

and if the amplifier with feedback is required to produce the same output as without feedback, or $E_o = E_o'$, the distortion is

$$D' = \frac{D}{1 - A\beta}. \tag{9-42}$$

If $|1 - A\beta| > 1$, the distortion with negative feedback is less than was present in the original amplifier, the amount of reduction depending on the magnitude of the feedback factor.

A comparison of Eqs. 9-39 and 9-42 shows that the distortion is reduced in just the same amount as the gain. This seems to indicate no advantage for negative feedback, but the difficulty is more apparent than real. Amplitude distortion occurs when large signal voltages are applied to the dynamic characteristic. In an ordinary amplifier such swings are usually available only at the grid of the last tube, and consequently nearly all amplitude distortion originates in the final stage of an amplifier. If the distortion can be eliminated there by feedback, additional gain can be added in small signal amplifiers ahead of the last tube, and the required gain obtained with a very real reduction in distortion.

Noise or hum components introduced by the amplifier inside the feedback loop are also reduced by the factor $1/(1 - A\beta)$. Suppose that a source of hum N_o exists inside the feedback loop in an amplifier at such a point that a gain of A_1 exists ahead of it and a gain of A_2 after it, where the total gain is $A_1A_2 = A$, as in Fig. 9-17. This

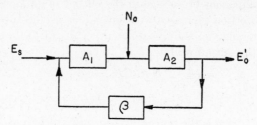

Fig. 9-17.   Effect of feedback on noise N_o introduced into an amplifier.

hum might, for example, be introduced by induced voltages from leads or filaments carrying alternating current of power-supply frequency.   The output with feedback then is

$$E_o' = A_2(N_o + A_1\beta E_o' + A_1E_s)$$

and

$$E_o' = \frac{A_2N_o}{1 - A\beta} + \frac{A}{1 - A\beta}E_s. \tag{9-43}$$

The second term on the right can be recognized as the desired output signal.   Since the hum or noise in the output would be A_2N_o without feedback, the first term on the right shows this output noise reduced by the factor $|1 - A\beta|$.

Obviously, as the gain is reduced by negative feedback, the input signal E_s must be increased to maintain the same output.   Rewriting Eq. 9-39 gives

$$\frac{A'}{A} = \frac{1}{1 - A\beta},$$

and for equal output

$$E_o = AE_s = E_o' = A'E_s',$$

so that for equal output voltages

$$E_s' = E_s(1 - A\beta). \tag{9-44}$$

Equation 9-44 shows that for negative feedback the signal input must be increased to maintain the same output.

Some of the above relations may be illustrated by an example.

Example. A certain amplifier has a gain **A** of 70 at an angle of 0°, distortion of 10 per cent, and normal input of 1.0 v rms. Find the effects of inverse feedback with a value of $\beta = -0.1$. The feedback factor $A\beta$ is then -7.0.

The gain is reduced to:

$$A' = \frac{A}{1 - A\beta} = \frac{70}{1 + 7} = 8.75.$$

Reduction in distortion to:

$$D' = \frac{D}{1 - A\beta} = \frac{0.10}{1 + 7} = 0.0125 = 1.25\%.$$

New input voltage:

$$E_s' = E_s(1 - A\beta) = 1.0(1 + 7) = 8.0 \text{ v.}$$

Output voltage without feedback:

$$E_o = AE_s = 70 \times 1.0 = 70.0 \text{ v.}$$

Output voltage with feedback, using E_s':

$$E_o' = A'E_s' = 8.75 \times 8.0 = 70.0 \text{ v.}$$

The actual grid voltage is

$$E_g' = E_s' + \beta E_o'$$
$$= 8.0 - 0.10 \times 70.0 = 1.0 \text{ v.}$$

The preceding example shows that although input-signal requirements are radically changed with feedback, the amplifier inside the feedback loop is operating under conditions identical with those existing before the feedback was added—that is, 1.0 v E_g was required to drive the amplifier to 70.0 v output without feedback. With feedback, E_g' is still 1.0 v for the same output; and although the input E_s' supplied is 8.0 v, 7.0 v is returned out of phase through the feedback loop to reduce E_g' to the original 1.0 v.

If the input E_s with feedback had remained at 1.0 v, the output would have been

$$1.0 \times 8.75 = 8.75 \text{ v.}$$

The reduction in output power, expressed in decibels, would then have been

$$\text{db} = 20 \log \frac{8.75}{70} = -20 \times 0.903 = -18.06.$$

The feedback has reduced the amplifier output by 18.06 db, or it is said that there has been 18.06 db of feedback applied to the amplifier.

9-9. Inverse-Feedback Circuits

Any network which will introduce into the grid circuit, in proper phase, a fraction of the output voltage can be used for inverse feedback. However, convenience and simplicity have dictated the use of two basic circuits, with modifications to fit various needs. These basic arrangements are known as *current-feedback* and *voltage-feedback* circuits.

In *current* feedback the voltage fed back to the input is proportional to the output *current*. In *voltage* feedback the voltage fed back is proportional to the output *voltage*. These two circuits achieve somewhat different results.

In current feedback the amplifier tends to maintain constant output current and therefore the output current is somewhat independent of changes in output load impedance. This is exactly the situation which occurs in the current-source equivalent circuit of Fig. 9-18(a), if r_p is made *large* and thereby draws a negligible portion of the constant current from the current source. It is therefore apparent that current feedback appears to raise the internal resistance of an amplifier.

For voltage feedback, the amplifier tends to maintain constant output voltage so that the load current varies if the output load impedance changes. Again with reference to Fig. 9-18(b), this would be the situation if r_p were made *small* and practically the entire current, $g_m E_g$, passed through it, giving a constant voltage across the load of value $g_m E_g r_p$. Thus it can be seen that voltage feedback appears to lower the internal impedance of an amplifier.

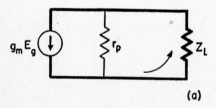

(a)

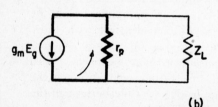

(b)

Fig. 9-18. Equivalent circuits for (a) current feedback, (b) voltage feedback.

Current feedback may be obtained in any circuit in which the drop across an impedance through which load current flows (other than the load itself) is fed back to the grid circuit in proper phase. A simple form of current feedback is shown at (a), Fig. 9-19. The

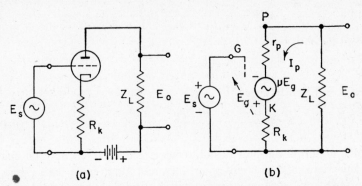

Fig. 9-19.   The basic current-feedback circuit and its series equivalent.

voltage which is fed back into the grid circuit is the I_pR_k drop appearing across R_k. Writing an expression for the cathode-to-grid voltage rise gives

$$E_g = E_s - I_pR_k \quad \text{and} \quad I_p = -\frac{E_o}{Z_L},$$

so that

$$E_g = E_s + \frac{R_k}{Z_L} E_o. \tag{9-45}$$

By reference to Eq. 9-37, which states that for a feedback amplifier

$$E_g' = E_s + \beta E_o',$$

it can be readily seen that for the current-feedback amplifier of Fig. 9-19

$$\beta = \frac{R_k}{Z_L}. \tag{9-46}$$

The current in the plate circuit is

$$I_p = \frac{\mu E_g}{r_p + R_k + Z_L} = \frac{\mu(E_s - I_pR_k)}{r_p + R_k + Z_L},$$

Since $E_o = -I_pZ_L$, the gain A' may be obtained as

$$A' = \frac{E_o}{E_s} = \frac{-\mu Z_L}{r_p(1 + g_mR_k) + R_k + Z_L}. \tag{9-47}$$

This equation shows that the tube, with current feedback added, appears to have a plate resistance which is greater than rated by a factor $(1 + g_m R_k)$, as was predicted above for current feedback.

Equation 9-47 may be changed in form to

$$A' = \frac{-\mu(Z_L/R_k)}{r_p(1/R_k + g_m) + 1 + Z_L/R_k};$$

and if $g_m \gg 1/R_k$,

$$A' = \frac{-\mu}{\mu\beta + \beta + 1}.$$

If μ is sufficiently large,

$$A' = -\frac{1}{\beta} = -\frac{Z_L}{R_k} \qquad (9\text{-}48)$$

which confirms the previous statement that the gain may be made independent of all circuit constants and tube coefficients, except the feedback-determining impedances. By the use of stable wire-wound resistors for R_k and Z_L, amplifiers of precision approaching that of the finest instruments can be engineered and built.

Another form of circuit giving current feedback is shown in Fig. 9-20.

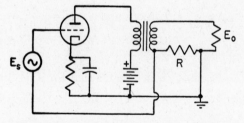

Fig. 9-20.   An example of current feedback.

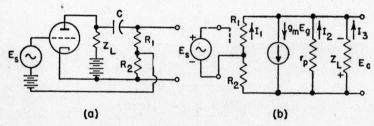

Fig. 9-21.   (a) A voltage-feedback circuit; (b) the current-source equivalent circuit for (a).

A circuit of the *voltage*-feedback type is shown in Fig. 9-21. This circuit produces voltage feedback because the voltage fed back, obtained by the drop across R_2, is proportional to the output voltage. The cathode-grid voltage rise is

$$E_g = E_s - I_1 R_2, \tag{9-49}$$

and

$$I_1 = \frac{-E_o}{R_1 + R_2},$$

$$E_g = E_s + \frac{R_2}{R_1 + R_2} E_o. \tag{9-50}$$

Comparison with Eq. 9-37 shows that for the voltage-feedback circuit

$$\beta = \frac{R_2}{R_1 + R_2},$$

with the feedback inverse, because $|1 - A\beta|$ may be shown greater than unity.

Writing a current equation for the current-source equivalent circuit of Fig. 9-21(b), under the assumption of $1/\omega C \ll (R_1 + R_2)$, gives

$$g_m E_g + E_o \left(\frac{1}{Z_L} + \frac{1}{r_p} + \frac{1}{R_1 + R_2} \right) = 0,$$

$$A' = \frac{E_o}{E_s} = \frac{-\mu Z_L}{r_p + Z_L \left(1 + \dfrac{r_p}{R_1 + R_2} + \mu\beta \right)}. \tag{9-51}$$

Further manipulation yields

$$A' = \frac{E_o}{E_s} = - \frac{\left[\dfrac{\mu}{1 + (r_p + \mu R_2)/(R_1 + R_2)} \right] Z_L}{\left[\dfrac{r_p}{1 + (r_p + \mu R_2)/(R_1 + R_2)} \right] + Z_L}. \tag{9-52}$$

If the factors in parentheses are considered as equivalent μ and r_p of the tube with voltage feedback, it can be seen that both are reduced by the same factor. This implies that g_m is unchanged. With reference to the circuit of Fig. 9-21(b), this means that the output current $g_m E_g$ is unchanged by the feedback; but since r_p has been decreased, the load voltage E_o will be reduced. If r_p can be made small with respect to Z_L, effects of variation of the load on the gain and output voltage can be minimized, and the feedback has the expected stabilizing effect. The reduction of r_p by addition of voltage feedback is in line with a previous prediction of this section.

It can be seen that the cathode follower is a form of voltage-feedback amplifier, since the voltage fed back and the load voltage are identical. Since the voltage fed back is E_o and the output is $I_p R_k$,

$$I_p = \frac{E_o}{R_k}; \quad\text{then}\quad E_g = E_s - \frac{R_k}{R_k} E_o,$$

and $\beta = -1$. This value of β gives to the cathode-follower circuit a very high stability.

Occasionally both voltage and current feedback may be combined in the same circuit. The value of β then becomes the sum of the values of β for each type of feedback. This combination has an advantage in permitting control of the internal impedance of the amplifier, the current feedback raising the impedance and the voltage feedback lowering the impedance.

Feedback may be applied across more than one amplifier stage. In such an application it is necessary to consider that for circuits of the grid input-plate output type there is an inherent 180° phase shift, or A is minus for one stage. For two stages the phase shift is 360°. Thus, to maintain $|1 - A\beta| > 1$ requires that the feedback voltage be introduced into the circuit properly. It has been seen that for voltage feedback, this β voltage is of such phase in single- or odd-stage amplifiers that it may be introduced into the grid circuit, but it is found for amplifiers of an even number of stages that the feedback voltage can most conveniently be introduced into the cathode circuit. These principles are illustrated in

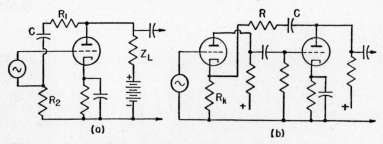

Fig. 9-22. Voltage feedback: (a) across an odd number of stages and (b) across an even number of stages.

Fig. 9-22. Some current feedback is also introduced into the first stage by this latter circuit.

Feedback from the secondary of an output transformer to the tube grid circuit may also be employed, the proper sign of $A\beta$ then being assured by choice of polarity of the transformer windings. The latter circuit has the advantage that frequency distortion introduced by the transformer may be reduced.

9-10. Stability of Inverse-Feedback Circuits

Since A and β are, in general, complex quantities and also frequency functions, it is impractical to predict that, because $|1 - A\beta| > 1$ at some midrange frequency, it will hold the same relation at all other frequencies. In other words, although an amplifier may be stable over a certain range of frequencies, for some other frequency range $|1 - A\beta|$ may be less than unity, or $A\beta$ may even be equal to $1 + j0$. It is apparent that for the first case the feedback will be positive and the amplifier regenerative, and the amplifier will oscillate under the second condition. Regeneration and oscillation are not desired and lead to instability, a condition which must be investigated.

Consider a plot of $A\beta\underline{/\theta°} = a + jb$ (θ includes the phase reversal of the tubes) in the complex plane for all frequencies, both positive and negative, from 0 to ∞. Nyquist (Ref. 8) has shown that such a plot is a closed curve. A critical condition exists where

$$|1 - A\beta| = 1$$

or

$$(1 - a)^2 + b^2 = 1.$$

This equation can be recognized as defining a circle of unit radius, with center at the point $1, j0$. If the $A\beta$ vector terminates inside this circle, obviously

$$|1 - A\beta| < 1 \qquad (9\text{-}53)$$

and the amplifier is regenerative, or the feedback is positive. If the $A\beta$ vector terminates outside this circle,

$$|1 - A\beta| > 1 \qquad (9\text{-}54)$$

and the amplifier is degenerative.

If the $A\beta$ vector terminates at $1, j0$, it is apparent from previous discussion that the amplifier will oscillate. Nyquist has shown that, in fact, if the $A\beta$ curve *encloses* the $1, j0$ point, the amplifier will oscillate. It is therefore obvious that one way to maintain stability and prevent oscillation is to ensure that $|A\beta|$ is less than unity when the angle θ equals zero, or when the feedback voltage appears in phase with the input voltage.

An $A\beta$ plot for a resistance-coupled grid input-plate output amplifier may be constructed from Figs. 9-6 and 9-7, with the diagram of Fig. 9-23(a) resulting. It is apparent that such an amplifier is stable at all frequencies. Frequency is found to increase in clockwise direction, with all midrange values plotted at the point on the negative real axis, since the gain in that range has an angle of 180°. The curve has been plotted under the assumption that any capacitance in the β circuit, used to block out d-c voltages, is infinite.

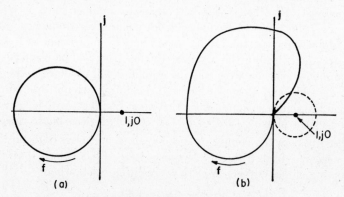

Fig. 9-23. Graphical presentation of the Nyquist criterion for stability in feedback amplifiers.

Figure 9-23(b) is that of a transformer-coupled amplifier in which the feedback voltage is taken from the secondary of the transformer. It can be seen that although the 1,j0 point is not encircled, the $A\beta$ vector terminates inside the unit circle at very high frequencies, indicating some regeneration. Further reduction in the gain at those frequencies, by design alterations, would probably be advisable to ensure stable performance.

In general, oscillation will not occur if the phase shift of the voltage fed back never differs as much as 180° from its midrange value, or if the absolute value of $A\beta$ becomes less than unity when θ reaches 360°. It is usually possible to design the amplifier so that at least the latter condition is met.

9-11. The Cathode-Bias R-C Circuit

The possibility of eliminating grid-bias batteries or other external sources and obtaining the bias voltage from the plate-supply source has been mentioned and such circuits have been indicated in the diagrams.   The advantages of such a practice are obvious.   However, if a resistor R_k is simply inserted in the common cathode lead of an amplifier with plate load Z_L, negative current feedback is set up and the gain reduced.   This reduction of gain may be undesirable and can be eliminated if R_k is paralleled or by-passed by a capacitor of reactance very small with respect to R_k at all frequencies of interest.   This condition being met, the d-c and a-c components may be assumed to divide, as in Fig. 9-24, with the alternating currents flowing through C_k and the direct current flowing through R_k.

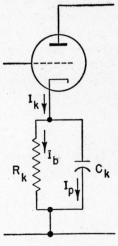

Fig. 9-24.   The cathode-bias R-C circuit.

If X_{c_k} is made not only small with respect to R_k, but actually of negligible value compared with other circuit impedances, the a-c voltage developed across the capacitor reactance may be considered negligible and the C_k-R_k combination completely eliminated from the a-c equivalent circuit.   No complications in analysis will then arise through such a method of obtaining grid bias.

The d-c voltage across R_k is

$$E_{cc} = I_b R_k;$$

and if a certain value of E_{cc} is desired and I_b is known, then by Ohm's law

$$R_k = \frac{E_{cc}}{I_b}. \tag{9-55}$$

The capacitance required for C_k may be determined by the requirement that

$$X_{c_k} \ll R_k$$

at the lowest frequency of interest.   If the inequality is true at that frequency, it will be even more true at any higher frequency. The inequality will often be satisfactorily met if $X_{c_k} \lessgtr R_k/10$.

If the capacitance is not sufficiently large, an a-c voltage of magnitude appreciable with respect to the input signal will appear across the R_k-C_k combination with a polarity such as to cause negative feedback. Because of the feedback, the gain will be reduced; this reduction will occur at the lower frequencies of the band, because at higher frequencies the value of X_{c_k} may be sufficiently small. Consequently, the use of a capacitor of too small capacitance may result in the introduction of frequency distortion at the low-frequency end of a band. The required capacitor sizes vary with different tubes and frequencies, but for audio frequencies the sizes required will range from 1 to 50 μf. Since these are nearly always electrolytic capacitors, physical size is not a serious factor, but costs rather than low distortion are frequently allowed to determine the capacity used.

9-12. Phase-Inversion Amplifiers

In providing input for the push-pull type of amplifier which will be discussed in Chapter 10, two equal voltages in phase opposition are required. Formerly this was done by a transformer with center-tapped secondary, but poor frequency response and cost have made preferable the use of specially designed small-signal amplifiers for the purpose. These circuits are called *phase inverters*.

The ideal phase inverter would change a single grounded potential into two equal voltages, balanced to ground or reference potential,

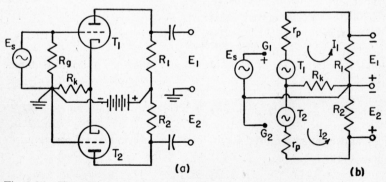

Fig. 9-25. The cathode-coupled phase inverter, and its equivalent circuit at (b). Polarities indicated are for positive voltage on G_1.

with 180° phase relation between the voltages.   Unfortunately, the circuits in current use do not always meet this ideal specification.

One widely used circuit is shown in Fig. 9-25.   Input E_s is supplied directly to the grid of tube T_1, with input to the second tube from the cathode circuit by the voltage drop across the cathode resistor R_k. The grid voltages are

$$E_{g1} = E_s - (I_1 - I_2)R_k, \qquad (9\text{-}56)$$

$$E_{g2} = -(I_1 - I_2)R_k. \qquad (9\text{-}57)$$

The two tubes are assumed identical in characteristics, but because of the indicated unbalance in grid voltages it is obvious that the output voltages E_1 and E_2 will not be equal in magnitude if R_1 and R_2 are equal.   It can be found that the output voltages will be in the ratio

$$\frac{E_1}{E_2} = \frac{[r_p + R_2 + (\mu + 1)R_k]R_1}{(\mu + 1)R_kR_2},$$

so that for equal output voltages the load resistors must conform to the relation

$$R_2 = \frac{R_1[(\mu + 1)R_k + r_p]}{(\mu + 1)R_k - R_1} = \frac{R_1\left(\dfrac{r_p}{\mu + 1} + R_k\right)}{R_k - \dfrac{R_1}{\mu + 1}}. \qquad (9\text{-}58)$$

This relation indicates that for R_2 to maintain a positive value, the values of μ or R_k must be large. As ordinarily employed with $R_1 = R_2$, unbalanced output voltages are to be expected.

A second and frequently employed form of phase inverter is the *paraphase* circuit of Fig. 9-26(a).   With the ordinary design of this inverter, $R_1 + R_2 = R_3$, and the tubes are assumed identical.   Essentially, tube T_1 is an ordinary amplifier, but a portion of its output is selected and again amplified, with the consequent introduction of an additional 180°

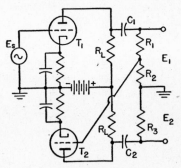

Fig. 9-26.   The paraphase inverter circuit.

phase shift and production of the desired out-of-phase voltages.   The ratio of resistors R_1 and R_2 is adjusted so that if A_2 is the gain of tube T_2, then

$$\frac{R_2}{R_1 + R_2} = \frac{1}{A_2},$$

with the consequent assurance that voltage E_2 will equal E_1 as

$$E_1 \times \frac{R_2}{R_1 + R_2} \times A_2 = E_2. \qquad (9\text{-}59)$$

The proper operation of the circuit is predicated upon a knowledge of the gain A_2 and constancy of this gain throughout the life of the tube. Some unbalance of the two voltages must be expected if the gain changes in tube T_2.

If capacitors C_1 and C_2 introduce any phase shift at low frequencies, the 180° phase relationship will be disturbed, since voltage E_1 passes through only one such capacitor-resistor combination, whereas voltage E_2 must pass through two such circuits.

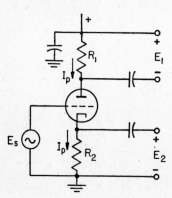

Fig. 9-27. The split-load form of phase inverter.

An inverter of the phase-splitting type is shown in Fig. 9-27. This is simply a cathode-output amplifier with an additional plate-circuit load. Since it uses only one tube, any changes in tube characteristics affect both voltage outputs in a similar manner; thus, if resistors R_1 and R_2 are equal, the output voltages will be balanced. Because of the cathode-output arrangement, the gain will be small; this is the major disadvantage of this circuit in comparison with those previously considered.

From the circuit equations

$$E_g = E_s - I_p R_2 \qquad (9\text{-}60)$$

and

$$\mu E_g = I_p(r_p + R_1 + R_2), \qquad (9\text{-}61)$$

the gain may be written as

$$A = \frac{\left(\dfrac{\mu}{\mu + 2}\right) R_1}{\dfrac{r_p}{\mu + 2} + R_1} \qquad (9\text{-}62)$$

if $R_1 = R_2$.

It is apparent that degenerative feedback with $\beta = 0.5$ is present, and consequently the distortion is low and gain stability is high. These characteristics make the circuit quite suitable for inclusion in instruments requiring stable calibration.

PROBLEMS

9-1. For the circuit of Fig. 9-28, find the gain at frequencies of 40, 80, 300, 500, 1000, and 5000 c, if $\mu = 30$, $g_m = 1200$ μmhos, $R_1 = 50,000$, and $R_2 = 50,000$ for values of

   (a) $C = 0.001$ μf.
   (b) $C = 0.01$ μf.
   (c) $C = 1$ μf.

Plot the three gain-vs-frequency curves on the same axes on a sheet of semilog paper.

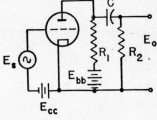

Fig. 9-28.

9-2. In Fig. 9-29 the tubes are two 6J5's (see Appendix). Plot a gain-frequency curve on semilogarithmic paper for frequencies from 30 to 7000 cycles, neglecting tube capacitances.

9-3. In Fig. 9-30, plot gain-vs-frequency and phase-shift-vs-frequency curves over the audible range, 40 to 10,000 c, if $\mu = 35$ and $r_p = 50,000$ ohms. Explain the unusual form of the low-frequency region.

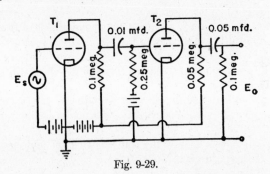

Fig. 9-29.

9-4. A tube with μ of 70, $r_p = 66,000$ ohms and a tube with $\mu = 22$ and $r_p = 10,000$ ohms are available. Design an amplifier to provide an output of 1.0 v across a load of 50,000 ohms at 1000 c, if the input is from a microphone giving an output of -63 db across a 100,000 ohm resistance (0.001-w reference). The amplifier gain is to be flat within 10 per cent of the 1000-c value from 100 to 7000 c.

9-5. For the circuit of Fig. 9-31, if $g_m = 1500$ μmhos, $r_p = 30,000$ ohms, $C_{in} = 50$ $\mu\mu$f, and $C_{pk} = 12$ $\mu\mu$f, find the low and high frequencies at which the gain is 70.7 per cent of the midband gain.

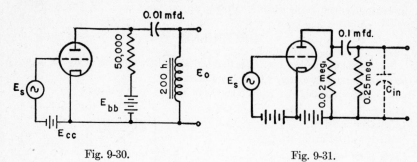

Fig. 9-30.   Fig. 9-31.

9-6. A transformer is used between two tubes having $\mu = 20$, $r_p = 15,000$ ohms. The ratio is $1 : 3$, primary to secondary, and the following values apply:

$$R_c \gg \omega L_p \qquad\qquad L_s = 540 \text{ h}$$
$$L_p = 60 \text{ h} \qquad\qquad C_2 = 150 \text{ }\mu\mu\text{f}$$
$$R_2 = 7000 \text{ ohms}$$

The leakage inductances may be considered 0.5 per cent each.

(a) Plot a gain-vs-frequency curve from 30 to 15,000 c.

(b) Determine the effect on the low-frequency response of a change in ratio to permit L_1 to be increased to 150 h.

9-7. Perform the necessary operations to obtain Eq. 9-13 from Eq. 9-5.

9-8. Derive Eq. 9-17, starting from Eq. 9-8.

9-9. (a) The circuit of Fig. 9-31 is to be used with a 6J5 tube. If E_{bb} = 300 v and $I_b = 0.0055$ amp, select a value of R_k which will replace the battery for $E_{cc} = -6$ v.

(b) Determine a satisfactory value for C_k if the lowest frequency of interest is to be 30 c, draw the equivalent circuit, and calculate the 30-c gain with C_k connected.

(c) With C_k removed, redraw the equivalent circuit and again find the gain without feedback formulas.

(d) What is the value of β for (c)?

9-10. (a) Determine the value of R_k needed for 10 per cent current feedback, to be added to the circuit of Fig. 9-30, with a tube having $\mu = 70$ and $g_m = 1500$ μmhos, at a frequency of 1000 c.

(b) Find the gain and phase shift with R_k added, at frequencies of 100 and 1000 c, and compare with gain and phase shift at the same frequencies without R_k. Bias voltage is to be assumed adjusted to compensate for the presence of R_k, so that the tube operates at the same Q point for both (a) and (b).

(c) Draw a Nyquist diagram for the circuit of Fig. 9-30.

9-11. Connect a 1-megohm resistor across the 200-h inductor of Fig. 9-30. Add voltage feedback to the amplifier by connecting the return of the E_s generator to a tap on the 1-megohm resistor at a point such as to provide 16 per cent feedback.

(a) At what point on the 1-megohm resistor should the tap be placed?

(b) If the tube has $\mu = 70$ and $r_p = 66,000$, plot curves of gain and phase shift over the range of 20 to 20,000 c.

(c) Draw a Nyquist diagram for this amplifier.

9-12. (a) Draw the current-source equivalent circuit for Fig. 9-32.

(b) Neglecting the reactance of C, develop an expression for gain in terms of tube and circuit constants.

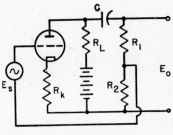

Fig. 9-32.

(c) Show that β is equal to the sum of the current- and voltage-feedback values for β.

9-13. For the circuit of Fig. 9-32, with $R_k = 0$, $R_1 = 100,000$ ohms, $R_2 = 12,000$ ohms, $C = $ large, and $R_L = 50,000$ ohms, plot gain as a function of μ for the range $\mu = 7$ to 20. Let $r_p = 100\ \mu$. This shows the effect of variation of tube parameters on amplifier gain with feedback.

9-14. In the circuit of Fig. 9-32, let $R_1 = 100$K, $R_2 = 15$K, and $R_k = R_L = 50$K ohms. Find the gain and the percentage of feedback, if the Q point is maintained by batteries, such that $\mu = 70$, $r_p = 66$K.

9-15. A generator of 1 v, 10^7 ohms internal resistance, and 1000 c is to connect to a load of 200 ohms resistance.

(a) Find the voltage across and the power available in the load.

(b) The same generator is used as a source with a cathode follower using a 6J5 tube under typical operating conditions. Find the value of R_k required for matching the 200-ohm load (load coupled to R_k through a large capacitor).

(c) Find the gain under (b) and the voltage across and a-c power in the load. Compare with (a).

9-16. In Fig. 9-20, $R = 1$ ohm, R_L across which E_o is measured is 8 ohms, the transformer has a ratio of 25 : 1, stepdown to the load. The tube has $\mu = 4$ and $r_p = 2000$ ohms. The tube appears to have a load $= a^2 R_L$.

(a) Find the value of E_s required to give an output of 0.1 w in the load.

(b) How many decibels feedback are being used in the circuit?

9-17. Write an expression for the gain of the circuit of Fig. 9-33, assuming identical tubes.

9-18. For the circuit of Fig. 9-31, the tube has a μ of 16, g_m of 1600 μmhos, with $C_{pk} = 2.8$ $\mu\mu$f, $C_{\text{in}} = 33$ $\mu\mu$f, and wiring capacity of 12 $\mu\mu$f.

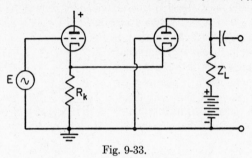

Fig. 9-33.

(a) Find the mid-frequency gain and the values of f_1 and f_2.

(b) Between what two frequencies is the amplifier gain less than 1 db down from the midband value?

(c) Between what two frequencies is the phase shift of the stage more or less than $180° \pm 15°$?

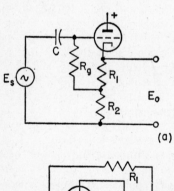

(a)

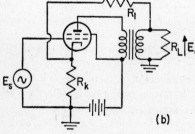

(b)

Fig. 9-34.

9-19. Write an expression for the gain of the circuit of Fig. 9-34(a).

9-20. Find an expression for the input impedance of the circuit of Fig. 9-34(a), excluding the usual tube capacitances, and neglecting C.

9-21. In Fig. 9-33, $Z_L = 50,000$ ohms, $R_k = 1000$ ohms, and the tubes are type 6J5. If $E_s = 1$ v rms, find the output voltage across Z_L.

9-22. In Fig. 9-34(a), $R_g = 10$ megohms, $R_1 = 2000$ ohms, $R_2 = 25,000$ ohms. The tube is a 6J5.

(a) Find the input impedance seen by the generator E_s. Neglect the reactances of C and the tube capacitances.

(b) If $E_s = 0.2$ v rms, find the output voltage.

9-23. The grounded-grid amplifier of Fig. 9-12 uses a tube having $\mu = 10$, $r_p = 9000$ ohms. If E_s is 1 v rms, find:

(a) The output voltage across Z_L when $Z_L = 50,000$ ohms resistance. The source resistance, R_1, is 200 ohms.

(b) The power gain in decibels.

(c) The impedance seen by the signal source.

9-24. A signal source has a resistance of 1000 ohms and a voltage of 0.01 v, 10^6 c. Using a grounded-grid amplifier with $\mu = 20$, $r_p = 7000$ ohms, design a circuit whose input resistance will be 1000 ohms. What output voltage will be obtained?

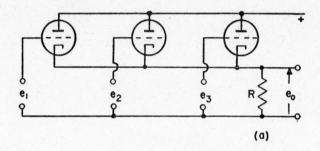

(a)

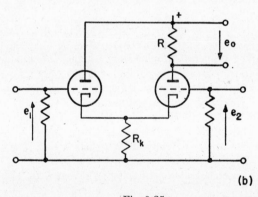

(b)

Fig. 9-35.

9-25. Referring to Fig. 9-21(a), if $Z_L = 25,000$ ohms, $\mu = 22$, $g_m = 2000$ μmhos, and considering all capacitive reactances negligible, select values for R_1 and R_2 such that the gain of the stage will be 5.

9-26. In Fig. 9-20 the output voltage is measured across a load of 16 ohms. If the transformer has a ratio of 22 : 1 stepdown to the load, and presents a load to the tube equal to $16a^2$, and if $\mu = 16$, $r_p = 5000$, find the value needed for resistor R if 6 db of negative feedback are to be introduced into the amplifier.

9-27. In Fig. 9-34(b), the tube is a tetrode with $g_m = 5200$ μmhos and $r_p = 33,000$ ohms operated at 350 v E_b, 250 v E_{c2}, -18 v E_{c1}, and I_b of 60 ma. The load R_L is 10 ohms, and the transformer has a ratio of 20 : 1 stepdown to the load. The load presented to the tube by the transformer is $a^2 R_L$.

(a) Specify values for R_1 and R_k if the tube is to operate at the above Q point and have 12 db of negative feedback.

(b) If E_s is 1.0 v rms, find the output power supplied to R_L.

9-28. Show that the output voltage e_o of Fig. 9-35(a) is proportional to the sum of the three independent input voltages. Assume the tubes identical, and employ the current-source equivalent circuit.

9-29. Show that the circuit of Fig. 9-35(b) can be employed for computing the difference of the input voltages e_1 and e_2, and that the output voltage can be written in the form

$$e_o = \frac{\mu R(e_1 - e_2)}{R + 2r_p}$$

if R_k is large.

REFERENCES

1. Ryder, J. D., *Networks, Lines, and Fields*, Prentice-Hall, Inc., New York, 1949.
2. Chaffee, W. L., *Theory of Thermionic Vacuum Tubes*, McGraw-Hill Book Company, Inc., New York, 1933.
3. Terman, F. E., "Universal Amplification Charts," *Electronics*, **10**, 34, June (1937).
4. ———, "The Inverted Vacuum Tube, a Voltage-Reducing Power Amplifier," *Proc. IRE*, **16**, 447 (1928).
5. Ramo, S., *Introduction to Microwaves*, McGraw-Hill Book Company, Inc., New York, 1945.
6. Black, H. S., "Stabilized Feedback Amplifiers," *Elec. Eng.*, **53**, 114 (1934).
7. Richter, W., "Cathode-Follower Circuits," *Electronics*, **16**, 112, November (1943).
8. Nyquist, H., "Regeneration Theory," *Bell System Tech. J.*, **11**, 126, July (1932).
9. Everitt, W. L., *Communication Engineering*, 2d ed., McGraw-Hill Book Company, Inc., New York, 1937.
10. Jones, M. C., "Grounded-Grid Radio-Frequency Voltage Amplifiers," *Proc. IRE*, **32**, 423 (1944).

11. Bode, H. W., *Network Analysis and Feedback Amplifier Design*, D. Van Nostrand Company, Inc., New York, 1945.

12. Valley, G. E., Jr., and Wallman, H., *Vacuum Tube Amplifiers*, McGraw-Hill Book Company, Inc., New York, 1948.

13. Learned, V., "Corrective Networks for Feedback Circuits," *Proc. IRE*, **32**, 403 (1944).

14. Dubridge, L. A., "The Amplification of Small Direct Currents," *Phys. Rev.*, **37**, 392 (1931).

15. Schlesinger, K., "Cathode-Follower Circuits," *Proc. IRE*, **33**, 843 (1945).

16. Wallman, H., MacNee, A. A., and Gadsden, C. P., "A Low-Noise Amplifier," *Proc. IRE*, **36**, 700 (1948).

17. Cohen, R. M., "Use of New Low-Noise Twin Triode in Television Tuners," *RCA Rev.*, **12** March (1951).

18. McProud, C. G., and Wildermuth, R. T., "Phase-Inverter Circuits," *Electronics*, **13**, 47, December (1940).

CHAPTER 10

LARGE-SIGNAL AMPLIFIERS—
CLASS A AND B

The dynamic grid characteristic of any vacuum tube is necessarily nonlinear. As the amplitude of the input signal is raised, the resultant amplitude distortion also increases. Analysis by use of the linear equivalent circuit is then inadequate, and the graphical method developed in Chapter 7 must be employed.

Such large input-signal amplifiers are usually the final, or output, tubes of an amplifier. A designer is primarily concerned here with fidelity or low distortion, power output, and power efficiency. Factors which affect such performance are the choice of proper load resistance, the operating d-c voltages, and the necessary input signal magnitude. Methods of making these choices and of determining the amplifier performance directly from the graphical load line are developed here.

10-1. The Load Line

Methods of drawing the a-c load line were developed in Section 7-9, for a circuit of the type of Fig. 10-1. With $R_1 = R_2 = 5000$ ohms, and $E_{cc} = -15$ v, the load lines appear as in Fig. 10-2. The Q point

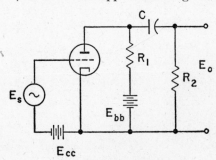

Fig. 10-1. Simple amplifier circuit.

272

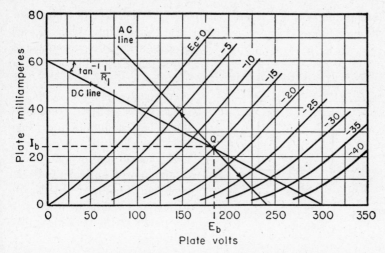

Fig. 10-2. Construction of the d-c and a-c load lines.

indicates $I_b = 23$ ma, $E_b = 182$ v. Thus the average power lost in the tube is

$$P_d = 182 \times 0.023 = 4.18 \text{ w.}$$

Since it was shown that

$$E_o = \frac{E_{\max} - E_{\min}}{2\sqrt{2}}, \qquad I_p = \frac{I_{\max} - I_{\min}}{2\sqrt{2}},$$

the fundamental a-c power output can be obtained in the resistive load as

$$P_o = \frac{(E_{\max} - E_{\min})(I_{\max} - I_{\min})}{8}. \qquad (10\text{-}1)$$

For the tube and circuit in question this will be

$$P_o = \frac{(212 - 148)(0.038 - 0.011)}{8} = 0.22 \text{ w.}$$

The total power supplied to the *circuit* is $E_{bb}I_b$, or

$$P_{\text{in}} = 300 \times 0.023 = 6.9 \text{ w.}$$

10-2. The Idealized Class A Power Amplifier

Any voltage amplifier furnishes some power in the output circuit as an incidental to voltage amplification, but when the tube and circuit are so chosen that power output is the major function, the combination is called a *power amplifier*. When specified and operated as a *Class A* power amplifier the usual implications of such operation are present: moderate power output, low distortion, and low power efficiency.

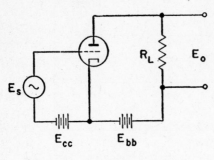

Fig. 10-3.   General load circuit for an amplifier.

Although no tube supplying large power output is entirely linear, an assumption of linearity or *idealized* operation is useful for an approximate study of the power amplifier. Under such an idealized condition, with the circuits of Fig. 10-3 the power in the load R_L can be found as

$$P_o = I_L{}^2 R_L = \left(g_m E_g \frac{r_p}{r_p + R_L}\right)^2 R_L$$

$$= \mu g_m E_g{}^2 \frac{R_L/r_p}{(1 + R_L/r_p)^2}. \tag{10-2}$$

The power output per input volt squared may be written

$$\frac{P}{E_g{}^2} = \mu g_m \frac{R_L/r_p}{(1 + R_L/r_p)^2}. \tag{10-3}$$

This ratio is defined as the *power sensitivity* of an amplifier and is considered a figure of merit of amplifier performance. Thus the power sensitivity is proportional to the product μg_m of the tube used. Since values of μ for pentodes and beam tubes are much greater than usual values for triodes, the power sensitivity of pentodes and beam tetrodes is greater than that of triodes in general.

To obtain large power output at nominal and safe voltages requires that R_L be of moderate value (a few thousand ohms or less). Fidelity requires that the choice of the desirable output load be based on allowable amplitude distortion, rather than on the condition of greatest power output.

The amplitude distortion of a triode is found to decrease with increase in load, so that a load somewhat above the value giving greatest power output is desirable. The power output may or may not decrease simultaneously with load increase, since by Eq. 10-2 the power output is also a function of E_g, and this may be increased as R_L is raised.   That is, as the load is increased the load line becomes flatter, giving a longer operating region without entering the region of nonlinearity.   The bias may then be made somewhat more negative to place the Q point in the center of the selected operating region, and the grid drive may be correspondingly increased without driving the grid positive.

Although selection of a desirable load for a triode is thus somewhat arbitrary because no definite statement of maximum permissible distortion can be made, values of load usually specified for triode operation are of the order of two to four times the value of r_p.   Frequently the statement is made that R_L should equal $2r_p$ as a desirable triode load, but this is true only in theory.

Considerations which enter into the selection of a load for a tetrode or pentode are also based on allowable and tolerable distortion. With the pentode some one value of load will produce minimum distortion, and deviations of load in either direction will increase the distortion.   Methods of determination of the desirable load are discussed in Section 10-8.

10-3. Output Circuits

In the circuit of Fig. 10-1, the direct plate current I_b flows through the resistor R_1, with a resultant power loss which serves no useful

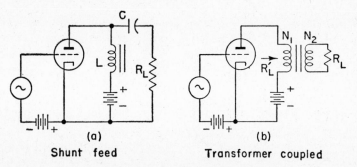

<table>
<tr><td>(a)</td><td>(b)</td></tr>
<tr><td>Shunt feed</td><td>Transformer coupled</td></tr>
</table>

Fig. 10-4.   Power-amplifier output circuits.

purpose.   It may be difficult to remove the heat, and the power efficiency of the circuit is reduced.

In cases where R_L is of a magnitude desirable as a load for the power-amplifier tube, a *shunt-feed* circuit, as shown at (a), Fig. 10-4, may be used.   Resistor R_1 is replaced with an inductor whose reactance will be very high with respect to R_L. The capacitor C, used to block the direct plate current out of R_L, should have a reactance small with respect to R_L at all frequencies of interest. If these conditions are met, the direct current flows entirely in L with negligible power loss, and the alternating current uses the path through R_L. The average voltage on the anode of the tube is raised to nearly the value of E_{bb}, and this higher voltage permits greater power output. The d-c load line will be drawn, starting at E_{bb}, with a slope determined by the d-c resistance of the inductor, and will usually be nearly vertical. After determination of the Q point, the a-c load line can be drawn with a slope fixed by the value of the a-c load R_L.

A second circuit which also eliminates the d-c power loss in the load is shown at (b), Fig. 10-4. In this circuit the load R_L is transformer-coupled to the plate circuit. The circuit is used wherever the value of R_L is too large or too small to serve as a load on the tube directly. The performance of the circuit of (b) is possible through the impedance-transforming properties of the transformer. The ideal or lossless transformer voltages and currents are related as

$$\frac{V_1}{V_2} = \frac{I_2}{I_1} = \frac{N_1}{N_2} = a,$$

from which $V_1 = V_2 I_2 / I_1$. The impedance seen from the primary side is then

$$Z_1 = \frac{V_1}{I_1} = \frac{V_2 I_2}{I_1^2} \times \frac{I_2}{I_2} = a^2 \frac{V_2}{I_2}.$$

It should be noted that V_2/I_2 is the secondary circuit impedance, and that

$$Z_1 = a^2 Z_2, \tag{10-4}$$

giving the impedance seen on the primary side due to any secondary load Z_2.

For instance, a loudspeaker with a voice coil impedance of 10 ohms may have to be used as a load on a tube whose desirable load has been determined as 5000 ohms. The transformer should have a turns ratio given by

$$a = \frac{N_1}{N_2} = \sqrt{\frac{5000}{10}} = 22.4.$$

The primary of the transformer would appear as a 5000-ohm load to the a-c current component, and would usually present low resistance to the d-c component of plate current. For graphic analysis of the circuit, the d-c load line would be nearly vertical from E_{bb}, the a-c load line through the Q point having a slope fixed by a^2R_L.

The ideal transformer concept is convenient in determining the power capabilities of a tube and circuit, and actual transformers can be built to approach the ideal transformer characteristics. Occasionally, however, poorly designed transformers must be used, which depart appreciably from the ideal-transformer assumptions. The actual impedance seen looking into the primary circuit can then be obtained from the equivalent circuit of the transformer in Fig. 10-5.

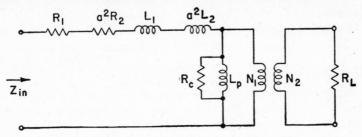

Fig. 10-5. Equivalent circuit of an output transformer.

The leakage inductance should be small to provide good high-frequency response, since the voltage drop across the leakage reactances is in series with the primary voltage. The iron should be of good quality and the winding resistances small to avoid power losses in the transformer. Well-designed transformers for the audio range may be found with efficiencies ranging up to 85 and 90 per cent, but many models can be found with efficiencies of 50 per cent or less.

It should also be pointed out that when a poor transformer is employed the tube load is no longer purely resistive. The load line then becomes an ellipse (see Section 10-13) and operation may be carried into the nonlinear tube characteristics, causing increased distortion.

Occasionally the circuit of (b), Fig. 10-4, is modified by placement of the output transformer in the cathode lead, the circuit then becoming a cathode-output amplifier, or cathode follower. It may be remembered that in such a circuit the tube appears to shunt the cathode load with a resistance of value $r_p/(\mu + 1)$. Thus the transformer primary is shunted with such a resistance, usually low in value, and the deleterious effects of low primary inductance are effectively swamped out. Such a circuit improves the frequency response of a poor output transformer but cannot, of course, improve the power efficiency of a low-efficiency unit.

The main disadvantages in the use of the cathode-output circuit are the loss in gain in the circuit and the large input-signal voltage which is required to obtain normal power output. This signal voltage will exceed somewhat in magnitude the expected output voltage across the transformer primary, and may be so large as to introduce nonlinear distortion through inability of the preceding stage to supply the required voltage and remain on a linear portion of its characteristic.

Desirable load values and expected power output remain the same for the cathode-output amplifier as for the plate-output circuit.

10-4. Plate-Circuit Efficiency

An amplifier is essentially a frequency converter, changing d-c power into a-c power. The power efficiency of the conversion process is called the *plate-circuit efficiency* and is defined as

$$\eta_p = \frac{\text{a-c power output}}{\text{d-c power input}} \times 100\%, \qquad (10\text{-}5)$$

where average power is ordinarily understood. Equation 10-5 then becomes

$$\eta_p = \frac{I_p^2 R_L}{E_{bb} I_b} \times 100\%, \qquad (10\text{-}6)$$

where R_L is the equivalent resistance through which the alternating plate current I_p flows. The output may also be defined as $P_o = E_p I_p \cos \phi$, where $\cos \phi$ is the cosine of the angle of the load-circuit impedance. The power supplied by the plate-voltage source must furnish the a-c output, the d-c power losses in the load resistor, or the primary of the output transformer, and the power P_p representative of the energy required to accelerate the electrons, which is converted to heat at the anode. If the tube is a tetrode or pentode, the additional loss as heat at the screen grid must be included as part of the input.

Again under idealized linear conditions, the plate characteristics of a triode with a series load resistor might be represented by straight lines as at (a), Fig. 10-6. Since distortion will be zero owing to the

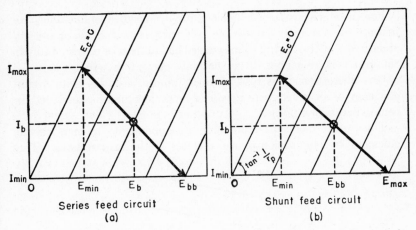

Series feed circuit
(a)

Shunt feed circuit
(b)

Fig. 10-6.   Idealized plate-circuit characteristics for development of theoretical maximum plate-circuit efficiency of triodes.

idealized linear characteristics, the grid may drive the plate current to zero at the negative maximum, so that the Q point may be placed on the load line halfway between I_{max} and zero current.   This implies that

$$\frac{I_{max} - I_{min}}{2} = \sqrt{2}\, I_p = I_m = I_b. \tag{10-7}$$

Equation 10-6 can then be written, for the theoretical idealized triode,

$$\text{theoretical } \eta_p = \frac{50 I_m^2 R_L}{E_{bb} I_m}\, \% = \frac{50 I_m R_L}{E_{bb}}\, \%. \tag{10-8}$$

It can be seen from the figure that

$$I_m R_L = E_{bb} - E_b,$$

so that

$$\text{theoretical } \eta_p = 50 \left(1 - \frac{E_b}{E_{bb}}\right) \%. \tag{10-9}$$

The efficiency will be a maximum when the second term in the parentheses is a minimum.   The value of E_b will decrease with increasing R_L.   For a very high value of R_L, the load line will be nearly horizontal and E_b will approach the value $E_{bb}/2$.   The maximum theoretical plate-circuit efficiency for an amplifier *with a series load resistor* can then be seen as 25 per cent.

For the efficiency to reach this value, the load resistance must be infinite, an obviously impossible condition from the power output standpoint. Also, owing to the curved characteristics of actual tubes, the grid voltage cannot drive the plate current to zero without excessive distortion. Because of these limitations, the plate-circuit efficiency of series-fed resistance-load amplifiers rarely exceeds 10 per cent in actual practice.

The transformer-fed circuit offers an opportunity to increase the efficiency by elimination of the d-c loss in the load resistor. The

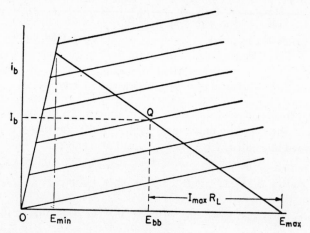

Fig. 10-7. Idealized plate characteristics for a transformer-fed pentode.

idealized characteristics with a load line for an effective a-c plate load of R_L ohms are drawn in (b), Fig. 10-6. The current relations of Eq. 10-7 hold, so that Eq. 10-8 can again be written

$$\text{theoretical } \eta_p = \frac{50 I_m R_L}{E_{bb}} \%. \tag{10-10}$$

For large R_L, the term $I_m R_L$ will approximate the value of E_{bb}, so that the maximum theoretical efficiency is 50 per cent for the *transformer-* or *choke-fed circuit*. Owing to the limitations discussed above, it rarely exceeds 25 per cent in practice.

Although the same theoretical maximum efficiency limits apply to any Class A amplifier, triode, tetrode, or pentode, Fig. 10-7 shows that for idealized pentode characteristics the value $I_m R_L$ may be larger for a given E_{bb} than is possible for the triode, since the value of the minimum anode voltage may be smaller. This condition results in a higher practical operating efficiency for pentodes or beam tetrodes than for triodes, even though the screen d-c losses must be charged against the pentodes.

10-5. Plate Dissipation

The plate efficiency of a shunt-fed amplifier may be written from Eq. 10-5 as

$$\eta_p = \frac{I_p^2 R_L}{I_p^2 R_L + P_p + I_b^2 R_L'}, \tag{10-11}$$

in which R_L is the apparent value of load resistance presented to alternating current in the plate circuit and R_L' is the d-c resistance of the load or output transformer primary through which I_b flows. The term P_p is the power lost in the tube, required to accelerate the electrons through the tube, and converted to heat upon impact of the electrons with the anode. The amount of power P_p dissipated by the anode is called the *anode loss*, or *plate dissipation*.

The power input to the plate circuit must be supplied by the d-c source, so that by the principle of conservation of energy the average power in the circuit will be distributed according to

$$\text{power input} = \text{a-c power output} + \text{losses},$$

or

$$E_{bb} I_b = I_p^2 R_L + \text{losses}. \tag{10-12}$$

Since

$$E_{bb} = E_b + I_b R_L',$$

$$\text{losses} = E_b I_b + I_b^2 R_L' - I_p^2 R_L.$$

The term $I_b^2 R_L'$ can be identified as the d-c loss in the load or coupling circuit. Since the remainder of the losses must occur in the tube, the plate loss is given by

$$\text{plate loss} = P_p = E_b I_b - I_p^2 R_L. \tag{10-13}$$

The input to the tube is $E_b I_b$, so that the loss in the tube is seen to be the average tube input minus the circuit a-c output. If at some instants there is no a-c grid signal, and consequently no a-c output, the entire input to the tube, $E_b I_b$, must be dissipated by the anode. Since designs must be based on the worst conditions to be encountered, the tube selected for a given service must be capable of radiating or dissipating the amount of power loss expected with no signal applied and without excessive temperature rise. As the a-c output increases, the plate loss decreases and the tube runs cooler.

The anode operating temperature is a critical limit in tube operation because to exceed it may result in liberation of gas from the metal tube parts and destruction of the high vacuum in the tube. Consequently, it is customary to state a value of maximum plate dissipation, in watts, as a rating of a tube to ensure that the anode operating temperature will be below the limiting value. This means that a vacuum tube is rated in terms of its allowable losses, not in terms of its possible output, as is customary for electric machinery. This is a very fundamental difference.

Equation 10-11 may be rearranged as

$$\text{a-c output} = I_p{}^2R_L = \frac{\eta_p \times \text{loss}}{1 - \eta_p}. \tag{10-14}$$

For a given *rated* plate loss, the output power possible from a tube of a given size is a function of the plate-circuit efficiency. Anything which may be done to increase the plate efficiency permits obtaining more power output from a given tube. Since initial and replacement costs of tubes are a major factor in operation of electronic equipment, any improvement in efficiency which allows a small tube to do the work of a larger and more expensive tube in providing a given output is economically worth while. The improvement in the economics of the situation goes far beyond the saving in cost of electric power input, although for high-power amplifiers the latter is also of importance. For instance, the 6L6 beam tetrode has a rated plate dissipation of 19 w, and at ordinary efficiencies in Class A operation, an output of 6.5 w. By use of special circuits for elimination of distortion, the same tube can be operated under Class AB conditions with an output of 23 w, solely owing to increased efficiency, the plate dissipation being within rated value in both cases.

10-6. Determination of Amplitude Distortion

The output voltage or current wave forms may be readily obtained by graphical means from the plate characteristics, and analyzed for harmonic components by conventional methods. However, the amplitude of various ordinates in the wave may be obtained directly from the load line, and the labor of plotting the output wave form can be avoided (Ref. 1).

A relation between plate current and signal voltage may be obtained by developing an equation for the dynamic grid characteristic of a tube. In the operating region, about a given E_b, I_b operating point, the dynamic curve can be expressed by a power series, derived as a Taylor's series, in terms of variations of voltage from the operating point. The following equation is of this type:

$$i_b = a_0 + a_1 e_g + a_2 e_g^2 + a_3 e_g^3 + a_4 e_g^4 + \cdots \qquad (10\text{-}15)$$

It can be seen that if only the first two terms on the right are used, the dynamic curve is approximated by a straight line; if the third term is added, the approximation is that of a straight line plus a parabola. Closer approximation to the curve is obtained by addition of the higher powers.

By reasoning that if $e_g = 0$, $i_b = I_b$, it is apparent that $a_0 = I_b$. Then applying to the grid of this tube a single voltage of the form

$$e_g = E_m \cos \omega t$$

leads to

$$i_b = I_b + a_1 E_m \cos \omega t + a_2 E_m^2 \cos^2 \omega t + a_3 E_m^3 \cos^3 \omega t \\ + a_4 E_m^4 \cos^4 \omega t + \cdots \qquad (10\text{-}16)$$

By use of trigonometric identities for multiple angles and by combining the resultant coefficients into a new set of constants, Eq. 10-16 may be written as

$$i_b = I_b + A_0 + A_1 \cos \omega t + A_2 \cos 2\omega t + A_3 \cos 3\omega t \\ + A_4 \cos 4\omega t + \cdots \qquad (10\text{-}17)$$

It may be reasoned that the higher-order harmonics will be small, and for triodes and pentodes all harmonics above the fourth may be dropped with negligible error. If the amplitudes of the various harmonics are to be determined, the five constants of Eq. 10-17 must be evaluated. This operation requires five equations, which may be written if the value of i_b is known for five instants in time.

The load line for the amplifier can be drawn on the tube characteristics, as in Fig. 10-8. With the indicated grid-signal amplitude, five values of current can be selected at five time instants spaced over both positive and negative half cycles. These are

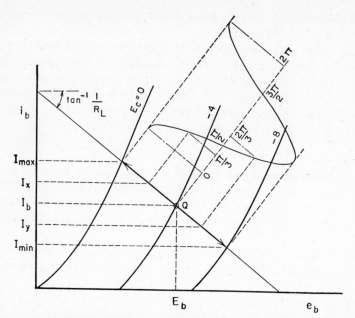

Fig. 10-8.   Calculation of distortion from the load line.

most easily chosen as $\omega t = 0$ with a current value I_{max} when the grid voltage is at the maximum value; $\omega t = 60°$ with a current value designated as I_x when the grid voltage is at half of the maximum value; $\omega t = 90°$ with current I_b when the grid voltage is at zero; $\omega t = 120°$ with a current designated as I_y when the grid voltage is at half of the negative maximum; and $\omega t = 180°$ with current I_{min} when the grid voltage is at the negative maximum.

Substitution of these values of time and current into Eq. 10-17 yields five equations:

$$\omega t = 0° \qquad I_{max} = I_b + A_0 + A_1 + A_2 + A_3 + A_4,$$

$$\omega t = 60° \qquad I_x = I_b + A_0 + \frac{A_1}{2} - \frac{A_2}{2} - A_3 - \frac{A_4}{2},$$

$$\omega t = 90° \qquad I_b = I_b + A_0 \qquad - A_2 \qquad + A_4, \qquad (10\text{-}18)$$

$$\omega t = 120° \qquad I_y = I_b + A_0 - \frac{A_1}{2} - \frac{A_2}{2} + A_3 - \frac{A_4}{2},$$

$$\omega t = 180° \qquad I_{min} = I_b + A_0 - A_1 + A_2 - A_3 + A_4.$$

Elimination among these five equations results in the following expressions for the amplitudes of the various components:

$$A_0 = \frac{1}{6}(I_{\max} + I_{\min}) + \frac{1}{3}(I_x + I_y) - I_b, \qquad (10\text{-}19)$$

$$A_1 = \frac{1}{3}(I_{\max} - I_{\min}) + \frac{1}{3}(I_x - I_y), \qquad (10\text{-}20)$$

$$A_2 = \frac{1}{4}(I_{\max} + I_{\min}) - \frac{1}{2}I_b, \qquad (10\text{-}21)$$

$$A_3 = \frac{1}{6}(I_{\max} - I_{\min}) - \frac{1}{3}(I_x - I_y), \qquad (10\text{-}22)$$

$$A_4 = \frac{1}{12}(I_{\max} + I_{\min}) - \frac{1}{3}(I_x + I_y) + \frac{1}{2}I_b. \qquad (10\text{-}23)$$

Once the amplitudes of the various harmonic components in the output wave of the tube have been obtained, it is possible to define percentage distortion due to a particular harmonic as the ratio of the harmonic amplitude to that of the fundamental times 100 per cent, or

$$D_2 = \frac{A_2}{A_1} \times 100\%, \qquad D_3 = \frac{A_3}{A_1} \times 100\%, \qquad D_4 = \frac{A_4}{A_1} \times 100\%.$$

The total harmonic distortion is then defined as the ratio of the effective value of all the harmonics to that of the fundamental, or

$$D = \frac{\sqrt{A_2{}^2 + A_3{}^2 + A_4{}^2 + \cdots}}{A_1} \times 100\%. \qquad (10\text{-}24)$$

In terms of the individual harmonic percentages, this may be written as

$$D = \sqrt{D_2{}^2 + D_3{}^2 + D_4{}^2 + \cdots}\,\%.$$

The power output into a resistance load for any harmonic is obviously given by $(A_n{}^2/2)R_L$, where A_n is the amplitude of the nth harmonic. The total a-c power output due to all frequencies is

$$\text{total power} = \frac{(A_1{}^2 + A_2{}^2 + A_3{}^2 + A_4{}^2 + \cdots)}{2}R_L. \qquad (10\text{-}25)$$

The harmonic distortion present in the output of a triode is predominantly due to the second harmonic; and if it is desired to neglect all higher harmonics as small, Eq. 10-17 may be written

$$i_b = I_b + C_0 + C_1 \cos \omega t + C_2 \cos 2\omega t. \qquad (10\text{-}26)$$

By use of a three-point voltage-current-time table, and by solution of the simultaneous equations, the values of the amplitude coefficients can then be obtained as

$$C_0 = \frac{1}{4} (I_{\max} + I_{\min}) - \frac{1}{2} I_b, \qquad (10\text{-}27)$$

$$C_1 = \frac{1}{2} (I_{\max} - I_{\min}), \qquad (10\text{-}28)$$

$$C_2 = \frac{1}{4} (I_{\max} + I_{\min}) - \frac{1}{2} I_b. \qquad (10\text{-}29)$$

These equations lead to some saving in time over the use of Eqs. 10-19 to 10-23 if it is known that harmonics of order higher than two are not important in the output. For tetrodes, pentodes, and beam tubes, the third harmonic is usually the most important, so that Eqs. 10-19 to 10-23 must be resorted to.

For harmonics of higher orders than the fourth, a schedule of time, grid-voltage, current points may be set up with sufficient points to provide the proper number of equations for solution for the harmonic amplitudes. For obtaining the amplitudes up to the nth harmonic, $(n + 1)$ points must be taken from the load line, preferably at equal grid-voltage increments.

10-7. Intermodulation Distortion

A sound wave is made up of a large number of sinusoidal harmonic components, so that rarely is the input to an amplifier tube a simple, single-frequency sinusoid. If the curvature of the dynamic characteristic is appreciable and two or more signal frequencies are simultaneously applied to the grid, an additional form of distortion, known as *intermodulation*, may result. This form of distortion produces additional frequencies in the output which are sums and differences of all the frequencies present. Harmonics introduced by amplitude distortion are generally harmonious with the original signal; but since the intermodulation products bear no definite relation to any input frequency, they are inharmonious. The output of intermodulation products, although generally small, is classed as noise which seemingly varies with the signal.

Assume that the dynamic characteristic can be expressed by the first three terms of Eq. 10-17, higher-order terms being neglected for simplicity; then

$$i_b = a_0 + a_1 e_g + a_2 e_g{}^2. \tag{10-30}$$

If an input consisting of two frequencies only, ω_1 and ω_2, is introduced into the grid circuit, so that

$$e_g = E_1 \sin \omega_1 t + E_2 \sin \omega_2 t,$$

then Eq. 10-30, with addition of $a_0 = I_b$ becomes

$$i_b = I_b + a_1(E_1 \sin \omega_1 t + E_2 \sin \omega_2 t)$$
$$+ a_2(E_1 \sin \omega_1 t + E_2 \sin \omega_2 t)^2. \tag{10-31}$$

After expansion and the introduction of trigonometric identities including

$$\sin \omega_1 t \sin \omega_2 t = \frac{1}{2}[\cos (\omega_1 - \omega_2)t - \cos (\omega_1 + \omega_2)t],$$

Eq. 10-31 may be written as

$$i_b = I_b + \frac{a_2}{2}(E_1{}^2 + E_2{}^2) + a_1 E_1 \sin \omega_1 t + a_1 E_2 \sin \omega_2 t$$

$$- \frac{a_2 E_1{}^2}{2} \cos 2\omega_1 t - \frac{a_2 E_2{}^2}{2} \cos 2\omega_2 t$$

$$+ a_2 E_1 E_2 \cos (\omega_1 - \omega_2)t - a_2 E_1 E_2 \cos (\omega_1 + \omega_2)t. \tag{10-32}$$

Not only are the usual second-harmonic-distortion frequencies present, but the new sum $(\omega_1 + \omega_2)$ and difference $(\omega_1 - \omega_2)$ frequencies are also in the output. If more frequencies are present in the input, additional sum-and-difference terms appear, but with the same coefficients as above, so that analysis on the basis of two sine waves is indicative of the general situation. Although these new frequencies may have small amplitude, they are quite noticeable as a background noise, or chatter, and add additional incentive to the design of amplifiers which are truly linear, or to the improvement of linearity with feedback.

10-8. The Plate Load for Maximum Power Output

The selection of a proper plate-load resistance for a vacuum tube, to provide maximum power output with minimum distortion, is an arbitrary problem. Although use of the condition $R_L = r_p$ will furnish the maximum possible power for a given value of signal, the amplitude distortion produced by this value of load will usually be greater than is considered allowable.   Higher values of load which permit use of greater driving voltages may raise the power output. Loads actually used lie in the range of two to four times the value of the plate resistance for triodes, and a small fraction of the plate

TABLE 6

RECOMMENDED LOAD VALUES FOR POWER AMPLIFIER TUBES*

Tube Type No.	μ	g_m	r_p	Recommended Load (ohms)	Power Output (w)	Per Cent Distortion
45 triode............	3.5	2,050	1,700	4,600	2.0	5
2A3 triode...........	4.2	5,250	800	2,500	3.5	5
6L6 tetrode..........		6,000	22,500	2,500	6.5	10
6V6 tetrode..........		3,750	77,000	8,500	5.5	12
6F6 pentode.........		2,550	78,000	7,000	4.8	9
6AQ5 tetrode........		4,100	52,000	5,000	4.5	8
50L6 tetrode.........		9,500	30,000	3,000	4.3	10
6AR5 pentode.......		2,300	68,000	7,600	3.4	11
6AG7 pentode.......		11,000	130,000	10,000	3.0	7
6AK6 pentode.......		2,300	200,000	10,000	1.1	10

* Data from *RCA Tube Handbook.*

resistance for tetrodes and pentodes.   The load actually is chosen to obtain a value of power output near maximum with a satisfactorily small value of distortion.   Typical values specified for various typical tube types are given in Table 6.

The selection of a maximum allowable percentage distortion is arbitrary, dependent as it is on subjective factors.   Many listeners tolerate 20 per cent distortion, whereas a highly trained musician may detect distortion of only a few per cent.   A value of 5 per cent distortion has been arbitrarily agreed upon as permissible, although many amplifiers are available which hold the distortion to only 1 or 2 per cent at rated output.

As a first step in graphical determination of the power-output capabilities of a tube, the rated dissipation line should be drawn on the plate characteristics.   This line will be a hyperbola drawn for

$$E_b I_b = k,$$

(10-33)

where k is the rated plate dissipation of the tube in watts. Since only shunt-fed or transformer-coupled output circuits with R_L' negligible are used when high power output is desired, $E_b = E_{bb}$, and the hyperbola will then be drawn for $E_{bb}I_b = k$. Any position chosen for the Q point must lie on or below this hyperbola, to avoid exceeding the plate dissipation rating. For maximum output, E_{bb} will be chosen as the highest-rated plate supply voltage, and the Q point will be fixed on the hyperbola at the value of I_b given by Eq. 10-33.

The second step is to decide on a value for I_{min}, selected so that operation will not carry far into the nonlinear characteristics at extremely low values of plate current. Draw a horizontal line on the characteristics at the value of I_{min} chosen to serve as a limit of operation on the load line. For Class A operation, the other extreme of the load line will end on the $E_c = 0$ line.

Through the Q point draw a load line with a slope such that it intersects the I_{min} line at a value of E_c equal to twice the E_c value at the Q point. Calculate the slope and value of load resistance for this line. Then draw a set of load lines through the Q point for a range of load values from one-half to twice the load for the first line. For each load line, calculate the power output and nonlinear distortion, using a value of grid swing sufficient to drive the grid either to $E_c = 0$ at the positive peak or to I_{min} at the negative peak, as determined by which of these limits is reached first.

If the tube is a pentode or beam tetrode, the first load line drawn through the Q point will probably pass through the $E_c = 0$ line near the knee of the curve. Draw the additional load lines to intersect the $E_c = 0$ curve at both sides of the knee. Then compute the power output for each line, and calculate the second-harmonic, third-harmonic, and total-harmonic percentages.

The construction of the rated dissipation and load lines is illustrated in Fig. 10-9 for both triode and pentode tubes. After calculating power output and harmonic percentages, plot them against load resistance, as is done in Fig. 10-10, for the load lines of Fig. 10-9. An arbitrary choice can then be made of a load giving nearly maximum power output with a desirable value of distortion. For the triode of (a), Figs. 10-9 and 10-10, this most desirable load might be 2500 ohms, although higher loads will reduce the distortion further. The choice of load can be seen as arbitrary.

The choice of load for the beam tetrode is more definite owing

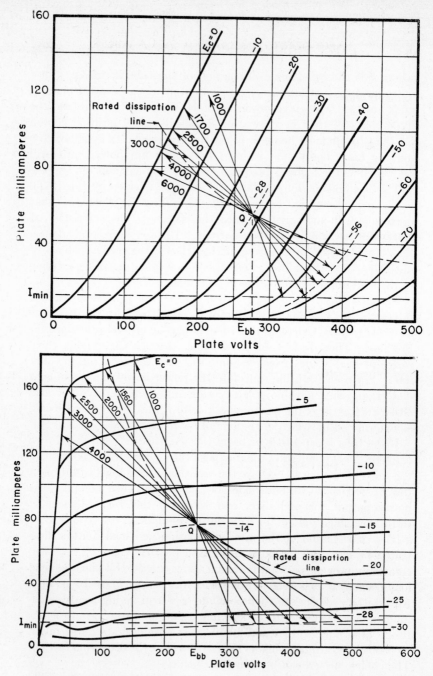

Fig. 10-9. Graphical determination of maximum power output: (a) triode, rated plate dissipation = 15 w, E_{bb} max = 275 v, μ = 5.8, r_p = 1700 ohms; (b) beam tetrode, rated plate dissipation = 19 w, E_{bb} max = 250 v, g_m = 6000 μmhos, r_p = 22,500 ohms.

TABLE 7

DETERMINATION OF OPTIMUM LOADS—DATA AND CALCULATIONS OBTAINED
FOR FIG. 10-9

(A) TRIODE OF FIG. 10-9(a)

R_L (ohms)	I_{max} (ma)	I_{min} (ma)	$I_{max} - I_{min}$	A_1	I_p (ma)	Power Output (w)	A_2	$\%D_2$
1000	118	12	106	53	38	1.40	5.0	9.5
1500	115	12	103	51	36	2.02	4.3	8.2
1700	112	12	100	50	35	2.12	3.5	7.0
2000	106	15	91	45	32	2.06	2.8	6.1
2500	99	19	80	40	28	2.00	2.0	5.0
3000	93	22	71	35	25	1.90	1.2	3.5
4000	87	27	60	30	21	1.80	1.0	1.7
6000	78	34	44	22	16	1.46	0.5	1.1

(B) BEAM TETRODE OF FIG. 10-9(b)

R_L (ohms)	I_{max} (ma)	I_{min} (ma)	I_x (ma)	I_y (ma)	A_1	I_p (ma)	Power Output (w)	$\%D_2$	$\%D_3$	$\%D_4$	Total Distortion (%)
1000	177	14	122	38	82	58	3.39	11.9	1.0	0.7	12.0
1560	171	14	120	38	80	56	4.95	10.4	1.4	0.8	10.5
2000	166	15	119	38	77	54	5.90	9.5	2.1	0.9	9.7
2500	158	15	118	39	74	52	6.85	7.2	3.4	0.1	8.0
3000	146	16	116	39	69	49	7.20	3.6	5.5	-0.4	6.6
4000	130	17	113	40	62	44	7.65	-1.9	8.9	-1.0	9.1
5000	120	18	109	41	57	40	8.00	-6.5	10.0	-0.9	12.0

to the minimum present in the total-harmonics curve. A desirable load for this tube might be 3200 ohms. The minimum in the total-harmonics curve is due to the fact that the second harmonic goes to zero magnitude at some load. For loads above this value, it reverses in phase. The value of zero second harmonic can be seen from Eq. 10-21 to occur at the point at which

$$\frac{1}{2}(I_{max} + I_{min}) = I_b.$$

This value will occur for a load line drawn in such a way that the Q point falls at a value of current exactly halfway between I_{max} and I_{min}.

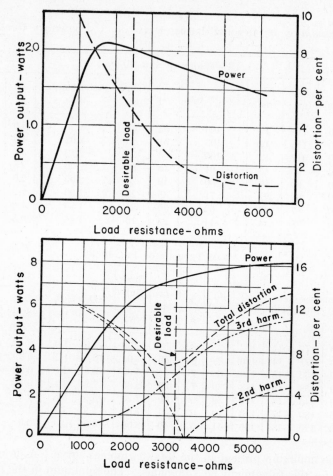

Fig. 10-10. (a) Power output and distortion vs load resistance
for the triode of Fig. 10-9(a); (b) power output and distortion
vs load resistance for the tetrode of Fig. 10-9(b).

The manner in which data may be tabulated and arranged for
the calculations incident to obtaining the curves of Fig. 10-10 is
shown in Table 7.

10-9. The Push-Pull Class A Amplifier

Higher power output can be obtained from a given tube by moving
the Q point to a higher bias and plate-voltage position on the rated

dissipation line. This operation permits a larger grid signal and a larger output voltage, but the output distortion may rise seriously. By the use of two tubes in a *push-pull* connection, the distortion can be largely canceled and a power output obtained which is greater than twice that of one tube operating under normal conditions.

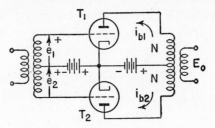

Fig. 10-11. Circuit for analysis of a push-pull amplifier.

The circuit of a push-pull amplifier using triodes is shown in Fig. 10-11. For pentodes and beam tetrodes, no changes other than a screen supply connection and by-pass capacitor are needed. On the assumption that the two tubes are identical in characteristics, the current in the anode circuit of either tube may be written as in Section 10-6:

$$i_b = I_b + a_1 e_g + a_2 e_g{}^2 + a_3 e_g{}^3 + a_4 e_g{}^4 + \cdots \cdot \quad (10\text{-}34)$$

By reference to Fig. 10-11, if a voltage

$$e_g = E_1 \sin \omega t$$

is applied to the primary of the input transformer, the individual a-c cathode-grid voltages are

$$e_1 = E_2 \sin \omega t \qquad\qquad\qquad (10\text{-}35)$$

$$e_2 = E_2 \sin (\omega t + \pi), \qquad\qquad (10\text{-}36)$$

because the transformer secondary constitutes one continuous winding, tapped at the center for the grid-bias return. The plate current of tube T_1 can then be written as

$$i_{b1} = I_{b1} + a_1 E_2 \sin \omega t + a_2 E_2{}^2 \sin^2 \omega t$$
$$+ a_3 E_2{}^3 \sin^3 \omega t + \cdots \quad (10\text{-}37)$$

and that of tube T_2 as

$$i_{b2} = I_{b2} + a_1 E_2 \sin (\omega t + \pi) + a_2 E_2{}^2 \sin^2 (\omega t + \pi)$$
$$+ a_3 E_2{}^3 \sin^3 (\omega t + \pi) + \cdots \cdot \quad (10\text{-}38)$$

By use of trigonometric relations, Eqs. 10-37 and 10-38 can be reduced to equations in terms of multiple angles or harmonics, as

$$i_{b1} = I_{b1} + B_0 + B_1 \sin \omega t - B_2 \cos 2\omega t + B_3 \sin 3\omega t \\ - B_4 \cos 4\omega t + \cdots \\ i_{b2} = I_{b2} + B_0 + B_1 \sin (\omega t + \pi) - B_2 \cos 2(\omega t + \pi) \\ + B_3 \sin 3(\omega t + \pi) - B_4 \cos 4(\omega t + \pi) + \cdots \tag{10-39}$$

By trigonometry,

$$\sin (\omega t + \pi) = -\sin \omega t \\ \text{and} \qquad \cos 2(\omega t + \pi) = \cos 2\omega t, \tag{10-40}$$

and similarly for all even and odd harmonics, so that the current in T_2 becomes

$$i_{b2} = I_{b2} + B_0 - B_1 \sin \omega t - B_2 \cos 2\omega t - B_3 \sin 3\omega t \\ - B_4 \cos 4\omega t \cdots .$$

Since the primary of the plate output transformer is one continuous winding tapped at the center for the B supply connection, and the currents have directions as shown, the magnetomotive force acting on the transformer core is proportional to

$$N_p i = N i_{b1} - N i_{b2}, \tag{10-41}$$

where all leakage is neglected.

If the transformer is considered ideal, the net primary ampere turns must be equal to the secondary ampere turns so that

$$N_2 i_2 = N(i_{b1} - i_{b2}) \\ = N(2B_1 \sin \omega t + 2B_3 \sin 3\omega t + 2B_5 \sin 5\omega t + \cdots). \tag{10-42}$$

For a resistive secondary load R_2, the secondary voltage will be

$$e_s = i_2 R_2 \\ = R_2 \frac{N}{N_2} (2B_1 \sin \omega t + 2B_3 \sin 3\omega t + 2B_5 \sin 5\omega t + \cdots). \tag{10-43}$$

Since all odd and even harmonics will have algebraic signs determined by Eq. 10-40, Eq. 10-43 shows that the push-pull connection with matched tubes will eliminate from the output all even-harmonic terms and will retain odd-harmonic terms.

Triodes with predominantly even-harmonic distortion may be operated at loads and Q points giving increased output, and the resulting even-harmonic distortion is canceled in the push-pull output circuit. By this means, outputs up to three times that possible from one tube may be obtained from two tubes, with distortion much less than from one tube operating normally. Tetrodes and pentodes, since the predominant distortion is odd-harmonic, are apparently not benefited so greatly by the connection. However, it may be noted in Fig. 10-10(b) that increased power output can be obtained from pentodes by operation at loads higher than normal, with the penalty largely in increasing second-harmonic distortion. Push-pull operation cancels the second harmonic present, leaving only the odd-harmonic distortion, and a higher load may then be used, giving higher output.

An added advantage for push-pull operation of power amplifiers is the elimination of d-c magnetomotive forces and fluxes in the output-transformer core, as is shown by Eq. 10-42, with consequent elimination of core saturation and distortion due to a nonlinear magnetization curve of the transformer iron. Since the direct plate currents I_b cancel, any power-supply ripple remaining in the filtered output of the plate supply rectifier will be in phase and will also cancel. This effect permits the use of a power supply for the power amplifier with less filtering than is required for the preceding voltage amplifiers.

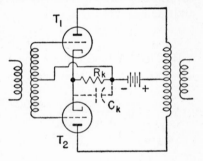

If a cathode resistor is substituted for the grid battery of Fig. 10-11 as a bias source, the cathode circuit will appear as in Fig. 10-12. If the cathode resistor R_k

Fig. 10-12. Grid bias by means of a cathode resistor, for a push-pull amplifier.

is used without a by-pass capacitor C_k, the current flowing through R_k will be

$$i_k = i_{b1} + i_{b2}.$$

Then the voltage drop across R_k, with matched tubes, is

$$e_k = R_k(2I_b + 2B_0 - 2B_2 \cos 2\omega t - 2B_4 \cos 4\omega t \cdot \cdot \cdot). \quad (10\text{-}44)$$

Here the odd harmonics cancel and the even harmonics remain. The phase relations will be such that the even-harmonic voltage components will produce negative-current feedback and thus will bring about further reduction in the even-harmonic distortion by degeneration. If the tubes are not matched and odd harmonics are present in the plate currents, the odd harmonics will have a phase relation such that positive feedback is introduced and odd-harmonic distortion will be increased. If there is a chance that unmatched tubes may be used, it is usually advisable to employ a cathode by-pass capacitor C_k. This recommendation is particularly applicable for beam tubes and pentodes, where odd-harmonic distortion is prevalent and where tube mismatches are common owing to variations in screen voltage and in construction.

With the cathode by-pass capacitor in place, the bias voltage is

$$E_{cc} = 2I_bR_k + 2B_0R_k. \tag{10-45}$$

This voltage will be a constant, ensuring a fixed Q point, only if B_0 (which from Section 10-6 can be shown equal to B_2, the second-harmonic distortion amplitude) is small at large values of grid swing E_g. This condition is usually met satisfactorily in Class A operation, and the bias voltage then can be taken as

$$E_{cc} = 2I_bR_k.$$

In Class AB operation, the second-harmonic distortion in each tube becomes very high owing to operation into the curved portion

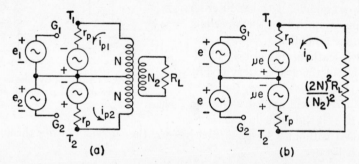

Fig. 10-13.   Derivation of the equivalent circuit for the push-pull amplifier.

of the tube characteristics, and the power output must be limited if cathode bias is used, on account of shift of the Q point. Fixed bias permits the full output to be obtained. In Class B operation, the first term on the right of Eq. 10-45 becomes small owing to operation with I_b near cutoff, and the second term may be quite large, so that cathode bias cannot be used and fixed bias becomes a necessity.

By drawing the equivalent circuit for each tube separately, as shown in Fig. 10-13(a), the equivalent circuit for the push-pull amplifier may be arrived at, as drawn in (b), with careful attention to polarities. At (a) both tubes are drawn independently but are operating on the half cycle in which the grid of T_1 is positive. It can be seen that the equivalent generators are effectively in series; and since the loads are equal, the plate circuit partakes of the form of a balanced bridge. Consequently, the line connecting the center point of the generators and the load will carry no alternating current and can be eliminated, resulting in the circuit at (b). This effect shows that the two tubes work in series into the common load and that the value of the plate-to-plate load is equal to the total reflected secondary load R_L',

$$R_L' = \left(\frac{2N}{N_2}\right)^2 R_L = 4\left(\frac{N}{N_2}\right)^2 R_L, \qquad (10\text{-}46)$$

where N is the number of turns in one-half of the primary winding and ideal-transformer conditions are assumed.

The equivalent circuit is based on assumptions of constancy of μ, g_m, and r_p, and can be used for operation in the linear regions of the tube characteristics only. Nonlinear operation in Class AB and Class B amplifiers cannot be analyzed from this equivalent circuit. Under the linearity assumptions, the equivalent circuit leads to

$$I_p = \frac{\mu E_g}{r_p + 2(N/N_2)^2 R_L} \qquad (10\text{-}47)$$

and the power output then is

$$P = \left[\frac{\mu E_g}{r_p + 2(N/N_2)^2 R_L}\right]^2 \left(\frac{2N}{N_2}\right)^2 R_L.$$

This expression may be rearranged to form

$$P = \left[\frac{\mu E_g}{r_p/2 + (N/N_2)^2 R_L}\right]^2 \left(\frac{N}{N_2}\right)^2 R_L = I_{eq}^2 R_{eq}, \qquad (10\text{-}48)$$

where I_{eq} is the current in an *equivalent* or *composite* tube, and R_{eq} is its load, or

$$I_{eq} = \frac{\mu E_g}{r_p/2 + (N/N_2)^2 R_L} \qquad (10\text{-}49)$$

and

$$R_{eq} = \left(\frac{N}{N_2}\right)^2 R_L. \qquad (10\text{-}50)$$

The composite tube performs in a manner equivalent to the complete push-pull amplifier, and according to Eq. 10-48 appears to be operating in a simple circuit as in Fig. 10-14.

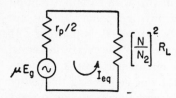

Fig. 10-14.   Equivalent circuit of the composite tube representing the push-pull amplifier.

The reduction of even harmonic distortion by the push-pull connection permits increased grid driving voltage and increased power output. In the case of a single tube this increased drive would generate excessive distortion, which the push-pull circuit cancels.   Thus the power output of a push-pull amplifier can be greater than twice that of a single tube.

10-10. Graphical Analysis of the Push-Pull Amplifier

A method of graphical analysis of push-pull amplifiers has been developed by Thompson (Ref. 3). Since the plate currents are subtractive in the output transformer, plate characteristics for the tubes used may be assembled with the characteristics of one tube inverted, the currents plotted as negative values, and the plate voltages plotted as increasing from right to left.   The sets of curves are adjusted along the zero-current axis, so that the normal operating tube voltages E_b are at the same point.   The construction is illustrated in Fig. 10-15 for two Type 2A3 triode tubes operating at $E_b = 250$ v and $E_{cc} = -45$.   The plate-voltage scales have been adjusted so that the 250-v line is at the same point for both tubes. Although the method is described for triodes, it is equally applicable to pentodes or tetrodes.

Since the effects of the tube currents in the output are subtractive and tube B has its current plotted as negative, *composite* or *effective* characteristics may be plotted point by point for the two tubes by adding algebraically the plate currents for grid-bias voltages at equal voltages each side of the operating-bias value—that is, the curve on tube A for x volts less than the operating bias is added to the curve of tube B for x volts more than the operating bias.   The composite curves are shown in Fig. 10-15 as solid lines; and if the

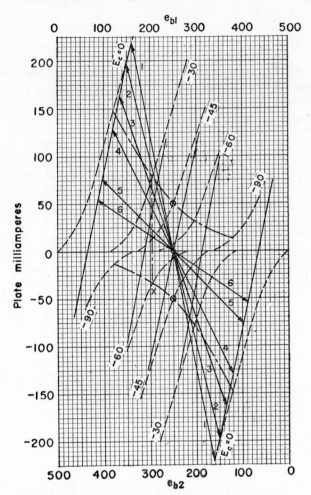

Fig. 10-15.   Determination of power output from a triode push-pull amplifier.   Tubes type 2A3, $E_b = 250$ v,
$E_{cc} = -45$ v, $\mu = 4.2$, $r_p = 800$ ohms.   Per tube loads
designated by number: (1) 400 ohms, (2) 500 ohms, (3)
700 ohms, (4) 1000 ohms, (5) 2000 ohms, (6) 3000 ohms.

two tubes are identical, the composite curves will be almost entirely
linear.

The linearity of the composite characteristics gives very low
values of distortion for matched tubes, as is indicated by the theory

of the previous section. The remaining distortion will be third- and higher-order odd harmonics, and for triodes can be small in magnitude. Consideration of Fig. 10-15 shows that for Class A operation, the slope of the solid-line composite characteristics yields a value of resistance of 400 ohms, or $r_p/2$. Thus the composite characteristics may be considered as those of the composite or equivalent tube whose circuit was developed in the preceding section.

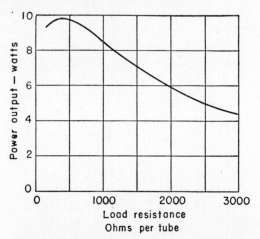

Fig. 10-16. Variation of power output with load resistance per tube for push-pull 2A3 tubes, Class A. Plate resistance of the composite tube = 400 ohms.

Comparison of Eq. 10-46 with Eq. 10-50 shows that the plate-to-plate load of the push-pull stage is four times the load of the composite tube. Variation of output for the load lines drawn in Fig. 10-15 is plotted in Fig. 10-16, which shows a maximum of almost 10 watts obtainable from the two tubes under the assumed grid input conditions, at a load of 400 ohms on the composite tube or a load of 1600 ohms plate-to-plate. To prevent extreme plate current swings and excessive odd-harmonic distortion which would not be canceled in the circuit it is desirable to choose a slightly higher load value. The load values for which the lines are plotted in Fig. 10-15 are equivalent tube loads, or are plate-to-plate values divided by 4.

In the case of pentodes and tetrodes, maximum permissible distortion must also be considered in the selection of a desirable load, since pentodes and tetrodes generate predominantly odd harmonics which are not eliminated with the push-pull connection. The desirable load is then a compromise between power and distortion.

If the tubes are not perfectly matched, the composite characteristics will not be linear, and considerable distortion may be present. Analysis for distortion can be carried out with the methods previously discussed.

Fundamental plate currents and power output may be computed from the load lines in a manner similar to that used for single-tube operation. For instance, with a 500-ohm equivalent-tube load, the peak plate current can be seen to be 197 ma. The power output then is

$$P = \left(\frac{0.197}{\sqrt{2}}\right)^2 \times 500 = 9.70 \text{ w.}$$

The path of operation for each tube is indicated by the dot-dash lines in Fig. 10-15, for the 1000-ohm load line. Intersections of the load line and the composite characteristics are projected upward and downward to the actual pair of tube characteristics which generated the composite line. For example, the intersection of the load line and the +15-v composite characteristic means that the individual tubes are operating at the anode voltages fixed by the intersection and on the −30-v E_c curve for the upper tube and the −60-v curve for the lower set of characteristics, fixing point x.

The curvature of the paths of operation indicates that the individual tube operation is nonlinear, but this action is balanced between the tubes. Peak tube swings are seen to be 147 ma at +45 signal volts and minimum currents are 14 ma at −45 signal volts for the 1000-ohm line. Power input and efficiency can be computed from the data given by these paths of operation.

10-11. The Class AB Push-Pull Amplifier

The previous section has shown that increased power output is possible from given tubes through raising the bias, thereby lengthening the positive-swing side of the load line, with even-harmonic distortion generated on the negative-swing side of the load line being eliminated by the push-pull connection. By increasing the Q-point bias and raising the plate voltage, keeping the plate dissipation at the rated value, the operating point and the lower set of characteristics of Fig. 10-15 may be moved further to the right. Thus, the load line for a given load value becomes longer, or larger output voltage swings may be obtained, with further increases in power output resulting. The tubes may be cut off for portions of the negative half-cycle swing, but the accompanying even-harmonic distortion is eliminated by the push-pull connection. Such operation is described as *Class AB*. The graphical methods of performance analysis developed in the preceding section still apply for quantitative results. In Class AB operation at 290 v E_b, -60 v E_{cc}, the two tubes of Fig. 10-15 are capable of over 15 w output with small distortion.

The subscript 1 is used, as in Class AB_1, to indicate that the grids are not driven positive and that no grid current flows at any time in the cycle. For even greater output, larger input voltages are used; and the subscript 2, as in Class AB_2, indicates that the grids are driven positive and that grid current flows at the peaks of the cycles. The amplifier driving the input circuit then is called upon to furnish power to the grid circuits during the positive peaks and must have good regulation, or low impedance, if distortion of the grid-voltage wave form is not to occur. The impedance reflected into the grid circuit from the driver tube can be reduced if a low-r_p tube, capable of voltage output much greater than needed, is used with a step-down ratio transformer to the grids of the Class AB_2 tubes. The transformer reduces the voltage by the turns ratio, but it reduces the reflected impedance by the square of the turns ratio.

Class AB_1 and AB_2 amplifiers are capable of large power outputs from small tubes, but with increased harmonic distortion. Also, since the tubes are operating in the nonlinear regions of their characteristics for a considerable portion of their cycles, the d-c component B_o is large and varies with the signal voltage. Such amplifiers require plate-voltage sources of large instantaneous-current capacity and good voltage regulation if distortion is not to be introduced owing to variation of E_{bb}.

10-12. The Class B Push-Pull Amplifier

If the bias voltage be increased to approximate cutoff, the effective Q point for the composite curves will remain at the same position, but the slopes of the composite curves will decrease, and in the limiting case in Fig. 10-17 will fall upon the plate characteristics.

This change will require a bias voltage that is not strictly cutoff for the value of E_b used, but any further increase in bias will cause the composite characteristics to depart considerably from straight lines. Such adjustment leads to approximate Class B operation. The slopes of the composite characteristics are the same as the slopes of the plate characteristics, or the resistance represented by the slope of the composite curve is r_p. This value requires a higher load resistance; and because of the increased length of positive swing

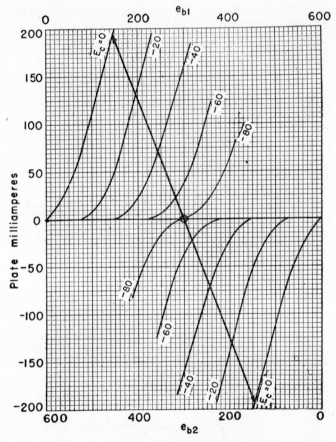

Fig. 10-17. Output of a Class B amplifier, formed by changing the operating conditions of the tubes of Fig. 10-16. $E_b = 300$ v; $E_{cc} = -60$; $R_L = 800$ ohms (3200 ohms plate to plate).

possible on the load line, a higher power output is obtained than was possible for Class A or AB operation. The negative swing on the operation line goes into cutoff, but the even-harmonic distortion present is canceled by the push-pull connection.

Operation of the Class B amplifier may be understood by reference to Fig. 10-18. The dynamic grid characteristic of tube B has been plotted upside down and reversed to that of tube A and with the grid-voltage scales adjusted so that the voltage E_{cc} corresponds on both scales. The value of E_{cc} is chosen by extending the linear portion of the dynamic curve to the zero-current axis. The value of bias obtained, which is slightly above cutoff, is called the *extended cutoff* voltage. Since the Class B amplifier is push-pull, a composite

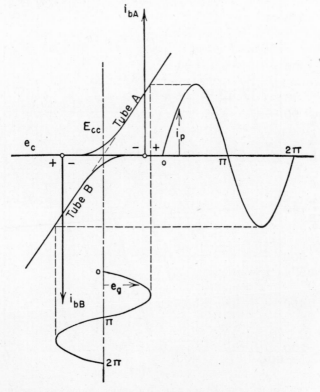

Fig. 10-18.   Operation of the Class B push-pull amplifier.

grid characteristic may be drawn by adding algebraically the plate-current values at each grid voltage. The result will be very nearly linear for most tubes, and especially so for tubes designed specifically for Class B service.

Application of a sinusoidal voltage in push-pull to the grids of tubes A and B causes tube A to carry current on the positive grid-voltage cycle and tube B to carry current on the negative grid-voltage cycle. Since the composite dynamic characteristic is linear, these current pulses will be sinusoidal in shape; and the output current wave, being the sum of the two pulses, will appear as the original sinusoidal input. The dynamic characteristic is usually linear for moderate grid-voltage swings into the positive grid-voltage region, so that a longer characteristic and increased output may be obtained by driving the grids to positive voltage values. Precautions must be taken to avoid grid-circuit distortion, as discussed under Class AB amplifiers, and the driving amplifier must be capable of supplying the power dissipated in the grid circuit owing to flow of grid current in the interval when the grids are positive.

The linearity of the composite dynamic curve permits drawing an analogy between the tube operating as a Class B amplifier and a linear diode rectifier. By drawing on the current relationships developed in Chapter 6, it can be seen that

$$I_{\text{d-c}} = \frac{2I_m}{\pi} \qquad \text{amp per two tubes.}$$

The alternating current represented by the output current wave of Fig. 10-18 is

$$I_{\text{rms}} = \frac{I_m}{\sqrt{2}}.$$

The total a-c power output then is

$$P_o = \frac{I_m^2 R_L}{2},$$

where R_L is the per tube load of the amplifier. The total d-c power input is

$$P_{\text{d-c}} = \frac{2I_m E_{bb}}{\pi}.$$

The plate-circuit efficiency of a linear Class B amplifier then is

$$\eta_p = \frac{\dfrac{I_m^2 R_L}{2} \times 100\%}{\dfrac{2I_m E_{bb}}{\pi}} = \frac{\pi}{4} \frac{I_m R_L}{E_{bb}} \times 100\%. \qquad (10\text{-}51)$$

The term $I_m R_L$ can be recognized as the peak departure of plate voltage from E_{bb}, or is equal to $(E_{bb} - E_{\min})$ or $(E_{\max} - E_{bb})$. Then

$$\eta_p = \frac{\pi}{4} \frac{E_{bb} - E_{\min}}{E_{bb}} \times 100\% = \frac{\pi}{4}\left(1 - \frac{E_{\min}}{E_{bb}}\right) \times 100\%. \qquad (10\text{-}52)$$

It can be seen that the minimum value that $E_{\min}$ can ever have is zero regardless of size of load, and consequently the maximum *theoretical* efficiency for a Class B amplifier is

$$\max \eta_p = \frac{\pi}{4} \times 100\% = 78.5\%. \qquad (10\text{-}53)$$

This is a notable increase over the efficiency possible for Class A amplification, and is responsible for the widespread use of Class B push-pull operation for high-power amplifiers.

From the current relations given above, it is also possible to write the a-c power output as a function of the direct plate current:

$$P_o = 2\left(\frac{\pi I_{\text{d-c}}}{2 \times 2}\right)^2 R_L = \frac{\pi^2 I_{\text{d-c}}^2 R_L}{8}, \qquad (10\text{-}54)$$

where $I_{\text{d-c}}$ is the plate current taken by the two tubes. If the signal output is small, the input d-c power is likewise reduced, and this is part of the reason for the increased efficiency of the Class B amplifier. The large signal input possible also contributes to the high efficiency possible in the circuit.

For the two 2A3 tubes of Fig. 10-17, operated near Class B with 300 plate volts, −60 grid volts, it can be found that the power output with the 800-ohm load line (3200 ohms plate-to-plate) is 15.0 w. The value of $E_{\min}$ is 145 v, so that the plate efficiency is 40.6 per cent; and the steady no-signal plate input is only 22.8 w, well below the rated value for two tubes. These results may be compared with those of Fig. 10-15, which for the same two tubes in Class-A push-pull gave only 9.7 w output at 400 ohms load (1600 ohms plate-to-plate load), with 25 watts input. The comparison could be made even more unbalanced in favor of the Class-B amplifier if the tubes were driven into the positive-grid region. The sacrifice made to achieve the higher output is in distortion, with both nonlinear and intermodulation types present.

In Class B operation, the power input is large only for large grid signals. The maximum plate loss must be calculated for large or maximum signal, rather than for zero signal as in a Class A amplifier. Tubes must be chosen with plate dissipation ratings large enough to handle the peak plate loss, which may occur for some value of signal near but not equal to that producing maximum output. The maximum value of plate loss may be computed through use of Eq. 10-54 in writing the plate loss P_p as

$$P_p = \text{input} - \text{output} = E_{bb}I_{\text{d-c}} - \frac{\pi^2 I_{\text{d-c}}^2 R_L}{8}.$$

Taking the derivative with respect to $I_{\text{d-c}}$ and setting it to zero shows that the d-c plate current at maximum loss is $4E_{bb}/(\pi^2 R_L)$. Using this value shows the maximum plate loss to be

$$\max P_p = \frac{2E_{bb}^2}{\pi^2 R_L} = 0.203 \frac{E_{bb}^2}{R_L} \tag{10-55}$$

and if this is likely to occur within the operating range of the amplifier, the plate dissipation rating of the tube must be chosen accordingly.

To avoid the necessity of a fixed bias supply of rather high voltage for biasing normal power triodes to cutoff, special tubes that operate at extended cutoff with zero bias voltage have been designed with high μ for Class B service. This implies that a signal will drive the grid positive during the whole of a half cycle; and since the grid of the second tube is positive over the other half cycle of grid voltage, grid current flows over the whole cycle and provides a much more constant load for the driver amplifier than is possible when grid current flows only in pulses at the peaks of the cycle. Grid-circuit distortion is much reduced by the use of zero-bias Class B tubes.

Linearity of the dynamic curve is necessary if distortion is to be low, since with only one tube operating at a time, distortion due to nonlinearity in one tube cannot be canceled by nonlinear distortion in the other tube except near cutoff, where the composite curve differs from the dynamic curves. If Class B tubes are overbiased, a discontinuity may be introduced near zero grid volts and may produce serious distortion, especially for small signals.

Class B amplifiers, although more efficient than Class A or AB amplifiers, have inherently higher distortion and are ordinarily employed only where costs dictate economy of power and tubes, or where the low current drain at no signal is desirable, as in battery-operated equipment.

10-13. Amplifiers with Reactive Loads

All analyses of large-signal amplifiers have so far been made with resistive loads. In practice, some reactance may be introduced, due to the load itself as in a loudspeaker, or in the output transformer. Owing to the angle between current and voltage in reactive loads, the plate current does not have the same value for increasing plate voltages that it has for decreasing plate voltages; and the load line, when plotted, becomes some form of ellipse, varying from the straight line for purely resistive loads to a circle for purely reactive loads.

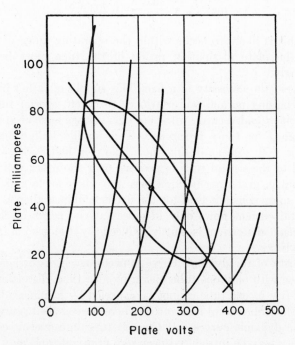

Fig. 10-19.   The load line for a reactive load on an amplifier.

The major axis of the ellipse will fall on the straight line plotted for a resistance load of magnitude equal to the impedance, so that for power output or other calculations involving only the extremes of grid-voltage swing, the load-line method previously discussed may be applied for a reactive load. However, a reactive load decreases the permissible grid-signal voltage, since the elliptical load line may carry the operating point into the region of low plate current and thereby introduce distortion. This effect is illustrated for the large grid voltage used in drawing the load line in Fig. 10-19. This elliptical load line is drawn for a load of $3200 + j2400$ ohms with a 2A3 triode tube, the grid-signal voltage being 40 v peak. No method exists, except a laborious point-by-point plot of the wave form, by which an analysis for distortion may be made when operation is in the nonlinear region of the tube characteristics with a reactive load.

That the curve is an ellipse for a reactive load is shown by the fact that load circuit voltage and current expressions are, respectively,

$$e_o = E_o \sin \omega t$$

and $$i_p = I_m \sin (\omega t + \phi). \tag{10-56}$$

These constitute the parametric equations of an ellipse.

PROBLEMS

Note: Characteristic curves for the tubes mentioned will be found in the Appendix.

10-1. (a) For series-feed loads of 5000, 10,000, 25,000, 50,000, and 100,000 ohms, determine graphically the values of E_b and I_b for a 6J5 tube operated at $E_{bb} = 250$ v, $E_{cc} = -6$ v.

(b) If a grid voltage of 4.0 v peak is applied, find the value of I_p fundamental for each of the above loads.

(c) What load resistance would be required to shift the Q point to $I_b = 6$ ma, $E_{cc} = -8$ v, with $E_{bb} = 320$ v?

10-2. A 6J5 tube is shunt-fed through a choke of 500 ohms d-c resistance and very high inductance. Neglect the reactance of the blocking capacitor.

(a) Draw load lines for each of the loads specified in Problem 10-1(a), with $E_{cc} = -8$ v.

(b) Calculate the voltage gain for each load, and plot a curve of load vs gain.

(c) Plot the dynamic grid characteristics for the 10,000- and 50,000-ohm loads from the load lines.

10-3. A 6J5 tube is used as an overload relay on a d-c motor circuit, as in Fig. 10-20. The relay has a coil resistance of 10,000 ohms, and closes the

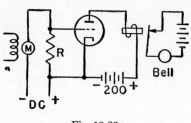

bell circuit at 4 ma coil current and opens at 5.5 ma coil current. If $R = 0.15$ ohm, at what motor currents will the bell start and stop ringing?

10-4. A 2A3 tube in the circuit of Fig. 10-21, with $E_{bb} = 250$, $I_b = 50$ ma, is to operate with a load of 5000 ohms = R_L. If the resistance of L is 500 ohms and reactance of C is negligible, find:

Fig. 10-20.

(a) Values of R_k and C_k for satisfactory operation down to 50 c.

(b) Power output if $E_s = 25$ v rms.

(c) Per cent of second-harmonic distortion.

10-5. (a) Determine the value of load to be used with a 2A3 tube operating in the circuit of Fig. 10-21, if the power output is to be the greatest

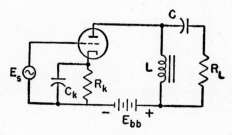

Fig. 10-21.

obtainable under Class A conditions and distortion is to be less than 6 per cent. The Q point is to be at $E_{cc} = -50$, $I_b = 50$ ma.

(b) If L has a resistance of 500 ohms, what value of E_{bb} must be used?

(c) Plot curves of power output and per cent distortion against load.

Note: Try load lines for values of $R_L = 1000$, 1500, 2000, 3000, and 5000 ohms.

10-6. Find the output power, plate circuit efficiency, plate dissipation, and second, third, and fourth harmonics for a 6F6 for loads of 2500, 7000, and 10,000 ohms coupled into the circuit through an ideal 1 : 1 transformer. Operation is with 300 v E_{bb}, $E_{c2} = 250$ v, and $E_{c1} = -20$ v, under Class A conditions with $I_{min} = 10$ ma.

10-7. A 6F6, with desired load of 5000 ohms, is to be transformer-coupled to a loudspeaker of 10 ohms resistance. If $E_{bb} = E_{c2} = 250$ v, $E_{cc} = -20$ v, 12 v rms signal and $I_{min} = 10$ ma, find:

(a) Transformer ratio needed, if the transformer is ideal.

(b) Transformer ratio required if the tube load is to remain at 5000 ohms, but the transformer efficiency is 75 per cent.

(c) Fundamental power output with the ideal transformer of (a).

(d) Second, third, fourth, and total harmonic distortion for (c).

10-8. A shunt-fed 6L6 tube, supplied through a choke of negligible d-c resistance and high reactance, is operated at $E_{bb} = 250$ v, $E_{cc} = -10$ v, and $E_{c2} = 250$ v, with a load of 2000 ohms. Find the fundamental power output, plate-circuit efficiency, per cent second- and third-harmonic distortion, and total distortion, with a driving voltage of 10 v peak value.

10-9. A 6F6 pentode is to be biased to -15 v. Without exceeding ratings, find the fundamental power output obtainable with a signal of 15 v peak and a load of 5000 ohms, shunt-fed. Also compute plate-circuit efficiency, per cent second and third harmonics, and plate dissipation, with and without the signal present.

10-10. (a) Find the fundamental power output, plate-circuit efficiency, and plate dissipation for a 2A3 tube operating with $E_b = 200$ v, and $E_{cc} = -30$ v, $E_. = 25$ v peak, with a series load of 3000 ohms.

(b) Find the value of E_{bb} needed to supply the circuit of (a).

(c) Repeat (a) and (b) if the load is shunt-fed through a choke of zero d-c resistance.

10-11. (a) A 6L6 tube is used in the circuit of Fig. 10-22. If R_L is 10 ohms, find the reflected primary load and transformer turns ratio required to obtain maximum possible power output with less than 8 per cent total

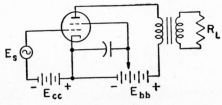

Fig. 10-22.

second- and third-harmonic distortion. The voltage E_{bb} is 250, screen voltage is 250, I_b is to be 65 ma, and $I_{min} = 10$ ma.

(b) Plot curves of power output, per cent total distortion, and plate-circuit efficiency against reflected primary load.

10-12. Using a 2A3 tube with a transformer-coupled output circuit having a transformer ratio of 24 : 1 with a secondary load of 8 ohms, $E_{bb} =$ 275 v, and assuming that the transformer is ideal, the grid is never positive, and i_b is always greater than 5 ma, find:

(a) Q point for plate dissipation of 15 w.

(b) Maximum possible power output under the assumptions.

(c) Value of E_g required for maximum output.

(d) Value of fundamental I_p.

(e) Plate-circuit efficiency.

(f) Per cent second and third harmonics.

(g) Current in the 8-ohm load.

10-13. A 6L6 operates at 300 plate volts, screen volts of 250, control grid bias of -18. The signal available is 15 v peak.

(a) Determine the shunt-fed load resistance for which the second harmonic distortion is zero.

With the load of (a), find:

(b) Power output.

(c) Power sensitivity, both theoretical and actual.

(d) Plate circuit efficiency.

10-14. Using a 6F6 tube in the circuit of Fig. 10-22, with $E_{cc} = -20$ v, $E_{bb} = 300$, $E_{c2} = 250$, and $R_L = 500$ ohms, and assuming that the transformer is ideal and that the tube is to work into a load of 7000 ohms with $E_s = 5.3$ v rms, 1000 c, find from the characteristics:

(a) I_b flowing.

(b) Transformer turns ratio required.

(c) Fundamental power output.

(d) Plate-circuit efficiency.

(e) Per cent total second and third harmonics.

(f) Voltage across the load.

(g) Average plate loss in watts, with and without E_s input.

10-15. The 6L6 has a rated plate dissipation of 19 w. Using the tube in the circuit of Fig. 10-22 with an effective primary load of 4000 ohms with $E_{bb} = 350$ and $E_{c2} = 250$ v, and assuming that the transformer is ideal, the grid is never positive, and the plate current is always greater than 10 ma, find:

(a) Transformer turns ratio required if $R_L = 12$ ohms.

(b) Q point with tube operating at rated dissipation with zero signal.

(c) Maximum possible power output under the stated conditions.

(d) Value of E_s in rms volts required for output of (c).

(e) Per cent total harmonics.

(f) Plate-circuit efficiency.

(g) Power sensitivity.

10-16. A 6J5 and a 6F6 are to be used in a two-stage amplifier to supply

3 w to a 10-ohm load. A 250-v plate supply is available, and cathode bias is to be used on both tubes. The 6J5 is resistance-coupled to the 6F6, and the operating frequency range is to be 100 to 5000 cycles.

Design the complete circuit for high efficiency and low amplitude and frequency distortion. The input signal required is to be 0.5 v or less. Draw the complete circuit diagram and specify the wattage ratings of all resistors called for.

10-17. Determine the value of all coefficients of the harmonic series up to A_7, in terms of I_{max}, I_x, I_y, I_r, I_s, I_r', and I_s', where I_r and I_s are taken at points of one-third and two-thirds peak grid voltage, respectively, and I_r' and I_s' are the corresponding values for negative grid voltage.

10-18. Two 2A3 triodes are operated in push-pull with $E_{bb} = 250$ v, $E_{cc} = -45$ v.

(a) Draw the composite characteristics.

(b) Draw a load line for a plate-to-plate load of 2400 ohms.

(c) For the load line of (b) construct the paths of operation of the individual tubes.

(d) Find the power output.

(e) Find the individual tube losses and the total power input from E_{bb}.

10-19. Two 6L6 beam tetrodes are used in push-pull with $E_{bb} = 250$ v, $E_{c2} = 250$ v, and $E_{cc} = -16$ v, all under Class A conditions.

Calculate and plot as a function of load per tube:

(a) Power output.

(b) Third-harmonic distortion.

(c) Plate-circuit efficiency.

Trial loads should range from 1000 to 10,000 ohms, plate to plate.

10-20. A 6L6 tube is operated with a load of $4000 + j6000$ ohms in a series-feed circuit with $E_{bb} = 300$ v and $E_{cc} = -10$ v. For a peak grid voltage of 5, plot the elliptical load-line diagram.

10-21. In Class AB₁ operation, two 2A3 triodes are operated at 290 v E_{bb}, -60 v bias. For the load giving maximum power output, find:

(a) Power output.

(b) Third-harmonic distortion.

(c) Plate-circuit efficiency.

(d) Total direct current.

10-22. A certain triode tube may be considered as having linear characteristics expressed by

$$i_b = 0.001(4e_c + e_b) \qquad \text{amp.}$$

(a) Compute the power sensitivity.

(b) For Class A operation, $E_{bb} = 300$ v, $E_c = -40$ v, find power output, efficiency, and d-c power input for a signal of 40 v peak, and load of 2000 ohms.

(c) Find value of load giving maximum power output under conditions of (b).

10-23. A push-pull triode circuit is operating Class B with a plate-to-plate load of 5000 ohms. The d-c milliammeter in the common anode circuit reads 122 ma for a steady sinusoidal signal. What is the a-c power output? If the anode-voltage supply is 1250, what are the plate-circuit efficiency and plate dissipation?

10-24. A pair of 2A3 tubes is to supply 6 w to a loudspeaker of 8 ohms resistance. The push-pull stage is to be driven by a phase-splitting, cathode-anode-output type of phase inverter (see Chapter 9). The plate supply for all tubes is 250 v. Design the complete circuit, giving all values of circuit constants, and specify the grid driving voltage required for the phase inverter if it uses a 6J5 tube.

REFERENCES

1. Espley, D. C., "The Calculation of Harmonic Production in Thermionic Valves with Resistive Loads," *Proc. IRE*, **21**, 1439 (1933).
2. Preisman, A., *Graphical Constructions for Vacuum-Tube Circuits*, McGraw-Hill Book Company, Inc., New York, 1943.
3. Thompson, B. J., "Graphical Determination of Performance of Push-Pull Amplifiers," *Proc. IRE*, **21**, 591 (1933).
4. Warner, J. C., and Loughren, A. V., "Output Characteristics of Amplifier Tubes," *Proc. IRE*, **14**, 735 (1926).
5. Barton, L. E., "High Audio Power from Relatively Small Tubes," *Proc. IRE*, **19**, 1131 (1931).

CHAPTER 11

GASEOUS CONDUCTION

A gas in its normal state is an excellent insulator for electricity. However, when a gas is confined at low pressure in a tube having properly placed electrodes and excited by a sufficient applied voltage, very complex phenomena take place. A current can be carried between the electrodes, and the discharge is usually accompanied by a visible glow in the gas, frequently showing streamers and other beautiful effects. The color of the discharge depends on the nature of the gas.

No satisfactory explanation of the phenomena was available until the discovery of the electron, and then the development of the theory was gradual. A major step was taken with the introduction, in 1913, of the Bohr atom theory, which gave for the first time a satisfactory explanation of the visible glow and the spectra exhibited by the gases in the discharge. An understanding of gaseous conduction, and thereby of the whole family of gaseous electron tubes, depends on an understanding of the structure of the atom.

11-1. The Bohr Atom

The early Thomson and Rutherford theories of the atom were discussed briefly in Chapter 1. The Rutherford atom consisted of a central nucleus, containing all the positive electric charge and nearly all the mass of the atom, around which were scattered the negative electrons in fixed positions. Difficulties encountered in explaining observed physical reactions with the Rutherford model led to further work which culminated in the Bohr theory of the atom. Some of these early difficulties were due to attempting to apply classical-mechanics theory for particles of observable dimensions, to particles of subatomic dimensions, which is now known as a particularly dangerous extrapolation.

The Bohr atom was an extension of the Rutherford theory, but with the electrons rotating in fixed orbital paths about the central nucleus of positive charge. In proposing this structure, Bohr set up certain postulates that were not wholly in accord with classical theory but which could permit explanation of line spectra and other points of difficulty. By further disregard of classical methods, a whole new field, called *wave mechanics*, has been set up which applies specifically to particles of subatomic dimensions.

Wave mechanics, although explaining much of the unknown, has unfortunately led to a less clear physical picture of the atom than that given by the original Bohr theory. For the understanding of gaseous conduction, however, the Bohr atom picture is wholly adequate; and when a change is made to the wave-mechanical viewpoint, a good approximation can be arrived at by replacing the statement "The electron *is* at such and such a place" with the sentence "It is *probable* that the electron is at such and such a place."

The Bohr atom model, similar to that proposed by Rutherford, had a central nucleus of positive charge surrounded by electrons. The difference lay in that Bohr placed the electrons in rotation in certain fixed circular orbits around the nucleus, much as in a miniature solar system. The difference between the various chemical elements is due to changes in the number of positive charges, or *protons*, within the nucleus. The number of positive charges is equal to the atomic number, and also determines the number of electrons in the normal or un-ionized state.

Bohr also specified that an electron *could exist in an atom only if it were in one of the fixed orbits*. Since the electron was in the field of the positive nucleus, the electron was required to have sufficient energy of rotation to maintain itself in that orbit, the force of attraction of the electron by the nucleus being balanced by outward centrifugal force due to rotation. However, circular motion implies a continuous acceleration toward the center, and classical electrodynamic theory requires radiation of energy by an accelerated charge. If the electron were to give up the energy needed for this acceleration, it would move progressively nearer and nearer the nucleus, eventually falling into it. Since most matter is believed to have been formed a long time ago, all the electrons would long since have fallen into their respective nuclei, and matter as we know it would have ceased to exist. Classical electrodynamics, therefore, provides an incorrect answer, and Bohr avoided the difficulty by arbitrarily setting up as his first postulate:

1. *An electron when in a stable orbit does not radiate or give up energy.*

Bohr made two other basic postulates:

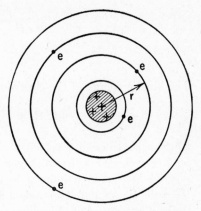

2. *The angular momentum of the electron in the orbit is quantized, or can have only certain definite values given by $nh/2\pi$, where h is Planck's constant and n may have only integer values 1, 2, 3, $\cdots$.*

3. *The energy given up when an electron jumps to an orbit of lower energy is radiated as a single quantum, or bundle of radiant energy (photon).*

Fig. 11-1.   The Bohr atom model.

With these three assumptions, Bohr was able to set up a theoretical atom model which was supported by experiment and gave a very satisfactory explanation of the origin of line spectra. A model of such an atom is shown in Fig. 11-1.

11-2. The First Bohr Postulate—Energy of an Orbit

In considering the first postulate, it is easy to calculate the energy that an electron must possess to maintain its position in any particular orbit in the field of the nucleus. For simplicity, the hydrogen atom H^1 may be chosen, having one electron of mass m and one positive electronic charge on the nucleus, the nucleus having a mass M. The electron revolves in an orbit about the central nucleus. Since $M \gg m$, the nucleus may be assumed at rest and unaffected by the motion of the electron. By Coulomb's inverse-square law, the force of attraction between the positive nucleus and the negative electron is

$$f_a = \frac{e(-e)}{4\pi\,\epsilon_v r^2} = \frac{-e^2}{4\pi\,\epsilon_v r^2}. \tag{11-1}$$

The system will be in equilibrium and the motion will be circular if f_a is balanced by an outward centrifugal force

$$f_c = \frac{mv^2}{r}, \tag{11-2}$$

or the net force acting on the electron is zero, and

$$\frac{mv^2}{r} - \frac{e^2}{4\pi \, \epsilon_v r^2} = 0,$$

$$mv^2 = \frac{e^2}{4\pi \, \epsilon_v r}. \tag{11-3}$$

The kinetic energy of the electron, due to its rotation in the orbit, is

$$\text{K.E.} = \frac{mv^2}{2} = \frac{e^2}{8\pi \, \epsilon_v r}, \tag{11-4}$$

where v is the orbital velocity. The potential at any point in the field of a charge is the work per unit of charge required to move a positive charge from infinity to the point under consideration. If the potential at infinity is taken as the zero reference in the field of the unit positive electronic charge on the nucleus, the potential of the orbit of radius r in the field of charge $+e$ is

$$V = \int_\infty^r \frac{f}{q} \, dr = \int_\infty^r \frac{-e}{4\pi \, \epsilon_v r^2} \, dr = \frac{e}{4\pi \, \epsilon_v r},$$

where V is measured from infinity to the orbit. From Chapter 2, the energy acquired by an electron moved through a potential V is $V(-e)$ joules. Consequently, the potential energy acquired by the electron in moving from infinity to the orbit of radius r is

$$\text{P.E.} = \frac{(-e)e}{4\pi \, \epsilon_v r} = \frac{-e^2}{4\pi \, \epsilon_v r}. \tag{11-5}$$

The negative sign indicates that the electron has actually done work or lost energy in moving to the orbit. This result is to be expected, since the electron moved under the attraction of a positive charge. The total energy possessed by the electron in the orbit is, then, the sum of the potential and kinetic energies, or, from Eqs. 11-4 and 11-5,

$$W = \frac{-e^2}{4\pi \, \epsilon_v r} + \frac{e^2}{8\pi \, \epsilon_v r} = \frac{-e^2}{8\pi \, \epsilon_v r}. \tag{11-6}$$

The negative sign is to be taken as meaning merely an energy less than that possessed by the electron at infinity. This is equivalent to stating that the potential energy of a book on the floor is negative, or less than the zero energy of a book at the reference level on the table top.

Although Eq. 11-6 was derived for the hydrogen atom, it holds in principle for atoms of higher atomic number and nuclear charge, despite the fact that the presence of additional negative electrons in other orbits alters the fields and prevents a simple extension of the theory.

11-3. The Second Bohr Postulate—the Quantum Theory

In 1913, influenced by earlier work of Max Planck on thermal radiation from hot bodies, Bohr was led to the apparently unusual assumption that the angular momentum of the electron in an orbit could have only certain values given by the relation $nh/2\pi$. Although this appears an inspired shot in the dark, it took a second equally inspired thought to clarify the matter and to place it on a basis of experimental fact. In 1924, Louis de Broglie postulated that even though electrons appeared to be particles, or corpuscles, they might have wave properties, or exhibit effects similar to those produced by light. The wavelength λ associated with the electron was assumed to be given by

$$\lambda = \frac{h}{mv} \qquad (11\text{-}7)$$

where h is Planck's constant, v the velocity, and m the relativistic mass of the electron. In 1928, C. J. Davisson and L. H. Germer proved this equation to be true, thus substantiating de Broglie's assumption, by measurement of diffraction of electron beams from crystals.

It is possible to correlate de Broglie's assumption concerning the wavelength of moving electrons with Bohr's second postulate that the angular momentum of an electron in an orbit could have only certain values given by

$$I\omega = mr^2\omega = \frac{nh}{2\pi}. \qquad (11\text{-}8)$$

In view of $\omega = v/r$, Eq. 11-7 becomes

$$mr^2\omega = \frac{hr}{\lambda}. \qquad (11\text{-}9)$$

If the wavelength is required to have the value $\lambda = 2\pi r/n$, the Bohr postulate is obtained as

$$mr^2\omega = \frac{nh}{2\pi}. \tag{11-10}$$

The requirement that $\lambda = 2\pi r/n$ implies that the orbit of an electron in an atom must have a circumference equal to an integral number of wavelengths.

For the hydrogen atom Eq. 11-4 may be rewritten in terms of angular velocity as

$$\frac{mr^2\omega^2}{2} = \frac{e^2}{8\pi \, \epsilon_v r}.$$

Upon substitution for ω^2 from Eq. 11-10, an expression for the radius of an orbit of a hydrogen atom can be obtained as

$$r_n = \frac{n^2 h^2 \epsilon_v}{\pi m e^2}. \tag{11-11}$$

The radii of the successive permitted orbits are then seen to be proportional to the squares of integers, 1, 2, 3, $\cdots$. These integers are called the *quantum numbers* of the various orbits. For hydrogen, the first orbit has a radius of 0.53×10^{-8} centimeter; the second will be four times as great; the third, nine times as great; and so forth. The exact solution for elements of higher nuclear charge and additional electrons is not possible, but by analogy the Bohr theory provides qualitative results for the heavier atoms.

From Eq. 11-6, the energy required for an electron's occupancy of an orbit in a hydrogen atom can be computed by use of the value of the radius in Eq. 11-11. The energy associated with the nth orbit is

$$W_n = -\frac{me^4}{8n^2 h^2 \, \epsilon_v^2}. \tag{11-12}$$

Substituting values for the constants and using $n = 1, 2, 3 \cdots$, gives for the energy of the first five orbits of the hydrogen atom

Orbit	Energy in Joules
First	-2.17×10^{-18}
Second	-0.54×10^{-18}
Third	-0.24×10^{-18}
Fourth	-0.13×10^{-18}
Fifth	-0.087×10^{-18}

These values, and the previous theory, are confirmed by spectroscopic observation, utilizing the Bohr radiation postulate of Section 11-4.

The lowest value of energy is that corresponding to the first orbit. Consequently, this orbit is the most stable and is the one occupied by the electron when the hydrogen atom is in its *normal state*. From this premise the general definition can be drawn that *an atom is in its normal state when the electrons are in their lowest energy condition.*

Although circular orbits have been assumed here, it is known that in the general case of motion of an electron around a heavy nucleus, or of a planet around the sun, the path is an ellipse with the central mass at one of the foci. A circle is, of course, a form of ellipse. Further analysis demonstrates that some of the orbits are elliptical, some circular. Interesting phenomena occur in the elliptical orbits: the velocity varies around the path, since the angular momentum $mr^2\omega$ must be constant, and the mass also varies with the velocity, so that the elliptical orbits themselves rotate slowly about the nucleus. For an engineering discussion, these distinctions need not be made, *the important fact being that a definite value of energy is associated with each orbit*, regardless of shape.

To describe more accurately all the conditions under which a given electron exists in an atom, a *set* of quantum numbers has been developed. The number n, used above, is known as the *total quantum number* and designates the orbit of the electron. A number l, called the *azimuthal quantum number*, designates the eccentricity of the elliptical orbits; s is the *spin* of the electron; and m describes the *orientation* of the spinning electron when the atom is in a magnetic field. The Pauli exclusion principle then states that in any atom no two electrons can have an identical *set* of quantum numbers. This might be paraphrased to say that at any instant no two electrons in an atom can exist under exactly identical conditions. The arrangement of electrons dictated by the Pauli exclusion principle can be used to build up the periodic table of the elements on a logical basis.

11-4. The Third Bohr Postulate—Radiation

The quantum conditions imposed by the experimentally proved concept of electronic wavelength, although in violation of the dictates of classical mechanics, provide a stable nuclear atom. No means, however, have been provided to explain electromagnetic radiation (light) from the atom, yet the spectrograph shows that atoms do radiate.

Corresponding to the larger quantum numbers are the greater absolute values of the energy W_n of the electron. If an electron initially in an outer orbit of energy W_2 falls, as a result of an atomic disturbance or instability, to an inner orbit of lower energy W_1, energy in amount given by

$$W = W_2 - W_1 \tag{11-13}$$

has disappeared. Since reliance can be placed in the principle of the conservation of energy, it may be assumed that this amount of energy, W, has been radiated.

Earlier work by Planck on the relation of the size of a quantum of energy to the frequency of the radiation had given

$$W = hf \qquad \text{joules.} \tag{11-14}$$

This equation states that a quantum, or single bundle of radiant energy called the *photon*, has a definite size for every frequency, or color, of the radiation; that is, a quantum is not a fixed quantity of energy, but the energy varies with the frequency of the radiation.

Equation 11-13 was applied to the relation of Eq. 11-14 by Bohr, yielding

$$f = \frac{W_2 - W_1}{h} \qquad \text{cycles per second,} \tag{11-15}$$

as the expression for the frequency of radiation emitted when an electron falls from an outer orbit of energy W_2 to an inner orbit of energy W_1. In terms of wave length of the radiation, this becomes

$$\lambda = \frac{hc}{W_2 - W_1} \qquad \text{m}$$

$$= \frac{10^{10}hc}{W_2 - W_1} \qquad \text{A,} \tag{11-16}$$

where $c = 3 \times 10^8$ meters per second, the velocity of light in space.

By use of the values of energy for the orbits of the hydrogen atom computed in Section 11-3, photons of wavelengths 4340, 4861, and 6563 A should be radiated when electrons fall from the fifth, fourth, and third orbits, respectively, to the second orbit of hydrogen.

These three wavelengths represent colors in the violet, blue, and orange portions of the visible spectrum, which is considered as running from 4000 to 7000 A. The lines are actually found in observed spectra of hydrogen as the so-called *Balmer series* of lines.

The possible transitions are not limited to jumps from the various outer orbits to the second orbit but may also occur from the outer orbits to the first, resulting in a series of spectral lines in the ultra-

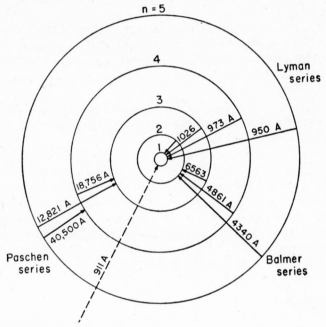

Fig. 11-2. Bohr model of the hydrogen atom, showing the origin of some of the spectral lines.

violet, called the *Lyman series*, and from the fifth orbit to the third or fourth, or the fourth to the third, giving a series of lines in the infrared, called the *Paschen series*. An electron may also come from outside the atom to enter any of the orbits, giving still another series of high-energy and short-wavelength lines. The model of the hydrogen atom shown in Fig. 11-2, with circular orbits assumed, indicates diagrammatically the orbital jumps that yield the various spectral series. In all these cases the Bohr theory predicts the value for the wavelength of the line, and experiment yields a check that thoroughly establishes the validity of the Bohr assumptions.

An electron can, at any instant, make only one jump and emit only one frequency. A discharge, as in a neon tube, is the integrated result of jumps occurring in a very large number of atoms. The number of atoms involved is so large, and so many transitions of each kind occur per second, that the colored light appears as if it were produced continuously and were constant in intensity. If a discharge due to only a few atoms could be observed, it would appear as intermittent flashes of the various colors. The differences in intensity observed for the various lines of the spectrum are due to the fact that certain jumps are more probable than others and that more electrons make these jumps per second, thereby producing a greater integrated light intensity.

Although it is not possible to calculate readily the frequencies of lines to be expected for heavier atoms, such as sodium or mercury, owing to the number of electrons in the outer orbits, it is possible to learn much by analogy with the case of the hydrogen atom. For instance, from the known spectral line frequencies it is possible to calculate the energies associated with the various orbits, although the radii of the orbits may not be easily obtained. From the known energies, most of the phenomena associated with ionization and conduction of electricity through gases can be explained.

11-5. Excitation, Ionization, Recombination

Although the preceding discussion has made liberal use of electrons falling from outer orbits to inner orbits and radiating the appropriate quanta of energy, no suggestion has been given as to how the electrons may be made to reverse the process. When an atom in the normal state receives external energy sufficient to raise one of its electrons to a higher than normal orbit or energy state, the atom is said to be *excited*, and the quantities of energy required for the transitions from the normal to the excited levels are called *energies of excitation*. These amounts of energy are exactly equal to the quanta radiated when the electron falls back to lower orbits. Since an electron in an orbit can have only a certain definite energy and has no capability for storing surplus energy, the energy taken up by an electron when it is raised to an excited level can be only the exact amount corresponding to the differences in energy of the levels.

An atom remains in an excited state for about 10^{-8} sec or less; then the electron falls back to a normal orbit, and the atom returns to the normal state. The fall back to a normal orbit may occur directly, or the electron may make the transit by jumps to one or several intermediate orbits on the way. Each jump is, of course, accompanied by emission of a photon of appropriate frequency or color, to radiate the amount of energy given up by the electron.

If the atom is given sufficient energy, an electron may be transported from a normal or excited orbit to a point a great distance from the atom—in brief, the electron is removed from the atom. The atom is then said to be *ionized* and the process is known as *ionization*. The electron becomes a free electron, and the atom is then an ion with one positive electronic charge. The minimum energy required to remove an electron from a normal atom is called the *ionization energy* and, when expressed in electron volts, the *ionization potential*.

By supplying even greater amounts of energy, it is possible to remove additional electrons from a positive ion, resulting in a multi-charged ion. Since such action involves removal of a negative electron from a positively charged body, the forces that must be overcome are very strong, and the energy required for removal of a second electron is considerably greater than for the first electron and becomes progressively greater for each additional electron removed. Ions with more than one charge are not common, although mercury ions have been reported with eight positive charges.

After ionization, the ion is free to move under any fields acting in the space and will obey the ballistic laws, provided that consideration is given to its great mass and the positive sign of its charge. Although the ionization energy for a particular gas is a constant, it is possible for an electron in a normal orbit to take up energy in excess of the amount required for removal from the atom or for ionization. This excess of energy then appears as kinetic energy of the free electron after the release.

A list of ionization potentials for a few common gases is given in Table 8.

As has been stated, an atom is in the normal state when the electrons are in the lowest-energy orbits. The unfilled orbits are then the outermost high-energy ones. The innermost electrons of atoms having a number of electrons are shielded from external influences by the outer electrons, so that it is the outermost electron which,

TABLE 8

IONIZATION POTENTIALS OF CERTAIN COMMON GASES AND VAPORS

Element	Ionization Potential (ev)
Argon	15.69
Helium	24.48
Hydrogen	13.6
Krypton	13.3
Mercury	10.39
Neon	21.47
Sodium	5.1
Xenon	11.5

with the least energy, can be excited or removed for ionization of the atom. It is the outermost electron or electrons that contribute not only to the electrical properties but also to the chemical properties of an element. Elements having balanced arrangements of outer electrons are stable elements, examples being the noble gases: helium, argon, krypton, xenon, and neon. As a result of their stability, these are the gases very often chosen for gaseous electron tubes. The elements that show the greatest degree of electronic unbalance among the outer exposed electrons are chemically very active; an example is the lithium-sodium-potassium group.

The energy required for excitation or ionization can be imparted to a gas atom in a number of different ways:

1. By collision of a high-energy electron with the gas atom.
2. By capture of a photon of proper energy by the atom.
3. By collision of positive ions with gas atoms.
4. By transfer of thermal energy to the atom, or collision between atoms.

The least energy required to produce excitation, or the least energy needed for the jump from a normal orbit to the next orbit above, is called the *first critical potential* when expressed in electron volts. An electron moving in a gas with energy less than the first critical potential of the gas will, upon collision with an atom, rebound elastically without appreciable exchange of energy, since the mass of the atom is very large with respect to the electron. If the electron has an energy equal to or greater than the critical energy, it may upon collision excite the atom and give up exactly the amount of energy needed to raise an internal electron from a normal to an excited orbit, or from a lower excited state to a higher one. Any excess of energy over that exactly needed remains with the first electron as kinetic energy.

If the original electron has a kinetic energy equal to or greater than the ionization energy, it may upon collision give up energy to cause excitation to any level, or it may supply enough energy to remove an electron completely from the atom and produce ionization. In the latter case, energy is transferred to the atom to supply the ionizing energy, and any remaining energy of the original electron may be shared with the electron removed from the atom.

If a photon of radiant energy strikes the atom, the atom may be excited or ionized. However, since a photon carries an amount of energy dependent on the frequency, and this energy cannot be subdivided, the energy of the photon must be exactly that needed for excitation of a particular orbital jump. Obviously, the frequency of the photon needed to raise an electron to a particular orbit is exactly the frequency that will be emitted when the electron returns to the original orbit.

Only certain discrete frequencies are able to produce excitation of a particular gas. If, however, a photon possesses energy greater than ionization energy, the atom may be ionized by the photon, and the excess energy of the photon will appear as kinetic energy of the emitted electron. This effect requires photons of relatively high energy, or frequencies in the ultraviolet, x-ray, and cosmic-ray regions. In every case of excitation or ionization of atoms by photons, the photon is totally absorbed and disappears.

Recombination of ions with free electrons to form neutral atoms occurs most readily on surfaces existing in the discharge. The surface of an anode, grid, cathode, or tube wall holds charges of one sign, and charges of opposite sign are attracted to the surface, combine, and form neutral gas atoms or molecules. Certain tubes in which it is desired to hasten the process of recombination are designed to have a large amount of electrode area available to the discharge as recombining surface. Although it might be thought that recombination would take place readily in the gas, owing to the natural affinity of ion and electron for each other, this is not the case. Such recombination occurs rarely in gases at low pressure.

11-6. Metastable States

Study of spectral data indicates that certain orbital jumps that would be expected from the energies of the known levels actually occur very rarely. That is, certain levels are known to exist by reason of electron jumps *to* those levels, but no indication of jumps *from* those levels to lower ones is found in the spectral lines. Energy levels from which it is very improbable for electrons to drop to lower levels are called *metastable levels*.

Electron release from a metastable state can occur only by giving the electron additional energy, thereby raising it to a higher level from which a drop to a lower or normal level then may take place. The reason for the existence of metastable states is not known, but it is found that one or more such levels do exist in many atoms.

The period during which an atom may exist in a metastable state on the average may be of the order of 10^{-4} sec, much longer than it can exist as an excited atom. During this relatively long time,

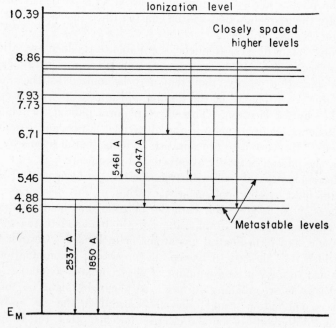

Fig. 11-3. Energy-level diagram for the mercury atom.

there is a very high probability of an additional collision with an electron having sufficient energy to complete the ionization process. That is, owing to the metastable state, ionization may take place in two steps, permitting ionization by electrons having energy much below the ionization energy for the gas. For instance, in mercury the ionization potential is 10.39 v, and the first metastable state is at 4.66 v. An electron with only 5 ev energy may collide with this atom, furnishing the energy to raise an electron to the first metastable state. Owing to the long life of the electron in this state, probabilities are excellent that a collision may occur with another electron having 5.73 or more volts energy, thereby ionizing the atom with individual electron energies well below the ionizing potential.

As an aid to understanding the transitions possible in one of the heavier atoms, an energy-level diagram for mercury is given in Fig. 11-3. This shows some of the energy levels most important in producing the mercury spectra, and the spectral lines which transitions between them will produce. Some of these lines are in the visible region, giving a mercury-vapor discharge its characteristic greenish hue, and others are in the ultraviolet and infrared regions. The 2537-A line is the one contributing most to the properties of the germicidal mercury ultraviolet lamp and to the fluorescent lamp.

It may be noted that although lines of 2656 A caused by a drop from the 4.66-ev level and of 2270 A excited by a transition from the 5.46-ev level to the normal level, E_m, should appear in the mercury spectrum, they do not appear there. These levels are metastable, and jumps downward from them are highly improbable, the spectral lines not being frequently detected.

11-7. Mean Free Paths

Experiment and theory give reason to believe that electrons and atomic nuclei have diameters in the range of 10^{-13} cm, and that the effective diameter of the atom is about 10^{-8} cm. Hence the volume of the atom is seen to be almost entirely free space, and the exact nature of atom-electron collisions cannot be readily determined. In fact, there is evidence that under certain conditions an electron can pass straight through an atom without mutual effects of any kind. As an atom and an electron approach each other, they experience forces due to the fields of the electrons and nucleus of the atom and to the electric field of the electron. The exact magnitude and sign of these forces might depend on the instantaneous positions of the electrons in the atom. A collision between electron and atom or between two atoms is actually more in the nature of a mutual deflection of paths due to these forces. As far as the results are concerned, however, collisions may continue to be considered as occurring between elastic spheres.

The distance that an electron moves between successive collisions with atoms in a gas is called the *free path*. The average length of the free paths is called the *mean free path* of the electron.

If the molecules have a radius σ which is assumed very large with respect to that of the electron, and if the velocities l of the electrons are large with respect to those of the molecules, the passage of an electron through a gas may be considered as equivalent to the situation shown in Fig. 11-4, wherein the large circles represent gas mole-

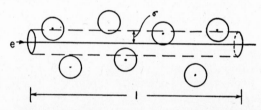

Fig. 11-4. Collision volume for electrons with velocity l meters per second in a gas of molecular radius σ.

cules. Any gas molecule whose center lies inside a hypothetical cylinder of radius σ will be struck by the electron. This cylinder is indicated by dashed lines in the figure and has a length l equal to the distance traveled per second by the electron. The number n of the molecules whose centers lie inside this cylinder is dependent on the volume of the cylinder and the density N of the molecules per cubic centimeter. Thus

$$\text{volume} = \pi\sigma^2 l \qquad \text{and} \qquad n = \pi\sigma^2 l N.$$

The average distance between collisions is then given by

$$\text{mean free path} = \frac{l}{n} = \frac{1}{\pi N \sigma^2}. \qquad (11\text{-}17)$$

The value of N may be determined from Avogadro's number as 2.69×10^{19} molecules per cubic centimeter at $0°C = 273°K$, and

760 mm mercury pressure. According to the gas laws, this value of
N will vary directly as the pressure and inversely as the absolute
temperature, so that in general

$$N = 2.69 \times 10^{19} \frac{PT_0}{P_0T} \quad \text{molecules per cc,} \quad (11\text{-}18)$$

where P_0 and T_0 are the above-mentioned standard gas conditions.
Data on the mean free path of an electron in various gases are given
in Table 9.

TABLE 9

THEORETICAL MEAN FREE PATHS OF ELECTRONS IN GASES AT 25°C

Gas	M.F.P. (cm) Pressure = 0.001 mm Hg	M.F.P. (cm) Pressure = 1 mm Hg	Number of Collisions per cm at 1 mm Pressure
Mercury..............	14.9	0.0149	67.0
Argon...............	45.0	0.0450	22.2
Neon................	78.7	0.0787	12.7
Hydrogen...........	81.7	0.0817	12.2

From Compton, K. T., and Langmuir, I., *Rev. Modern Phys.*, **2**, 208 (1930).

When gas pressures are high, the mean free path is short, and an
electron can acquire ionizing energy during transit of distances commensurate with the mean free path only if the field intensity is high.
As the pressure is reduced, the mean free path lengthens, making it
possible to ionize, or break down, the gas with a lower field intensity.
However, when the gas pressure is further reduced, it is found that
the field intensity needed for breakdown becomes high again, since
there are then so few gas atoms that the probability of an electron's
colliding with a gas atom during flight from cathode to anode becomes
small; that is, the mean free path between collisions at very low pressure may be much longer than the cathode-anode distance.

A curve of breakdown potential plotted against gas pressure for
an electrode distance of 1 mm is shown in Fig. 11-5. The curve is
for air, but similar curve shapes would be obtained for other gases.
The minimum in the breakdown potential curve is clearly shown.

At atmospheric pressure there are about 10^{19} gas molecules per
cubic centimeter. When the pressure is reduced to that referred to
as *high vacuum*, where the pressure is of the order of 0.001 micron

or about 10^{-9} atm, there are still about 10^{10} molecules of gas per cubic centimeter. Yet the molecules are so small and the spaces between them so great that electrons can travel over 10^4 cm on the average before colliding with even one molecule. In vacuum tubes having electrode spacings of 1 mm, the probability that an electron will collide with gas atoms during cathode-anode transit is very

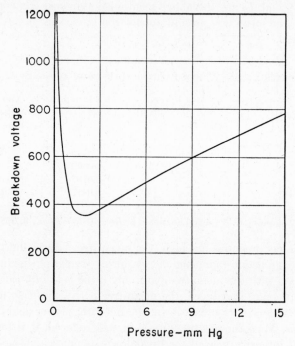

Fig. 11-5. Breakdown potentials for air between electrodes spaced 1 mm.

small. With gas tubes which depend upon collisions and ionization for their operation, it is necessary to ensure gas pressures of the order of 0.001 to 0.1 mm of mercury so that electronic mean free paths are much less than interelectrode distances, and the collision probabilities are thereby increased.

11-8. The Gas Discharge Between Cold Electrodes

Any gas may be ionized by radiation of sufficiently high energy, usually by ultraviolet or x radiation, cosmic rays, and the like.

The gas enclosed at low pressure between the electrodes of the tube in (a), Fig. 11-6, will have a few ions present owing to cosmic rays, but more ionization may be produced by exposure to ultraviolet light. If the potential E be increased from zero, a few of the ions and free electrons liberated in the gas will be attracted to the electrodes and a very minute current will flow in the circuit. As the potential is increased, a greater number of the ions and electrons

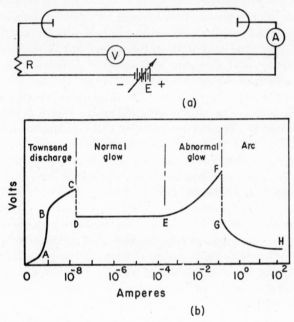

Fig. 11-6. (a) Circuit for obtaining the volt-ampere curve of a gas discharge; (b) volt-ampere characteristic of a gas discharge tube.

being formed by the radiation are attracted to the electrodes, and the current increases linearly as in the portion of the curve labeled OA in (b), Fig. 11-6.

Further increases of potential are not matched by corresponding increases in current, and the region AB of constant current independent of potential indicates that saturation has been reached, and that the ions and electrons are being drawn to the electrodes by the applied electric field as rapidly as they are being formed.

An increase in radiation intensity would result in additional ion formation and more current. Upon removal of the source of radiation, the current would cease, since there would be no continuing ion source, and the discharge would be *non-self-maintaining*.

An additional increase in potential raises the electric field intensity and imparts higher energy to the ions and the electrons in the gas. As the point *B* is passed, the energy gained by a few of the electrons in the field is just sufficient to produce ionization by collision with gas atoms. For every electron ionizing by collision, two electrons and an additional positive ion are then free in the discharge. Further increase in potential may provide the second pair of electrons with ionizing energy, and then four electrons and associated ions reach the electrodes for each single electron liberated by the radiation.

Higher potentials will cause additional ionization, with a general exponential increase in current with voltage, as shown in the region *BC* of the curve. The region *O* to *C* of the volt-ampere curve was investigated in 1901 by J. S. Townsend and is now called the *Townsend discharge*. The Townsend discharge is non-self-maintaining, although the value of current induced by the radiation is increased by gas ionization in the *BC* region. Gas photoelectric cells make use of this gas amplification of current for operation.

At some potential *C*, the field intensity becomes high enough that the energy accumulated by the positive ions in traveling through the gas is sufficient to allow the positive ions to bombard the cathode so strongly as to cause secondary electronic emission. The secondary-emission coefficient for positive ions is usually small, so that some large number of ions *n* may have to bombard the cathode to produce one secondary electron. If the emitted secondary electron can in turn ionize *n* atoms during its transit, *n* positive ions will reach the cathode and again cause emission of one electron. The discharge then regenerates itself, becomes *self-maintaining*, and is independent of the source of radiation for its electrons and ions. At this potential, when the discharge becomes self-maintaining, the gas is said to *break down*, and the value of voltage is called the *breakdown potential*, or *ignition potential*.

Upon breakdown, the potential across the tube falls abruptly to a point *D*, and a visible glow appears in the gas and on a portion of the cathode surface. The discharge is accompanied by a relatively constant tube-voltage drop for a wide range of current from

D to *E*. This constant-voltage feature is applied in various forms of voltage-regulator tubes. The glow on the cathode, called the *normal glow*, at first will cover only part of the cathode surface. As the current is increased by increase of applied potential, the glow covers more of the cathode area, keeping approximately a constant current density on the cathode surface. When the whole cathode area becomes covered with the glow, further increases in current force the current density to rise, and the tube-voltage drop also begins to increase, as is shown in the region *EF*. The discharge is then called the *abnormal glow*.

As the current in the abnormal-glow region is increased, the bombardment of the cathode by the positive ions becomes more intense, creating high values of secondary-emission current and heating of the cathode. A transition results, as at point *F*, in which the cathode's current density further increases, and the discharge tends to concentrate at some point on the cathode. The voltage across the tube falls, and the discharge becomes an *arc* that operates in the *G-H* region of Fig. 11-6.

Owing to the concentration of the discharge on the cathode, the cathode's metal surface may be sputtered off by ionic bombardment; and if the high current density is allowed to continue, the cathode may become so hot as to melt. The voltage drop across the tube in the arc region is of the same order as the ionizing potential of the gas, or even less. Such a value indicates that much of the ionization may be taking place by way of the metastable states of the atoms. An arc is usually characterized by an intense glow throughout the gas.

The arc discharge ordinarily shows the downward slope of the volt-ampere curve from *G* to *H*, indicating negative resistance properties. The current flowing in the tube is then determined largely by the value of resistor *R* in the circuit. Without *R*, the current would continue to rise indefinitely until limited by some tube or circuit failure. The arc is economically the most important form of the gas discharge because with it currents of hundreds of amperes, representing large amounts of power, can be handled.

Arcs are divided into four main types according to the manner in which the electrons that are needed to maintain the discharge are obtained.

Thermal arcs are those in which the cathode is heated by positive ion bombardment, providing both secondary emission and thermal emission of electrons.   An example of this type is the well-known carbon arc lamp.

High-field emission arcs obtain emission of electrons for the discharge by development of a high-field intensity at the cathode surface; tubes with mercury-pool cathodes are of this type.

Thermionic cathode arcs derive their electron emission from indirectly heated cathodes or filaments, and no emission by secondary or high-field phenomena is needed or desired; gas-filled diodes and thyratrons are of this type.

The fourth class is the *metal* arc obtained in the opening of a switch in air or gas.

11-9. Conditions in the Discharge

Positive ions are heavy, and for a given amount of energy their velocity is low.   The ions remain in the space in the tube much longer than the high-velocity electrons; consequently, for a given number of electrons or a given current, there may be more positive ions in the space at a given instant than there are electrons.   These positive ions then produce a positive space charge which successfully *neutralizes* the negative space charge due to the electrons, and even replaces it with a positive space charge.   An electron near the cathode then is accelerated, rather than opposed, by the space charge.   The neutralization of space charge is the major reason for using gas in certain electron tubes.

In the normal glow operation, electrons are released from the cathode by secondary emission through bombardment by positive ions.   The secondary electron energy is low on emission, but the electrons are in a positive-field region created by positive ions drifting toward the negative cathode.   The electron need travel only a short distance to attain ionizing, or exciting, energy, and then upon collision an atom may be excited, or ionized.   If excited, the atom will return to normal and release a flash of characteristic radiation, which accounts for the bright glow seen close to the cathode surface.

In arc discharges the conditions are essentially the same.   At the cathode are congregated slow-moving positive ions in great density, setting up a positive space charge which limits the positive-ion current flowing to the cathode.   The three-halves-power law actually applies here to the positive ions, with the space region constituting the source and the cathode receiving the ions.   As in the normal glow, electrons emitted from the cathode are quickly accelerated by the positive field and reach ionizing energy, contributing further to the positive-ion density near the cathode. The gathering of positive ions near the cathode is called the *cathode sheath.*

Because of the shielding of the cathode from the anode by the positive-ion sheath, electric force lines from the cathode terminate on positive ions close by. Since no electric field can exist between two positive charges, the field between the anode and the positive ions is zero. Consequently, an intense electric field exists in a very narrow region near the cathode, with a large potential drop in this region. Only a small field intensity occurs over the remainder of the tube length, and the potential drop is low; hence it appears that almost the entire voltage drop across the tube occurs in the cathode sheath.

In the *plasma* an equilibrium is reached at about equal numbers of positive ions and negative electrons, all moving slowly and in somewhat random directions owing to the low value of electric field present. If insufficient ions are produced, the current reaching the anode falls because of increase of negative space charge. The lower current reduces the voltage drop in R, resulting in a higher potential across the tube. A higher anode potential accelerates the electrons in the plasma and they produce more ionizing collisions, returning the space-charge conditions to near zero. Overproduction of positive ions produces a converse effect, and equilibrium is again reached at nearly neutral conditions in the plasma. The plasma is, therefore, a region of visible glow, containing slow-moving electrons and ions in practically equal numbers, with normal and excited gas atoms also present.

PROBLEMS

11-1. A doubly-ionized helium atom is equivalent to a bare hydrogen nucleus except for charge and mass.

(a) With atomic weight of helium equal to 4.002, calculate the radii of the first four orbits.

(b) Determine the energy of the above four orbits.

(c) Find the spectral wavelengths to be emitted by an electron in coming from infinity to each of the four orbits.

(d) Compute the wavelengths radiated from jumps from each orbit to the normal ($n = 1$) orbit.

11-2. Brackett has observed lines in the hydrogen spectrum of wavelengths 40,500 A and 26,300 A, representing jumps from the fifth and sixth orbits, respectively, to the fourth. Determine the wavelengths of lines to be expected for jumps from the fifth and sixth orbits to the first.

11-3. (a) Find the minimum velocity needed by an electron to ionize a neon atom.

(b) How far would the electron have to travel to acquire this velocity in a field of 100 v per centimeter?

11-4. A mercury atom has an electron in the first metastable level with 4.66 ev energy.

(a) What is the wavelength of a photon of light needed to raise this electron to the next, or 4.88-ev, level?

(b) If the atom then emits a flash of light of wavelength 2537 A, what has happened?

11-5. A sodium atom is ionized by a photon, and the electron has 1.0 ev energy upon being freed.

(a) Find the wavelength and frequency required for the photon.

(b) If the ion recombines with an electron that reaches the normal state by passing first to a level of 2.11 ev above the normal, what will be the wavelengths of the photons emitted?

11-6. Calculate the mean free path of an electron in argon at a pressure of 0.15 mm mercury, and temperature of 40°C. The argon atom radius is 1.43×10^{-8} cm.

11-7. The pressure in a neon-filled tube is 0.01 mm mercury at a temperature of 70°C.

(a) What should the anode-cathode spacing be if an electron is to make 10 collisions, on the average, in passing between cathode and anode.

(b) What potential would be needed between anode and cathode if each such collision is to produce an ion? The radius of the neon atom is 1.17×10^{-8} cm.

11-8. Compute the wavelength of an electron in the second circular orbit of a hydrogen atom. Show that the requirement that the orbit be an integral number of wavelengths in circumference is met. Repeat for the fourth orbit.

11-9. (a) Find the velocity an electron must have to excite the ultraviolet mercury line at 2537 A.

(b) What would be the minimum frequency which a photon could have if it is to be capable of ionizing mercury vapor?

11-10. An electron, after falling through 8.5 volts potential, collides with a mercury atom having an electron in a metastable state of 4.66 ev energy. If the atom is ionized, what will be the velocities of the two electrons after the collision, assuming the excess energy to be equally shared?   Neglect energy given to the ion.

11-11. Plot a curve of the mean free path of an electron in mercury vapor for the range of pressures 0.01 to 10 mm mercury pressure, and standard temperature conditions.   The radius of the mercury atom is 1.82×10^{-8} cm.   The curve may best be plotted on semilogarithmic paper.

11-12. What is the minimum field intensity required for electrons to produce ionization in each of the following gases:

> Mercury, at 0.15 mm mercury pressure, 0°C, $\sigma = 1.82 \times 10^{-8}$ cm.
> Argon, at 1.2 mm mercury pressure,   30°C, $\sigma = 1.43 \times 10^{-8}$ cm.
> Neon, at 0.70 mm mercury pressure,   30°C, $\sigma = 1.17 \times 10^{-8}$ cm.

11-13. If the cathode-anode spacing of a diode is 0.5 mm, and the gas is argon at 0.1 mm mercury pressure, 20°C temperature, what is the probability of any particular electron having a collision with a gas atom during its transit through the tube?

11-14. If objects can be "seen" only if their dimensions are greater than a wavelength of the "light" used in a microscope, what is the smallest object which can be resolved in an electron microscope using a beam of electrons accelerated by 50,000 v, using relativistic corrections? How does the size of this object compare with that visible in an optical microscope using violet light of 0.4 micron wavelength?

REFERENCES

1. Tonks, L., "Electrical Discharge in Gases," *Trans. AIEE*, **53,** 239 (1934).
2. Jeans, J. H., *An Introduction to the Kinetic Theory of Gases*, 4th ed., Cambridge University Press, London, 1940.
3. Dow, W. G., *Fundamentals of Engineering Electronics*, John Wiley & Sons, Inc., New York, 1937.
4. Langmuir, I., and Compton, K. T., "Electrical Discharges of Gases," *Revs. Modern Phys.*, **2,** 171 (1930).
5. Richtmyer, F. K., and Kennard, E. H., *Introduction to Modern Physics*, 4th ed., McGraw-Hill Book Company, Inc., New York, 1947.
6. Crowther, J. A., *Ions, Electrons and Ionizing Radiations*, 7th ed., Longmans, Green and Company, New York, 1939.
7. Cobine, J. D., *Gaseous Conductors*, McGraw-Hill Book Company, Inc., New York, 1941.
8. Maxfield, F. A., and Benedict, R. R., *Theory of Gaseous Conduction and Electronics*, McGraw-Hill Book Company, Inc., New York, 1941.

CHAPTER 12

GAS DIODES

Since truly high vacuums were difficult to obtain, tubes containing small quantities of gas were studied very early in electronic history, and it was well known that the properties of such tubes were widely different from those in which a good vacuum existed. In fact, at one time it was believed that electronic conduction through space was impossible without the presence of gas. Langmuir subsequently disproved this, and in studying conduction in both high vacuums and in gases he contributed greatly to progress in both fields.

Subsequent development, building on the work of Langmuir and others, has made available a great variety of gaseous conduction tubes. The gas tube is similar to the vacuum tube in general construction but differs radically in some applications. It is designed to rectify and control large quantities of electric power. Because of its high efficiency and low maintenance costs, the gas tube has displaced some types of rotating electric machinery.

12-1. Formation of the Arc

The gas diode consists of an anode and cathode sealed in an evacuated container into which has been introduced an inert gas at a pressure ranging from a few microns to a few millimeters of mercury (1 micron is 10^{-6} m Hg pressure). The anode is usually made from nickel, molybdenum, or graphite, whereas the cathode may be a coated metal plate, a pool of liquid mercury, or a heated thermionic cathode. The gases most frequently used are argon, neon, hydrogen, xenon, and mercury vapor.

If electrons are emitted from the cathode but no positive potential is applied to the anode, the cathode will be surrounded by a space charge of negative electrons. If a very small positive voltage is connected to the anode, an electron current whose value is determined by the negative-space-charge laws will flow to the anode. Since the cathode-anode spacing in gas tubes is relatively large, the current will be very small. As the anode potential is increased further, electrons emitted from the cathode are given higher energy, although the current is still limited by the negative space charge.

At a value of anode voltage somewhat above the gas-ionization potential, a few electrons will obtain sufficient energy to cause ionization when they collide with gas atoms, with the resultant formation of a few positive ions and free electrons. The positive ions neutralize part of the space charge, allowing more electrons to flow and to acquire ionizing energy: these electrons produce still more ions which neutralize additional space charge in a cumulative effect. This process leads to the formation of an arc discharge, with positive space charge surrounding the cathode and a large electron current flowing with small voltage drop. The whole operation from formation of the first positive ion to complete operation as an arc may take place within 10 μsec. The main function of the gas in the space is to form positive ions which *neutralize the negative space charge*, thus permitting large anode currents to flow.

The arc can be maintained only by a continuing source of electrons. These electrons may be obtained from the cathode by either thermionic, secondary, or high-field emission. Frequently these types of emission may be combined in a single tube.

In general, the conditions in the arc are those discussed in Chapter 11. The potential required to start the arc is the breakdown voltage, and for mercury vapor this may approximate 15 to 20 v at gas pressures usually employed. After the arc is established the tube potential falls somewhat; the final level depends on the type of cathode but is usually somewhat above the ionizing potential of the gas. In some cases where ionization by metastable states occurs, the voltage across the tube may be less than the ionization potential.

With the thermionic cathode, part of the energy of ionization is supplied to the electrons as energy of emission. When the electron emission is produced by positive-ion bombardment of the cathode to obtain secondary electrons, the work function energy must be supplied by the positive ions. The tube voltage, or *tube drop*, will be higher in such tubes to provide this energy.

Most of the tube drop will appear across the positive-ion sheath close to the cathode surface. The electrons leaving the cathode are accelerated by the field and are then capable of producing ionization along their path. Outside the cathode sheath, practically equal numbers of ions and electrons fill the space in the plasma. The field intensity is small in this region owing to the small potential between cathode sheath and anode. Electrons drift in a random manner with a net movement toward the anode at a rate sufficient to maintain the anode current.

12-2. The Thermionic Cathode in a Gas Tube

The most efficient thermionic cathodes and those most adaptable to design for large emission currents are oxide-coated. When used in a gas discharge the cathode, being negative, is bombarded by positive gas ions. If the voltage across the tube is sufficiently great, the energies acquired by the gas ions become large enough to knock off particles of the oxide coating from the cathode, thereby adversely affecting cathode life. In fact, under certain conditions, the entire cathode coating can be removed in a few seconds' bombardment. With the oxide coating gone, the cathode becomes base metal, operated at a temperature so low that the emission is negligible. The effect on the cathode is much as if the gas ions had sharp corners and sand-blasted the cathode surface.

Hull (Ref. 1) discovered that the destruction rate of the cathode could be minimized and reasonable cathode life obtained if the energies of the positive ions could be kept below a certain value. For mercury vapor, if the voltage across the tube is maintained at values less than 24, the rate of loss of cathode material by bombardment will be low enough to permit the economical construction of oxide-coated cathodes having 10,000 or more hours of operating life. Since the ionizing potential of mercury is 10.4 v and normal tube voltages of approximately this magnitude can be maintained under proper gas pressures, mercury vapor tubes with oxide-coated cathodes can be operated with reasonable factors of safety. Safe operating voltages in other gases may be higher owing to the lower mass of the ions.

If voltages are kept under the safe limit, the energies of the ions are also below the value at which secondary emission by ionic bombardment can occur at the cathode. Consequently, to operate the cathode safely, no dependence can be placed on secondary emission as a source of electrons from the cathode. The cathode must then be designed to deliver by thermionic emission all the electrons needed to maintain the desired or rated maximum anode current in the external circuit. For a given oxide coating the emission is a function of the area of surface available, and this can be readily set at a value to give any desired emission.

The cathode efficiency depends not only on the ability of the emitting surface but also on the heat input required to raise the surface to the operating temperature. If a means can be found to shield a given amount of cathode area from radiant heat loss, the heat required will be reduced, and the emission efficiency will rise correspondingly.

In the vacuum tube, any confined spaces near the cathode must be eliminated or the electron concentrations built up will produce high negative space-charge values, thereby cutting off the emission. The gas atoms, by collision with electrons in a gas tube, cause the electron paths to be quite random in direction, and the collisions make possible turning of the electrons from straight-line paths. Concentrations of negative space charge in cathode recesses are neutralized by the presence of positive gas ions in the gas discharge, so that cathodes can be built in confined spaces, the electrons still will be able to find an exit, and no limiting of the emission will occur. As a result, a heated cathode surface for a gas tube may be placed in a confined space and shielded to reduce heat loss by radiation, and the designed emission may still be obtained.

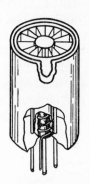

Fig. 12-1. Heat-shielded indirectly heated cathode as used in a hot-cathode gas tube.

Such cathodes for gas tubes, called *heat-shielded cathodes*, are generally used with much increased efficiency. An example of a nonshielded cathode is in the 9C25 transmitting triode with a thoriated-tungsten filament requiring 1710 w of heating power for a rated cathode current of 4 amp. The type FG-172 mercury-vapor tube with a thoroughly heat-shielded cathode requires only 50 w heating power for a rated cathode current of 1.25 amperes. Heat-shielded cathodes are usually made with nickel fins radiating from a nickel tube containing a tungsten-wire heater coil. The surfaces of the fins and tube are coated with a barium-oxide layer. The whole is surrounded by several concentric heat shields of polished nickel sheet, with openings at one end for the electrons to emerge.   A cathode of this type is illustrated in Fig. 12-1.   Similar cathodes are also built with heat shields surrounding a filament, which is folded or bent to fit into a very small space.

If the resistance in the external anode circuit is reduced to a point where the current drawn from the cathode is greater than the emitted value, the voltage across the tube will rise and positive ions will be given greater energy, so that the additional emission needed is obtained by secondary emission, and the tube will provide the additional load current.   However, while bombarding the cathode and producing the needed secondary electrons, the positive ions may also be destroying the cathode surface.

If the anode voltage is applied at the same time as the filament or heater potential, the current demanded by the external circuit will be greater than the emission during the time taken for the cathode to come up to operating temperature.   Positive-ion bombardment and possible damage to the cathode may result, large particles of cathode surface even being seen flying off the cathode as apparent sparks.   To avoid damage, the anode potential should not be applied until the cathode has had sufficient time to reach operating temperature, although some small tubes may be started under anode potential.   For different tube sizes and designs the cathode heating time may run from 5 sec to 30 min.

In mercury-vapor tubes, low ambient temperature will cause a low pressure of the mercury vapor.   This will make production of ions by collision difficult owing to the smaller number of gas atoms free in the space.   If insufficient ions are produced to neutralize the space charge, the tube voltage will rise, and the electrons will then acquire more energy, making ionization easier or more probable. The positive ions also receive more energy and may damage the cathode by bombardment.   Low ambient temperatures are thus to be avoided in mercury-vapor tube operation, possibly by the use of heating elements near the tubes.   Tubes containing atmospheres of other gases change their pressures only slightly with temperature, and no precautions need be taken to avoid low temperatures.

The anode in such a gas tube is not a source of emitted electrons. Therefore, upon reversal of polarity of the applied voltage, the positive ions in the space will migrate to the anode and the tube walls, recombining with electrons available or attracted there, and the

space will be said to have been *deionized*.   Since no current can flow
in the reverse direction, all gas diodes of the type described are
inherently rectifiers.

12-3. Hot-Cathode Gas Diodes

An envelope of glass or steel containing a gas at low pressure,
and enclosing an anode and a thermionic cathode, is called a *gas-
filled* diode, or *phanotron*, meaning a tube with a visible glow.   The
cathodes are usually oxide-coated, and for small current capacities
are filamentary.   The filaments are usually wound in spirals or are
deeply corrugated to provide partial heat shielding.   In larger tubes,
indirectly heated cathodes are preferred to provide greater emission
area, and these are usually very completely heat-shielded to raise
the emission efficiency.   The anodes for small tubes are simple
circular plates of nickel; but in tubes of higher ratings, large blocks
of graphite are provided because of the excellent heat-radiating
properties of the material.

Any of the inert gases, such as argon, may be used at a pressure
of 0.1 to 0.5 mm of mercury.   The inert gases change in gas pressure
only slightly with changes in temperature, and consequently the
tube characteristics are almost independent of ambient temperature.
A more common gas is mercury vapor, provided by distilling into
the tube a few drops of mercury during the exhaust process.   Tube

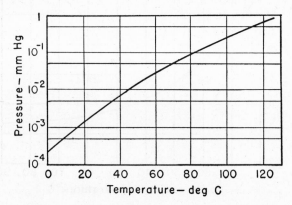

Fig. 12-2.   Variation of mercury vapor pressure with
temperature.

voltages to be expected with argon and the other gases are usually somewhat higher than for mercury, resulting in increased tube losses. Mercury vapor is preferred for applications in which variations of characteristics with temperature are not critical. For mercury, the pressure corresponds to that of mercury vapor at the temperature of the point at which condensation occurs in the tube; the variation in pressure is shown in Fig. 12-2. The usual operating

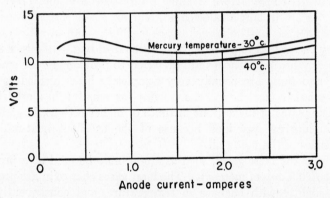

Fig. 12-3.   Variation of the tube drop with load current for FG-32 phanotron.

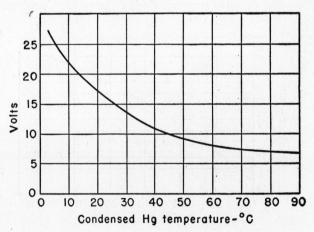

Fig. 12-4.   Variation of tube drop with condensed-mercury temperature.   Current constant at 2.5 amperes.

temperature of the condensing point will be in the range of 20° to 80°C, resulting in pressures between 0.001 and 0.1 mm of mercury.

With mercury vapor the tube-voltage drop will approximate 10 to 12, and at such a low value of tube voltage the possible efficiency is high. Since the internal loss at the anode is equal to the product of tube-voltage drop and plate current, the anode power dissipation is not a serious consideration.

The tube-voltage drop, *tube drop*, or *arc drop* is measured by passing various direct current values through the tube and measuring the voltage across the tube. If the condensed mercury temperature is

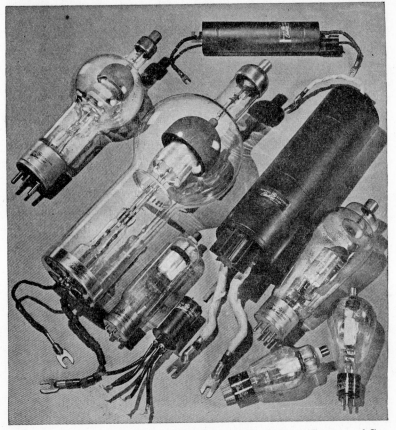

Fig. 12-5. Collection of hot-cathode mercury vapor diodes. (Courtesy of General Electric Co.)

maintained constant, the tube drop may be found to vary with load current as shown in Fig. 12-3. These curves show that the tube drop is almost entirely independent of current flow through the tube.

The tube drop may be measured at several values of temperature with a constant current flowing and the effect of changes of gas concentration in the discharge shown by the changes in tube voltage. At low temperatures there are few mercury atoms in the space, and the probability of collisions between electrons and atoms is reduced, thereby decreasing the number of positive ions formed. The tube drop therefore rises owing to less complete neutralization of negative space charge and is shown in Fig. 12-4. To avoid operation with tube voltages above the disintegration voltage of the cathode, the temperature of the condensed mercury should never be less than some low limit. This is frequently chosen as 20°C, producing a tube drop of about 17 v, with the disintegration value near 24 v. Allowance is thus made in the voltage values for a safety factor to provide for variations in different tubes.

Several sizes of gas diodes are shown in Fig. 12-5. Compared with vacuum tubes, gas diodes have very large power-handling capabilities, since the losses are small owing to the low tube drop. Tubes with current ratings ranging from 0.125 to 75 amp are available, with peak inverse voltage ratings up to 15,000.

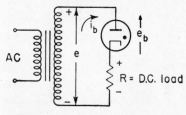

Fig. 12-6. Simple circuit for the hot-cathode gas diode. The dot inside the symbol indicates a gas-filled device.

In the simple rectifier of Fig. 12-6, a circuit equation written while the applied alternating voltage has the polarity indicated would be

$$e = e_b + i_b R.$$

The value of e_b, the tube drop, is relatively constant and is independent of current, so that as the applied emf e is increased, i_b must increase to maintain the voltage equation in balance. Likewise, if R is reduced, the current will increase. It can then be seen that the value of R is the factor which limits the current flowing in the circuit; if R were zero, the current would increase without limit until tube damage occurred. Consequently, *arc discharge tubes must always be operated in series with sufficient resistance load to limit the current to a safe value.*

12-4. Mercury-Cathode Rectifiers

An early and widely used form of gaseous discharge tube was the *mercury-arc*, or *mercury-pool*, rectifier. A simple form of early design is shown in Fig. 12-7 connected for use as a single-phase full-wave, or biphase, rectifier. Such a tube consists of a glass chamber, highly evacuated, and containing a pool of liquid mercury as a cathode in conjunction with one or more metal or graphite anodes. The space above the pool cathode will then be filled with mercury vapor at a pressure determined by the temperature of condensing mercury at the coolest spot on the bulb.

Electron emission from a liquid cathode, such as the mercury pool, occurs when a *cathode spot* is formed on the mercury surface. The cathode spot shows itself as one of more bright points of light which dance over the

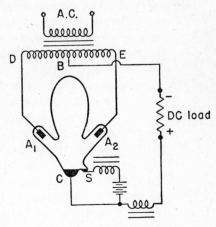

Fig. 12-7. Early form of the mercury-arc rectifier in a usual circuit.

mercury surface. Measurements indicate that the current densities at the point of emission run quite high, up to as much as 100 amp per square millimeter, and that the number of the spots varies to maintain roughly constant current density per spot. The cathode spot can best be initiated by a small spark at the surface of the mercury. The spark seems to produce the first electrons and positive ions; and if one of the anodes happens to be positive with respect to the cathode, the electrons are attracted to the anode, thereby producing additional ionization on the way which neutralizes the negative space charge and establishes the arc to the anode.

The theory of operation of the mercury-pool cathode is not well established. Langmuir has suggested that the cathode arc is maintained by a form of high-field emission. He theorized that the spark forms a positive space-charge sheath of ions very close to the cathode surface, so that the electric-field intensity established is sufficient for the emission of large numbers of electrons.

That the effect is not thermionic in nature is shown by measurements of the temperature of the cathode spot. These data are obtained by observations of the rate of evaporation of mercury from the spot, and show temperatures of only 250° to 350°C, much too low to permit thermionic emission of currents of the magnitude observed. The current densities are much higher, and the cathode area and volume are much smaller, than those encountered in other forms of electron emission; therefore it cannot be said definitely that the usual theories of emission apply. At present, however, the high-field theory seems to explain the phenomena satisfactorily.

The spark to start the cathode spot can be produced in several ways. One means is illustrated in Fig. 12-7, where a small pool of mercury is contained in a side arm of the tube and is connected to the main cathode through a battery and inductance coil. The discharge is started by mechanically tipping the tube until mercury from the main cathode pool C flows into the side arm, establishing a current flow through the inductor. The tube is then tipped back, and when the pools separate (breaking the current in the inductive circuit) a spark jumps between the pools, thereby forming the cathode spot. If either anode A_1 or A_2 is positive, the discharge carries over to that anode and establishes current flow in the load circuit.

A second starting method replaces the side-arm mercury pool with a steel block sealed into the tube on a spring and connected to the inductor and battery. A magnet may then be used for pulling the steel block into the mercury. Removal of the magnet allows the steel to fly out of the mercury, opening the inductive circuit and causing the spark on the mercury surface. A third method uses a steel plunger operated externally by a solenoid coil to close and open the starting anode circuit. All these methods are mechanical and slow, and are unsuitable for use except at infrequent intervals.

If the arc initially starts to anode A_1, it will continue until the voltage between anode and pool cathode falls below the value of the arc drop. The arc will then go out; the positive ions will diffuse to the anode and tube walls and recombine to form neutral atoms; and the space will become deionized. By the time the voltage on anode A_2 on the other half cycle becomes sufficiently positive to support the arc, no positive ions or cathode spot will exist. The tube would then have to be restarted each half cycle by tipping or by one of the other mechanical means, an obviously impossible situation for these devices. If, however, an inductance is placed in series with the load, the current is maintained after the supply voltage at D reaches zero by the induced voltage in the inductor; and when the anode A_2 becomes sufficiently positive to pick up the arc, the current commutates smoothly to this anode, the cathode spot having been maintained during the cycle zero. Starting devices are then needed only to renew the arc after a shutdown.

While the current shifts from anode A_1 to anode A_2 and back, depending on which anode is positive, the current flowing through the load will be pulsating but unidirectional, so that rectification occurs. The d-c voltage on the load will equal the average value of the applied a-c half-sine waves less the drop in the tube. The tube drop will be found to be practically constant and may average 15 v. The tube drop is higher for the mercury-pool cathode than for a hot-cathode because the emission energy must be supplied by the arc drop rather than by an external heating circuit. Owing to the constant voltage characteristics, a resistance load must always be maintained in the circuit to limit the current to a safe value, as in the hot-cathode tube.

Bombardment of the cathode by positive ions can do no damage other than to dislodge a few mercury atoms, but more atoms are always available below. Accordingly, peak currents are not limited by cathode emission but by the instantaneous current that can be carried without cracking the seals as a result of overheating, or breaking the leads because of magnetic stresses. High peak currents can be carried with only slight rises in tube voltage. Obviously, the mercury-pool cathode is more rugged than the hot cathode, and higher ratios of peak to average currents can be carried by pool cathodes.

The large central bulb of the rectifier in Fig. 12-7 is needed to provide a cooling surface for the mercury vapor evaporated from the pool by the cathode spot. The vapor is able to condense on this surface, and the liquid flows back down the sides to the cathode pool. For proper operation and to avoid failures due to *arc-backs* (Section

12-5), the vapor pressure and temperature must not be allowed to exceed a certain upper limit.

The glass-tube form of mercury-arc rectifier was superseded by similar structures built inside large steel tanks, with 6, 12, or 18 anodes. In this form, capacities up to 9000 kw have been built with voltages in the range from 200 to 3000. The large number of anodes is desirable to produce a smoother d-c output voltage, the anodes carrying current in rotation from 6, 12, or more phases provided by proper transformer connections (Section 12-12).

The steel tank acts as a container for the mercury cathode. The seals may not be totally vacuum-tight, and vacuum pumps, automatically controlled by vacuum gages to operate whenever the gas pressure exceeds a certain amount, are assembled as part of the tank equipment.

Although the mercury-pool rectifier can operate under heavy peak surges and short-time overloads better than the hot-cathode diode, it requires a mechanical form of starter, whereas the hot-cathode tube is ready to start at all times that the cathode is heated. The mercury-pool rectifier can be built in much larger current capacities than can the hot-cathode tube, which at present is limited to 75 or 100 amp per tube. Owing to inability to maintain desirable high-vacuum conditions, the voltage limits of the mercury-pool tube are now set at about 3000 output. The hot-cathode tube can be constructed to provide output voltages up to 15,000. Hence the applications of these two types of rectifiers are not entirely competitive.

12-5. Arc-Back in Gas Tubes

While the arc current of Fig. 12-7 is flowing to either anode, the full transformer secondary voltage is impressed across the tube between anodes A_1 and A_2. Since the anodes are made of a material that is a very poor emitter at a low temperature, there is no source of electrons for a self-maintained discharge. Also the gas pressure in the tube is made so low that the voltage between the anodes is below the sparking potential for the distance. Without a source of emission on the anode which is momentarily negative, the low-voltage discharge occurs to the mercury-pool cathode.

However, if in some way the gas between anodes should break down or if a source of emission should occur on the anode that is negative, current would flow from anode to anode, thereby producing a short circuit on the transformer. The only impedance in the circuit capable of limiting the short-circuit current is the impedance of the transformer, since the arc drop is small and relatively constant. Transformer impedances are usually small, allowing currents of several thousand per cent of normal to flow. These currents, if not quickly interrupted by the circuit breakers, will destroy the rectifier. An accidental discharge of this nature is called an *arc-back*.

Arc-backs are random in occurrence, but several factors are known to contribute to their cause. High gas pressure produced by high operating temperature increases the probability of arc-back by reducing the sparking potential of the gas between the anodes, and by slowing down the deionization of the space near the negative anode. The variation of arc-back voltage with condensed mercury

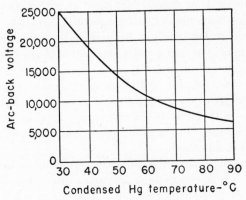

Fig. 12-8. Variation of arc-back voltage with condensed-mercury temperature.

temperature is shown in Fig. 12-8 for an average tube. Considerable variations are to be expected between different tubes. Arc-back, therefore, sets a maximum temperature limit for mercury-vapor tubes, the temperature limit determining the maximum inverse voltage that may be allowed to appear between the anodes of the tube.

An additional factor that contributes to the cause of arc-backs is splashing of mercury on the anode surface, making possible a momentary cathode spot. Evaporation of oxide material from the cathode to the anode is also a factor in hot-cathode tubes and may make anode emission possible. Emission of gas from an anode is also believed to be a possible cause, especially when the gas is released by positive-ion bombardment during deionization of the space surrounding the anode.

Arc-backs occur sufficiently often at high voltages that rectifier equipment must be protected by high-speed circuit breakers. Arc-back in hot-cathode diodes is not too difficult to control, since no ionization exists in the space during most of the negative half cycle. The causes of arc-back for hot-cathode tubes are similar to those for pool-cathode tubes, although since a better vacuum can be maintained, the most common causes seem to be breakdown by reason of excessive gas pressure and the sputtering of cathode material onto the anode.

12-6. Gas Tube Ratings and Definitions

The performance of gaseous-discharge tubes is notably different in many ways from that of other electric apparatus. As a result, certain definitions and ratings have been developed which, unless understood, may lead to improper application of gas electronic tubes with other electric equipment.

Average Anode Current. Although gas tubes are ordinarily operated on alternating current, they are given ratings in maximum average current that can be carried rather than in *rms* quantities. The average current is that value which can be carried continuously without excessive heating.

The major loss in the tube, excepting the cathode heating power, is the power lost in overcoming the tube drop. The instantaneous value of power loss is the product of tube drop and instantaneous current. Since the tube drop is essentially constant, the average power lost is proportional to the *average* value of the current flowing.

Since many tubes operate in circuits with unusual wave forms or in intermittent service, the tube manufacturer specifies a time over which the average is to be taken. This time for averaging may run from 15 to 60 sec or more, depending generally on the physical size and heat-storage capacity of the tube.

Peak Anode Current. Although a current of 100 amp flowing for 1 sec would have the same average value as a current of 10 amp flowing for 10 sec and might be entirely within the average current rating, the 100-amp value of current might exceed the cathode emission or current capacity of the leads, and damage the tube. Accordingly, to protect the tube, a peak current rating as well as the average current rating is used. The peak anode current is the maximum current that may be permitted to flow at any instant.

Tube Drop. The voltage across the tube during the conduction interval is called the *tube drop,* or *arc drop.* For mercury-vapor tubes, this approximates 10 to 20 v. Since the tube drop is relatively independent of current flowing, analysis of circuits is simplified by the assumption that the tube drop is a constant.

Peak Inverse Voltage. To maintain a gas diode as a one-way device, or as a rectifier, and to avoid arc-back, the voltage across the tube in the portion of the cycle in which an anode is negative with respect to the cathode must be kept below the potential that might cause breakdown of the gas. The maximum peak inverse voltage specifies the largest tube voltage that may occur with negative anode without breakdown.

Temperature Limits. In order to furnish a high enough vapor pressure and to provide a plentiful supply of ions for neutralization of space charge while a low tube drop is being maintained, the condensed mercury temperature must not fall below a certain value for a given tube. Too low a temperature may cause a high tube drop, thereby leading to cathode bombardment and destruction.

At high temperatures and gas pressures, the arc-back voltage falls, as shown in Fig. 12-8; and if the temperature rises too high, the applied voltage may exceed the arc-back voltage, leading to frequent arc-backs and possible tube destruction.

The two factors mentioned place both an upper and lower limit on condensed mercury temperature for mercury-vapor tubes. This range is usually taken as 30° to 80°C condensed mercury temperature, which means approximately 20° to 60°C in terms of ambient temperature. If these limits cannot be maintained, external heaters or cooling means must be provided.

An additional factor which must be considered in the use of hot-cathode tubes is the time required to heat the cathode and bring the mercury to operating temperature. This heating time may vary from a few seconds to many minutes depending on the size of tube and cathode.

12-7. Half-Wave Gas-Diode Rectifier—Resistance Load

A hot-cathode gas diode may be used in a circuit such as Fig. 12-9 to provide d-c output into a resistance load from an a-c source.

In order to design such circuits properly and to operate the tubes under rated conditions, it is desirable to analyze the circuit and to determine certain factors. These factors may be the current wave form in the load, the average load current, the peak load current, the power loss in the tube, the circuit efficiency, and the output-voltage regulation.

When anode voltage is applied and increased from zero, the arc does not start until the tube voltage reaches the breakdown voltage. Current then flows, and the tube voltage falls back to the tube-drop value. Since the breakdown voltage is usually only a few volts

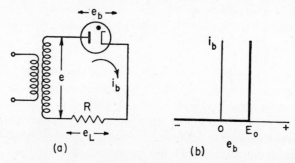

Fig. 12-9.   (a) Gas diode half-wave rectifier circuit; (b) ideal gas diode volt-ampere characteristic.

above the tube drop, no great error is introduced by assuming that breakdown and tube voltages are equal, especially if the peak of the applied a-c voltage is large with respect to the tube drop value.   To simplify the analysis, it is also customary to assume that the tube drop has a constant value during the conduction interval, and that this constant is E_0 volts.   Under these assumptions a volt-ampere curve for a gas diode becomes that shown in Fig. 12-9(b).

Writing a voltage equation around the mesh of (a), Fig. 12-9, gives for the voltages during the conduction part of the cycle

$$e = i_b R + E_0. \tag{12-1}$$

If the input voltage is assumed sinusoidal, the current may be written as

$$i_b = \frac{E_m \sin \omega t - E_0}{R}. \tag{12-2}$$

A reverse, or negative, current through the diode is impossible as a normal condition; therefore the current i_b must be zero for all negative values of the numerator of Eq. 12-2. Setting the numerator of Eq. 12-2 to zero to obtain the starting angle for conduction gives

$$\alpha_1 = \sin^{-1}\frac{E_0}{E_m}. \tag{12-3}$$

If the breakdown voltage were sufficiently different from E_0 to be considered, E_0 should be replaced by the breakdown value in Eq. 12-3.

The cutout or stopping angle, α_2, is

$$\alpha_2 = 180° - \sin^{-1}\frac{E_0}{E_m}; \tag{12-4}$$

and if the breakdown voltage has been neglected in calculating α_1, then

$$\alpha_2 = 180° - \alpha_1.$$

Gas-tube rectifier circuits are frequently employed to operate d-c motor armature circuits from a-c supply circuits. When they are so used, the counter emf of the armatures must be considered in the circuit equations. A like situation exists when a diode is used to charge a battery. The battery emf or the counter emf will add to the tube-drop term in the equation, and the term $E_m \sin \omega t$ will have to rise to a higher value before conduction can start. The proper emf values must be introduced into the circuit equations, and will thus be effective in altering the values of α_1 and α_2. The first step in analysis then is to write a mesh equation during a conducting interval, followed by determination of the conduction angle as above.

From observation of the current wave form in (b), Fig. 12-10, the wave form can be seen as the top of a sinusoid, E_0/R units being sliced horizontally from the base. This is the wave form that would be expected from a tube with an idealized volt-ampere characteristic as at (b), Fig. 12-9.

The dashed curve in Fig. 12-10(a) is the voltage appearing across the tube during the cycle. Starting at zero, the voltage rises until the discharge starts at $\omega t = \alpha_1$ and then remains constant during conduction at the value E_0. At $\omega t = \alpha_2$, the circuit voltage becomes less than the tube drop, and conduction ceases. During the nega-

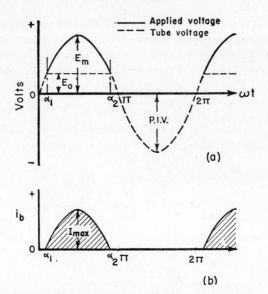

Fig. 12-10. (a) Voltage waveforms in the half-wave gas diode rectifier; (b) current wave forms in the same circuit.

tive half cycle, the tube constitutes an open circuit and the entire circuit voltage appears across the tube. The maximum value of this negative voltage is the peak inverse voltage of the circuit.

The output current of interest in the load is the d-c or average value of i_b over a cycle of alternating supply voltage. If i_b is written as

$$i_b = \frac{E_m \sin \omega t - E_0}{R} \qquad (\alpha_1 < \omega t < \alpha_2) \qquad (12\text{-}5)$$

and

$$i_b = 0 \qquad (\alpha_2 < \omega t < 2\pi + \alpha_1), \qquad (12\text{-}6)$$

the average current $I_{\text{d-c}}$ may be obtained by

$$I_{\text{d-c}} = \frac{1}{2\pi} \int_0^{2\pi} i_b \, d\omega t = \frac{1}{2\pi} \int_{\alpha_1}^{\alpha_2} \frac{(E_m \sin \omega t - E_0)}{R} \, d\omega t$$

$$= \frac{E_m}{2\pi R} \left[-\cos \alpha_2 + \cos \alpha_1 - \frac{E_0}{E_m} (\alpha_2 - \alpha_1) \right]. \qquad (12\text{-}7)$$

By use of trigonometric identities and Eqs. 12-3 and 12-4, Eq. 12-7 may be simplified to

$$I_{\text{d-c}} = \frac{E_m}{\pi R}\left[\cos\alpha_1 - \left(\frac{\pi}{2} - \alpha_1\right)\sin\alpha_1\right]. \qquad (12\text{-}8)$$

The output d-c voltage across the load is $I_{\text{d-c}}R$, so that

$$E_{\text{d-c}} = \frac{E_m}{\pi}\left[\cos\alpha_1 - \left(\frac{\pi}{2} - \alpha_1\right)\sin\alpha_1\right]. \qquad (12\text{-}9)$$

From the definition of the angle $\alpha_1 = \sin^{-1} E_0/E_m$, it can be seen that as the value of E_m increases, angle α_1 decreases, and both $E_{\text{d-c}}$ and $I_{\text{d-c}}$ rise, approaching limiting values of

$$I_{\text{d-c}} = \frac{E_m}{\pi R}, \qquad E_{\text{d-c}} = \frac{E_m}{\pi}. \qquad (12\text{-}10)$$

For many applications in high-voltage rectifiers, the angle α_1 is very small, and Eqs. 12-10 may be used with negligible error.

As the conduction angle $(\alpha_2 - \alpha_1)$ becomes smaller with decreasing values of E_m, the peak value of anode current is forced to increase to provide a given value of d-c output. The peak anode current is an important gas-tube limitation, and its value can be obtained from the current expression, Eq. 12-5. The current will be a maximum when $\sin\omega t = 1$, so that

$$I_{\text{peak}} = \frac{E_m - E_0}{R} = \frac{E_m}{R}(1 - \sin\alpha_1). \qquad (12\text{-}11)$$

The ratio of the peak current to the average value then is

$$\frac{I_{\text{peak}}}{I_{\text{d-c}}} = \frac{\pi(1 - \sin\alpha_1)}{\cos\alpha_1 - (\pi/2 - \alpha_1)\sin\alpha_1}. \qquad (12\text{-}12)$$

The variation of the ratio $I_{\text{peak}}/I_{\text{d-c}}$ is plotted as a function of $E_0/E_m = \sin\alpha_1$ in Fig. 12-11. The curve shows that very high ratios of peak to average currents may be reached for short conduction angles.

The average power input to the rectifier circuit from the transformer in Fig. 12-9 may be calculated from the basic average power relation,

$$P_{\text{a-c}} = \frac{1}{2\pi}\int_0^{2\pi} ei_b\,d\omega t = \frac{1}{2\pi}\int_{\alpha_1}^{\alpha_2} E_m\sin\omega t\,\frac{(E_m\sin\omega t - E_0)}{R}\,d\omega t.$$

After integration and the use of the definitions of α_1 and α_2 and of certain trigonometric identities, the power-input expression becomes

$$P_{\text{a-c}} = \frac{E_m^2}{2\pi R}\left[\frac{\pi}{2} - \alpha_1 - \cos\alpha_1\sin\alpha_1\right]. \qquad (12\text{-}13)$$

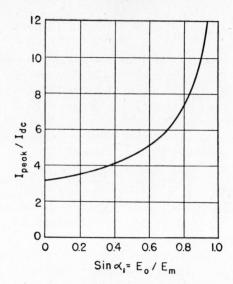

Fig. 12-11. Ratio of peak current to average tube current as a function of E_0/E_m for the half-wave gas diode.

For high-voltage rectifiers where $\alpha_1 \cong 0$ the power is

$$P_{\text{a-c}} = \frac{E_m{}^2}{4R}. \qquad (12\text{-}14)$$

Part of the power input is lost in the rectifier tube, and the tube loss can be found as

$$P_p - \frac{1}{2\pi} \int_0^{2\pi} e_b i_b \, d\omega t = \frac{1}{2\pi} \int_{\alpha_1}^{\alpha_2} E_0 \left(\frac{E_m \sin \omega t - E_0}{R} \right) d\omega t.$$

The factor E_0 has been assumed constant over the interval and may be taken outside the integral sign. The remaining integral can then be recognized as that which leads to the average current $I_{\text{d-c}}$, so that

$$P_p = E_0 I_{\text{d-c}} \qquad (12\text{-}15)$$

independent of current wave form.

The efficiency with which the rectifier converts a-c power to d-c power is the rectification efficiency, and by use of Eqs. 12-8 and 12-13, this can be written

$$\eta_R = \frac{P_{\text{d-c}}}{P_{\text{a-c}}} = \frac{2[\cos \alpha_1 - (\pi/2 - \alpha_1) \sin \alpha_1]^2}{\pi[\pi/2 - \alpha_1 - \cos \alpha_1 \sin \alpha_1]} \times 100\%. \qquad (12\text{-}16)$$

The rectification efficiency is independent of the value of load current flowing, which fact is a valuable characteristic of gas-diode rectifiers.

Equation 12-16 may be investigated for the maximum attainable efficiency, and it is found that it occurs when $\alpha_1 = 0$, or tube drop E_0 is negligible with respect to E_m. The variation of efficiency with $E_0/E_m = \sin \alpha_1$ is plotted in Fig. 12-12. The maximum theoretical

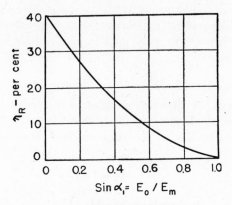

Fig. 12-12. Variation of efficiency of rectification with the ratio E_0/E_m for the half-wave rectifier of Fig. 12-9.

efficiency attainable when $\alpha_1 = 0$ has a value of $4/\pi^2 \times 100$ per cent, or 40.6 per cent, for single-phase half-wave rectifiers supplying a resistance load.

The rectification efficiency should not be confused with the over-all efficiency of a rectifier, which would include the power losses in transformers, and cathode heating power. Consideration of the wave forms of current in the circuit shows that the direct current is accompanied by harmonic frequencies of alternating current. Flowing through the load, these harmonic currents represent power input which is unavailable as direct-current power. This is the reason for the low maximum theoretical efficiency.

The peak inverse voltage is the maximum voltage appearing across the tube during the time in which the anode is negative. Since, from the circuit of Fig. 12-9(a), it is obvious that during the nonconducting period the voltage e_b across the tube is equal to the applied voltage $e = E_m \sin \omega t$, the peak inverse voltage for a half-wave rectifier is

$$\text{P.I.V.} = E_m = \sqrt{2}\,E_{\text{rms}}. \qquad (12\text{-}17)$$

In the half-wave rectifier, the d-c load current flows through the transformer secondary and impresses a d-c magnetomotive force on the iron of the core. If the transformer is not built with an air gap in the core, d-c saturation of the iron may result and may raise the primary current to dangerously high values. Because of the expense of building special transformers with large air gaps, the half-wave rectifier is not ordinarily used in applications involving large d-c output currents.

12-8. Full-Wave Gas-Diode Rectifier—Resistance Load

The full-wave, or biphase, rectifier circuit employing two gas diodes or a two-anode mercury arc is shown at (a), Fig. 12-13, supplying a resistance load. The tube currents, obtained by writing

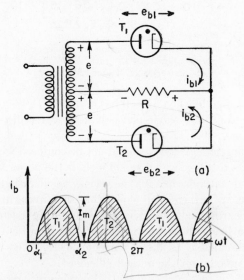

Fig. 12-13. (a) Full-wave (biphase) rectifier with gas tubes; (b) current pulses through the load of (a).

mesh equations during the conduction intervals, are

$$i_{b1} = \frac{E_m \sin \omega t - E_0}{R} \left.\vphantom{\begin{array}{c}a\\a\end{array}}\right\} \quad \alpha_1 < \omega t < \alpha_2, \tag{12-18}$$
$$i_{b2} = 0$$

$$i_{b1} = 0$$
$$i_{b2} = \frac{-E_m \sin \omega t - E_0}{R} \left.\vphantom{\begin{array}{c}a\\a\end{array}}\right\} \quad (\pi + \alpha_1) < \omega t < (\pi + \alpha_2), \tag{12-19}$$

where $E_m \sin \omega t$ is the instantaneous voltage e for each half of the transformer. The resulting current pulses through the load are drawn in (b), Fig. 12-13. The angles α_1 and α_2 are given by the same expressions as for the half-wave rectifier (Eqs. 12-3 and 12-4), assuming equal tube drops for the two tubes.

By use of the fact that there are two pulses of current and voltage per cycle, instead of one as in the half-wave rectifier, an analysis for the pertinent design and performance factors may be made for the full-wave rectifier in a manner exactly similar to that for the half-wave rectifier. The results of such an analysis for the full-wave rectifier may be stated as follows:

The d-c load current:

$$I_{d\text{-}c} = \frac{2E_m}{\pi R} \left[\cos \alpha_1 - \left(\frac{\pi}{2} - \alpha_1 \right) \sin \alpha_1 \right]. \tag{12-20}$$

The output d-c voltage:

$$E_{d\text{-}c} = \frac{2E_m}{\pi} \left[\cos \alpha_1 - \left(\frac{\pi}{2} - \alpha_1 \right) \sin \alpha_1 \right]. \tag{12-21}$$

For high-voltage rectifiers, where $\alpha_1 \cong 0$, $I_{d\text{-}c}$ and $E_{d\text{-}c}$ approach limiting values of

$$I_{d\text{-}c} = \frac{2E_m}{\pi R}, \qquad E_{d\text{-}c} = \frac{2E_m}{\pi}. \tag{12-22}$$

It should be noted that E_m is the peak value of voltage for one-half of the transformer, so that $2E_m$ is the peak of the full transformer secondary voltage. For a given value of voltage applied to a diode, the d-c voltage obtained for the full-wave rectifier is twice that for the half-wave circuit.

Since each tube individually operates under the conditions of the half-wave circuit, the ratio of peak tube current to average tube current is not altered, and Fig. 12-11 may be used unchanged. The full-wave rectifier is simply two half-wave rectifiers with a common load, and the power input will be twice the input for the half-wave rectifier. The power output is proportional to I_{d-c}^2 and is thus four times that of the half-wave circuit. Variation of the rectification efficiency with E_0/E_m is plotted in Fig. 12-14.

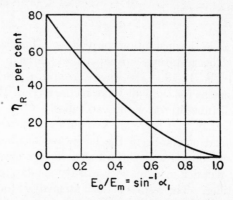

Fig. 12-14. Variation of efficiency of rectification with the ratio E_0/E_m for the full-wave rectifier.

Writing an emf equation around the outside mesh of the full-wave circuit in Fig. 12-13 gives

$$2e = 2E_m \sin \omega t = e_{b1} + e_{b2}. \qquad (12\text{-}23)$$

If a half cycle is chosen in which tube T_2 conducts and T_1 is open-circuited, the voltage e_{b1} across T_1 is

$$e_{b1} = 2E_m \sin \omega t - E_{02}.$$

The maximum value of this voltage occurs at $\sin \omega t = 1$, so that if E_m is large with respect to E_{02}, the peak inverse voltage for the full-wave rectifier may be specified as

$$\text{P.I.V.} = 2E_m. \qquad (12\text{-}24)$$

In the full-wave rectifier, the d-c components of the tube currents flow through the transformer secondary in opposite directions, each away from the center tap. As a result, if the tubes are approximately balanced, the d-c magnetomotive forces due to the two cur-

rents will cancel.   No saturation of the iron will occur, and ordinary
transformer core construction will suffice.

12-9. The Bridge Rectifier

A connection of four diode rectifiers and a two-terminal transformer, as shown in Fig. 12-15, is called a *bridge rectifier* for obvious
reasons.   In the half cycle in which the a-c transformer voltage has
the polarity shown, current
flows through the tubes T_1 and
T_4 and the load R in the directions indicated by the arrows.
Tubes T_3 and T_2 have negative
anodes and are nonconducting.
On the next half cycle, T_3 and
T_2 carry current from anode to
cathode, causing another pulse
of current in the load in the
same direction as the pulse
from the first half cycle.   The

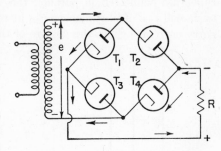

Fig. 12-15.   The bridge rectifier circuit.

circuit is thus a full-wave rectifier in which two tubes conduct simultaneously and *in series*.

Since the bridge rectifier circuit has a tube drop equal to that of
two tubes, it is most often used on high voltage, where the effect
of the tube drops can be neglected.   Another reason for its use is
the possibility of employing a transformer without a center tap.
For high-voltage operation this is an advantage, because the same
d-c voltage can be obtained from a transformer in the bridge circuit
as from another transformer having twice the number of secondary
turns in a full-wave or biphase circuit.   Since current flows continuously in the secondary for the bridge rectifier, and only half the
time in each winding for the full-wave transformer, the current
rating for a transformer when used in a bridge circuit is only about
two-thirds that for the same transformer in full-wave connection.

Observation of the bridge circuit will show that the inverse voltage
across either of the nonconducting tubes is equal to the transformer
voltage.   If this circuit is contrasted with the ordinary full-wave
circuit, it can be seen that when a tube of given P.I.V. rating is used,
approximately twice as large a d-c voltage can be obtained with the
bridge rectifier.

Analysis of the bridge circuit may be made on the same basis as that of the full-wave circuit, with allowance being made for the effect of the tube drop of two tubes in series.

12-10. Parallel Operation of Gas Diodes

Assume that two gas diodes have the ideal volt-ampere characteristics shown by the heavy lines of (a), Fig. 12-16. If these tubes are connected in parallel, the voltage at the beginning of a cycle will rise until it reaches E_{02}, at which tube T_2 will conduct and carry current. Since the voltage of the parallel combination cannot

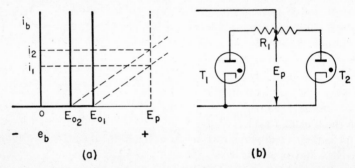

Fig. 12-16. (a) Ideal volt-ampere curve for two gas diodes, including the effect of load-dividing resistors; (b) circuit for parallel operation of gas diodes.

rise above that point, tube T_1 never will conduct, and tube T_2, the tube with the lowest tube drop, will carry all the load. Parallel operation of tubes with the characteristics of gas tubes is not possible without special circuit precautions.

If a small resistor is connected in series with each tube anode, as shown at (b), Fig. 12-16, the individual tube-circuit characteristics will change to the sloping dashed lines of (a). If the resistor in series with tube T_2 is large enough that at some current less than full load the voltage E_p across the resistor and tube T_2 becomes greater than the tube drop of T_1, then T_1 will conduct and share the load at a common voltage of E_p, as shown in Fig. 12-16(a).

The resistors may need to be only a few ohms in value, depending on the current to be carried. Tubes may differ in tube drop by as much as 6 or 7 v, and if the resistors can produce a drop of this value at the desired tube current, operation will be satisfactory. To avoid power loss, a small center-tapped reactor may be used in place of the resistor, thereby producing a voltage drop by reason of its reactance.

Parallel operation may occasionally be needed to enable a small half-wave rectifier to carry a load, but for large rectifiers it is usually more economical to purchase one large rectifier tube than two small tubes plus a reactor.

12-11. Effect of Transformer Leakage Inductance

The analysis to this point has considered the transformers supplying rectifiers as perfect, without leakage inductance. A full-wave rectifier, with leakage inductance L_s for each half or phase of the transformer represented in the anode leads, is shown in Fig. 12-17(a).

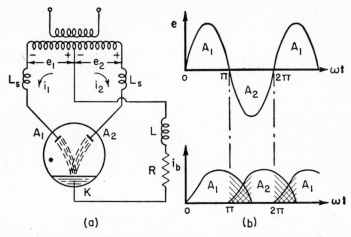

Fig. 12-17. Conditions in the full-wave circuit during current commutation, showing the effect of transformer leakage inductance L_s.

During the analysis of rectifiers with resistance loads, with leakage inductance neglected, it has been assumed that the current flow to one anode ceases before that to the next anode begins. Actually, owing to the effect of the leakage inductance L_s in maintaining the current, the second anode may start to conduct before the first anode ceases, with a resulting overlap of the two currents. If there is appreciable inductance in the transformer or the load, the total current will tend to remain constant, so that as one tube begins to carry current the other drops its load at the same rate, as shown by the crosshatched overlap region in (b), Fig. 12-17. The result is a delay, or angle of lag, of rectifier current with respect to the voltage of a particular anode. The transfer of current from one anode to another is spoken of as *commutation of the arc.*

With the assumption that anode A_2 has just become positive and has started conducting before A_1 has ceased, an emf equation written through both transformer secondaries and both arc streams gives

$$e_1 + e_2 - L_s \frac{di_1}{dt} - L_s \frac{di_2}{dt} + e_{b1} - e_{b2} = 0, \qquad (12\text{-}25)$$

the negative sign appearing on $L_s(di_1/dt)$ because of the direction of current change. If the arc drops may be neglected,

$$e_1 + e_2 = L_s \frac{di_1}{dt} + L_s \frac{di_2}{dt}, \qquad (12\text{-}26)$$

and this equation shows that the whole transformer voltage appears across the leakage inductances. If this were not the case, the transformer would be effectively short-circuited through the two arcs to the cathode.

During the overlap interval, the voltages appearing across the leakage inductances subtract from the voltage appearing across the load, and as a result a lower d-c voltage is obtained than would be the case if the transformer had no leakage inductance. Hence a transformer with appreciable leakage will affect the voltage regulation of a rectifier adversely. Since the transformer leakage inductances are usually small, the effect is not great and may usually be neglected.

The two currents add up to an approximately constant sum during the overlap interval, so that the lag of current behind the voltage may be overlooked and the conduction in a given tube considered as occurring in phase with the voltage. In effect, this means taking the crosshatched area of a given current wave in Fig. 12-17(b) from the rear of the wave and using it to fill in the front of the wave. For simplification in analysis of rectifier circuits, the current is then assumed as flowing to the most positive anode at any given instant.

12-12. Polyphase Rectifiers

Conversion of large blocks of alternating power into d-c power involves operation from three-phase circuits, since that is the manner of generation and distribution of large amounts of electric power. Also, a single-phase full-wave rectifier will produce two pulses of current per cycle; a three-phase half-wave circuit will produce three pulses; a six-phase circuit, six pulses; and so forth. The voltage of the applied a-c waves will also not fall to zero for commutation to take place (Fig. 12-19). The percentage of ripple will be reduced; and because of the increased number of pulses, the ripple frequencies will be raised, both factors leading to greater ease in filtering of the direct current over that possible in a single-phase rectifier. A large number of phases also gives improved efficiency. Consequently, rectifiers with large numbers of phases are desirable.

Individual anode, steel-tank rectifiers are best suited to rectifying large amounts of power. At present they are limited to d-c voltages of about 3000. For producing d-c power at voltages up to 15,000, hot-cathode gas diodes are suitable, but these are limited in power capacity by the cathode emission available.

A great many circuits are available for rectification of polyphase power, but only a few elementary circuits are considered here as an illustration of the principles involved. For analysis of more complex types, Refs. 6, 7, and 8 are available.

In the analysis that follows, the effects of transformer resistance, leakage inductance, and current overlap are neglected, and it is assumed that voltages employed are sufficiently large that the tube drop may be overlooked.

12-13. The Three-Phase Half-Wave Rectifier

The simplest polyphase rectifier is the three-phase half-wave of Fig. 12-18, with star-connected transformer secondary. Since this circuit has a common cathode connection, it is suitable for either mercury-pool, hot-cathode tubes, or ignitrons (Chapter 13). The secondary voltages to neutral are illustrated in Fig. 12-19.

Under the assumption of negligible transformer reactance, a voltage equation written around phase 1 of the rectifier will give, if A_1 is conducting,

$$e_{01} - E_0 - e_k = 0, \qquad (12\text{-}27)$$

where e_k is the potential of the cathode above that of the transformer neutral. From this equation it can be seen that the cathode potential is

$$e_k = e_{01} - E_0, \qquad (12-28)$$

or the cathode is only 10 or 15 v lower than anode A_1. Considera-

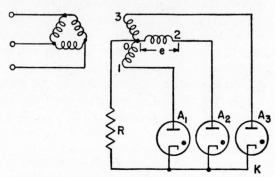

Fig. 12-18. Three-phase half-wave mercury diode rectifier.

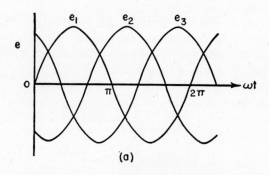

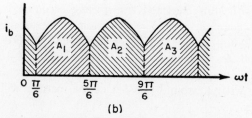

Fig. 12-19. Voltages to neutral, and load current in the three-phase half-wave circuit of Fig. 12-18.

tion of the voltage curves of Fig. 12-19 shows that with A_1 conducting, anode A_2 is negative with respect to its cathode and is unable to conduct until its voltage exceeds the cathode potential by the amount of the tube drop. But if Eq. 12-28 gives the cathode potential, anode A_2 may conduct when

$$e_{02} - E_0 \geq e_k = e_{01} - E_0. \tag{12-29}$$

If the tube drops are equal, this requires that anode A_2 conduct when

$$e_{02} \geq e_{01}, \tag{12-30}$$

which occurs at $\omega t = 5\pi/6$ or $150°$ with respect to the voltage e_1. Since e_{01} at this point is dropping in value, anode A_1 is not able to maintain the arc and ceases conduction, the arc having transferred, or commutated, to A_2. A similar process will occur at $270°$, or $9\pi/6$ radians, when the current commutates between tubes A_2 and A_3. The arc conducts to the most positive anode at any instant. The current wave form per anode is represented by the crosshatched areas of Fig. 12-19(b).

A mesh equation may be written as

$$E_m \sin \omega t - E_0 - i_b R = 0; \tag{12-31}$$

and if the tube drop is neglected, the current during conduction of anode A_1 may be written as

$$i_b = \frac{E_m \sin \omega t}{R} \qquad \frac{\pi}{6} < \omega t < \frac{5\pi}{6}. \tag{12-32}$$

The direct load current may then be obtained as three times the average current of one anode, or

$$I_{\text{d-c}} = \frac{3}{2\pi} \int_{\pi/6}^{5\pi/6} \frac{E_m \sin \omega t}{R} \, d\omega t = \frac{0.827 E_m}{R}. \tag{12-33}$$

The power input from the secondary of the transformer is

$$P_{\text{a-c}} = \frac{3}{2\pi} \int_{\pi/6}^{5\pi/6} \frac{E_m^2 \sin^2 \omega t}{R} \, d\omega t = \frac{0.706 E_m^2}{R}. \tag{12-34}$$

Since the tube drop and losses are neglected, the maximum theoretical value for the efficiency of rectification is readily obtained as

$$\max \eta_R = \frac{(0.827 E_m)^2 / R}{0.706 E_m^2 / R} \times 100\% = 96.5\%.$$

·Tube and transformer losses would reduce this value.

Writing

$$E_{\text{d-c}} = I_{\text{d-c}} R = 0.827 E_m \qquad (12\text{-}35)$$

formulates a relation between the d-c output voltage and the a-c voltage per phase required to produce it. The peak current per tube is E_m/R and the average current per tube is $I_{\text{d-c}}/3$, so that

$$\frac{I_{\text{peak}}}{I_{\text{d-c}} \text{ per tube}} = 3.63. \qquad (12\text{-}36)$$

The peak inverse voltage between anode A_1 and the cathode K occurs when $\omega t = 4\pi/3$, and is

$$\text{P.I.V.} = \sqrt{3}\, E_m = 2.09 E_{\text{d-c}}. \qquad (12\text{-}37)$$

The ripple will be due to three pulses per primary cycle, so that its lowest frequency is 180 cycles. Its magnitude may be computed by finding I_{rms}, the effective value of the load current:

$$I_{\text{rms}} = \sqrt{\frac{3}{2\pi} \int_{\pi/6}^{5\pi/6} \frac{E_m^2 \sin^2 \omega t}{R^2}\, d\omega t} = \frac{0.838 E_m}{R}. \qquad (12\text{-}38)$$

The form factor then is computed as the ratio of $I_{\text{rms}}/I_{\text{d-c}}$, which has a value of 1.014 for this circuit. The ripple percentage then is

$$r = 100\% \sqrt{F^2 - 1} = 100\% \sqrt{1.014^2 - 1} = 17\%. \qquad (12\text{-}39)$$

The direct current of each anode flows in the a-c secondary winding of each phase and may cause considerable transformer saturation with its resultant high magnetizing current. Since transformers which are designed to avoid this effect and at the same time to handle large amounts of power are expensive, this circuit is not in extensive use. It has been presented here as a simple illustration of methods of analysis which may be used for more complex circuits.

12-14. Three-Phase Half-Wave Zigzag Rectifiers

A modification may be made to avoid the d-c saturation inherent in the three-phase half-wave rectifier transformer. The modified circuit is shown in Fig. 12-20. Windings on the same core are indicated by being drawn parallel to each other. Consequently, on each core are two windings which carry d-c current components I_0 in opposite directions, thereby neutralizing the d-c magnetomotive force in the cores. Since the anode voltage e must be derived from

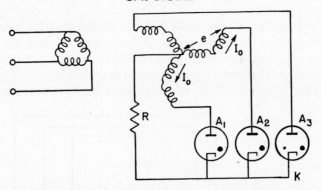

Fig. 12-20. Three-phase zigzag half-wave rectifier, showing cancellation of d-c saturation due to d-c tube currents I_0.

the sum of two voltages at 60°, a larger and special transformer is required, and the utilization efficiency is decreased. However, the avoidance of d-c saturation makes the use of the circuit worth while and economic.

By vector addition, the voltage of each winding of a zigzag pair can be found to be $0.575e$.

12-15. m-Phase Rectifiers

For reasons of efficiency, transformer availability and cost, and low ripple, rectifiers are frequently built having many more than three anodes (6, 12, 18, 24, or more) connected to as many phase voltages. By analogy to the previous section it can be seen that rectification of m phases in a star-connected secondary requires the use of m anodes, each of which then conducts for $2\pi/m$ radians per cycle. The load-current wave form will appear as in Fig. 12-21.

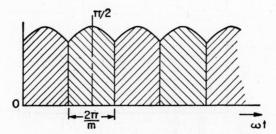

Fig. 12-21. Current pulses in the m-phase rectifier.

Such a definition of m requires that the single-phase full-wave and bridge rectifiers be considered as biphase circuits, which they are. It does not cover the single-phase half-wave circuit, since current conduction in that circuit is not continuous.

Figures 12-22 and 12-23 are introduced for the six-phase, star-

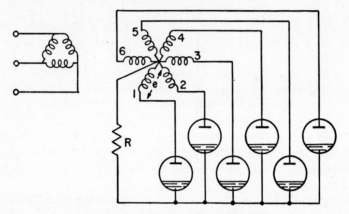

Fig. 12-22.   Six-phase half-wave rectifier.

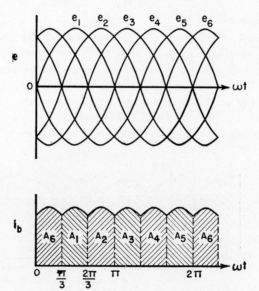

Fig. 12-23.   Voltage and current wave forms for the six-phase half-wave rectifier.

connected rectifier, to illustrate further the type of circuit under discussion here.

Under the assumption of negligible tube losses it is possible to build up a number of general polyphase rectifier expressions. The d-c load current may be found to be

$$I_{\text{d-c}} = \frac{m}{2\pi} \int_{\pi/2 - \pi/m}^{\pi/2 + \pi/m} \frac{E_m \sin \omega t}{R} \, d\omega t$$

$$= \frac{E_m}{R} \frac{m}{\pi} \sin \frac{\pi}{m}. \tag{12-40}$$

Since $E_{\text{d-c}} = I_{\text{d-c}} R$, it is possible to write

$$\frac{E_{\text{d-c}}}{E_m} = \frac{m}{\pi} \sin \frac{\pi}{m} \tag{12-41}$$

as a dimensionless ratio to show the effect of variation of m on the d-c voltage output. This ratio is plotted in Fig. 12-24.

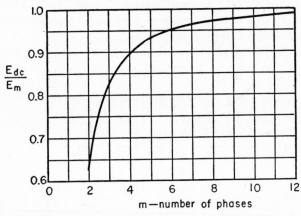

Fig. 12-24. D-c output voltage in the m-phase rectifier.

The voltage E_m is the peak value of the anode voltage to neutral. The d-c voltage produced by a rectifier increases with m, although there is little gain in going above six phases.

The d-c power output can be written as

$$P_{\text{d-c}} = \frac{E_m{}^2}{R} \left(\frac{m}{\pi} \sin \frac{\pi}{m} \right)^2, \tag{12-42}$$

and the rms value of current flowing through *each diode* found as

$$I_{\text{rms}} = \sqrt{\frac{1}{2\pi} \int_{\pi/2-\pi/m}^{\pi/2+\pi/m} \frac{E_m{}^2 \sin^2 \omega t}{R^2} d\omega t}$$

$$= \frac{E_m}{R} \sqrt{\frac{1}{2\pi} \left(\frac{\pi}{m} + \sin \frac{\pi}{m} \cos \frac{\pi}{m} \right)}. \qquad (12\text{-}43)$$

The a-c power input from the transformer is then obtainable as m times the power input per phase, $mI_{\text{rms}}{}^2 R$, or

$$P_{\text{a-c}} = \frac{m}{2\pi} \frac{E_m{}^2}{R} \left(\frac{\pi}{m} + \sin \frac{\pi}{m} \cos \frac{\pi}{m} \right),$$

after which the maximum theoretical rectification efficiency becomes

$$\max \eta_R = \frac{(2m/\pi) \sin^2 (\pi/m)}{\pi/m + \sin (\pi/m) \cos (\pi/m)} \times 100\%. \qquad (12\text{-}44)$$

A curve of maximum theoretical efficiency plotted against m is drawn in Fig. 12-25. An improvement is shown with increase in m, although a value of 99.8% at $m = 6$ leaves little room for improvement with larger values of m.

The variation of ripple percentage can be calculated from Eqs. 12-40 and 12-43, the latter multiplied by $\sqrt{m}$ to obtain the total rms

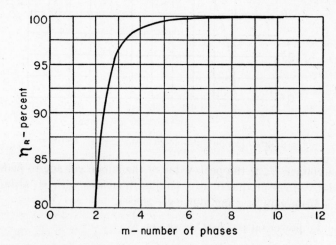

Fig. 12-25. Theoretical rectification efficiency in the m-phase rectifier.

load current. The resultant curve of Fig. 12-26 shows that the ripple decreases rapidly with increase in the number of phases. This condition, plus the increase in the lowest frequency present in the ripple, makes the output of rectifiers having six or more phases easy to filter. Distortion of the primary-current wave form is also much less with rectifiers having m large. This is important because harmonics introduced into the primary circuit may cause interference in adjacent telephone lines.

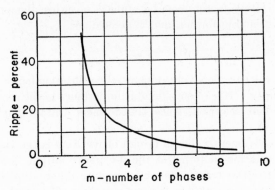

Fig. 12-26. Variation of ripple percentage with number of phases.

From study of Figs. 12-23, 12-24, 12-25, 12-26, it can be seen that the use of six or more phases is desirable from the standpoint of d-c voltage output, ripple, and efficiency. Other factors, such as peak current, P.I.V. rating, telephone interference, and transformer utilization, are also considered in the choice of the actual circuit to be used.

12-16. Transformer Utilization Factor

Transformers for power use are designed for normal sinusoidal current flow and for a power output commensurate with that current. Transformers supplying rectifiers do not always have sinusoidal current wave forms, and may carry current in various windings only over small portions of the time of a cycle. The larger the number of phases, the shorter is the time of current conduction in a given winding. The distorted current wave forms indicate the presence of harmonics, and the harmonic currents cause transformer heating, yet produce no useful output.

To provide for these harmonic currents, a transformer rated at more than the d-c power output is required. This condition is much the same as that due to power factor in a-c circuits; the harmonic currents increase the input volt-amperes without adding to the d-c power output. A measure of the ability of a transformer in a given rectifier circuit to supply d-c power in the rectifier output is called the *utilization factor* of the transformer.

The utilization factor may be applied to either the primary or secondary of a transformer, and is defined as

$$\text{U.F.} = \frac{P_{\text{d-c}}}{\text{volt-amperes}}. \tag{12-45}$$

Because of the harmonic volt-amperes, the utilization factor is always less than unity. It is of considerable importance in the economics of rectifier circuit selection, since transformers are a major item in rectifier costs.

A more convenient value in design of rectifiers is the transformer volt-ampere rating in terms of the d-c power output desired from the rectifier. The transformer may require different primary and secondary ratings, so that it is necessary to specify which is meant. The transformer rating can be obtained as

$$\text{transformer volt-amperes} = \frac{P_{\text{d-c}}}{\text{U.F.}}. \tag{12-46}$$

As an example, the utilization factor may be computed for the six-phase rectifier of Fig. 12-22, by use of the general rectifier relations with $m = 6$. The rms current through one diode is then

$$I_{\text{rms}} = \frac{E_m}{R}\sqrt{\frac{1}{2\pi}\left(\frac{\pi}{m} + \sin\frac{\pi}{m}\cos\frac{\pi}{m}\right)} = \frac{0.390E_m}{R}. \tag{12-47}$$

The total secondary volt-amperes are

$$\text{sec. V.A.} = 6 \times \frac{0.390E_m}{R} \times \frac{E_m}{\sqrt{2}} = \frac{1.656E_m^2}{R}. \tag{12-48}$$

The d-c power output can be obtained from Eq. 12-40 as $(0.955E_m)^2/R$, so that the secondary utilization factor becomes

$$\text{sec. U.F.} = \frac{(0.955E_m)^2/R}{1.656E_m^2/R} = 0.550,$$

and the total transformer secondary rating must be

$$\text{sec. V.A. rating} = \frac{P_{\text{d-c}}}{0.550} = 1.82P_{\text{d-c}}.$$

Two opposite secondary windings are supplied by a single primary-phase winding in the circuit under discussion. The effective current in the primary phase winding is then the effective value of two current pulses. By the definition of rms value, this primary-phase current, from Eq. 12-47, is

$$\text{pri. } I_{\text{rms}} = \sqrt{2} \times \frac{0.390E_m}{R} = \frac{0.550E_m}{R}.$$

The total primary volt-amperes will be

$$\text{pri. V.A.} = \frac{3E_m}{\sqrt{2}} \times \frac{0.550E_m}{R} = \frac{1.168E_m{}^2}{R}, \qquad (12\text{-}49)$$

from which the primary utilization factor can be found as

$$\text{pri. U.F.} = \frac{(0.955E_m)^2/R}{1.168E_m{}^2/R} = 0.781, \qquad (12\text{-}50)$$

and the volt-ampere rating of the primary transformer bank must be

$$\text{pri. V.A.} = \frac{P_{\text{d-c}}}{0.781} = 1.28P_{\text{d-c}}. \qquad (12\text{-}51)$$

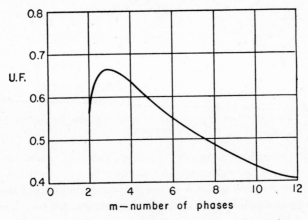

Fig. 12-27. Secondary utilization factor in the m-phase rectifier.

It is also possible to write a general expression for the utilization factor of the transformer bank secondary as

$$\text{sec. U.F.} = \frac{(2m/\pi)\,\sin^2\,(\pi/m)}{\sqrt{\pi(\pi/m + \sin\,\pi/m\,\cos\,\pi/m)}}, \qquad (12\text{-}52)$$

and a curve of this function is presented in Fig. 12-27. It can be seen that a maximum occurs near $m = 3$.

Values of primary and secondary volt-ampere ratings for other rectifier circuits are given in Table 10 (Section 12-18). Computations for circuits in which the d-c components neutralize in a given transformer secondary follow the method outlined. Circuits such as the single-phase and three-phase half-wave, which produce an unbalanced d-c component in a transformer secondary, cannot be analyzed without further knowledge of primary-current wave forms. This phase of the subject is beyond the scope of the treatment given here.

12-17. Some Other Polyphase Rectifiers

The six-phase rectifier circuit of Fig. 12-28 employs the zigzag method of avoiding transformer saturation. Observation will show

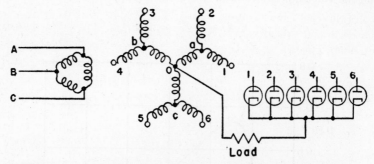

Fig. 12-28. Another type of transformer connection for the six-phase rectifier.

that there are three secondary windings deriving power from each primary phase. For instance, secondaries *0-c*, *a-2*, and *b-3* are obtained from primary phase *A-C*; it must also be noted that secondary *0-c* carries two pulses of current for every one carried by *a-2* and *b-3*, thus secondaries *0-a*, *0-b*, *0-c* must have volt-ampere ratings $\sqrt{2}$ larger than those of the branch secondaries. This gives improved utilization of *0-a*, *0-b*, and *0-c* since they carry current for longer intervals. Analysis will also show that d-c magnetization of the transformer cores is avoided.

The scheme is the basis on which may be developed circuits with larger numbers of phases, by further branching connections at termi-

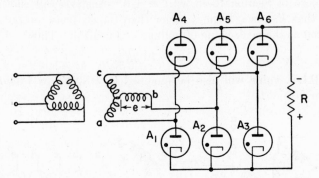

Fig. 12-29. Three-phase full-wave or bridge rectifier.

nals 1, 2, 3, 4, 5, and 6. Only three multiwinding transformers will ordinarily be required.

Another special circuit is that of Fig. 12-29, which partakes of the form of a bridge rectifier, but is sometimes called a three-phase full-wave circuit. Each transformer secondary carries current on both half cycles as in the case of the single-phase bridge circuit. It can also be seen from the crosshatched current pulses of Fig. 12-30 that each tube conducts for two 60° pulses per cycle in series with

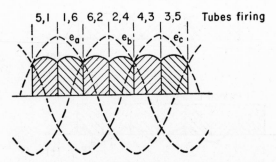

Fig. 12-30. Current pulses, and voltages to neutral, in the three-phase full-wave rectifier.

one other tube. A study of the circuit and the voltage-to-neutral
waves of the figure shows that during conduction the designated
firing tubes have positive anodes or negative cathodes.

The shape of the current pulses in the load is identical with those
of a six-phase rectifier, and current, ripple, and efficiency relations
are those of Section 12-15 with $m = 6$. Analysis will show, however, that E_{d-c} is $\sqrt{3}$ times larger than the six-phase output, if E_m
is taken as the peak value of voltage e to neutral. Thus

$$E_{d-c} = 1.65E_m. \qquad (12-53)$$

The P.I.V. value will also be modified to $1.732E_m$ or $1.045E_{d-c}$ in
similar fashion.

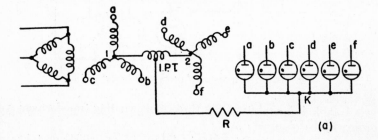

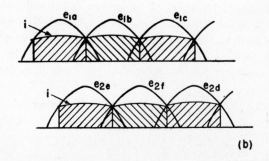

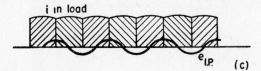

Fig. 12-31. (a) Three-phase double-Y circuit; (b) current wave forms;
(c) interphase reactor voltage approximate wave form.

The circuit provides good transformer utilization and because of the low P.I.V. value is usually applied for high-voltage service. Since the transformer secondaries carry only an a-c current component, no d-c saturation trouble exists.

The circuit of Fig. 12-31 employs six secondary windings connected in two stars, the neutrals interconnected by an interphase reactor. At any instant there are two anodes carrying current, one in each group, and each anode conducts for 120°. In effect, the two star transformer banks constitute two rectifiers which are connected in parallel by the interphase reactor. Point by point addition of the two current waves shows that the load current will have a ripple frequency which is six times that of the supply.

By reason of the unequal instantaneous currents flowing in the two halves of the reactor a three-phase voltage of amplitude $E_m/\sqrt{2}$ will appear across the reactor, as shown in Fig. 12-31(c). The circuit is sometimes employed in preference to the six-phase half-wave circuit because of improved transformer utilization, the current flowing in a given winding for 120° instead of for 60° as in the simple six-phase circuit.

Combinations of the circuit of Fig. 12-31 and the transformer connection principles of Fig. 12-28 lead to a variety of further circuits.

12-18. Summary—Polyphase Rectifiers with Resistance Load

Theoretical data for various rectifiers analyzed by the methods of the previous sections is summarized in Table 10.

12-19. Polyphase Rectifiers with Inductance Filters

Although the ripple present in the output of polyphase rectifiers is small, this ripple is undesirable in many applications, and an inductance may be connected in series with the d-c load as a filter. Because of the small ripple value and the high ripple frequency, nominal inductance values give substantial smoothing of the current. The tube currents may then be assumed as constant during the con-

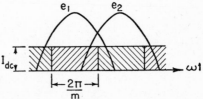

Fig. 12-32. Current pulses in an m-phase rectifier with large series inductance.

TABLE 10
THEORETICAL* DESIGN DATA—RECTIFIERS WITH RESISTANCE LOAD

Rectifier Performance	1ϕ Full-wave	1ϕ Bridge	3ϕ Half-wave	3ϕ Bridge	3ϕ Double-Y	6ϕ Half-wave
Value of m	2	2	3	6	6	6
Av load current, I_{d-c}	$0.636E_m/R$	$0.636E_m/R$	$0.827E_m/R$	$1.65E_m/R$	$1.65E_m/R$	$0.955E_m/R$
Av current/tube	$I_{d-c}/2$	$I_{d-c}/2$	$I_{d-c}/3$	$I_{d-c}/3$	$I_{d-c}/6$	$I_{d-c}/6$
Peak current/tube	$1.57I_{d-c}$	$1.57I_{d-c}$	$1.21I_{d-c}$	$1.21I_{d-c}$	$0.60I_{d-c}$	$1.05I_{d-c}$
E_{d-c}	$0.636E_m$	$0.636E_m$	$0.827E_m$	$1.65E_m$	$0.955E_m$	$0.955E_m$
Fund. ripple freq.	$2f_1$	$2f_1$	$3f_1$	$6f_1$	$6f_1$	$6f_1$
Ripple %	47%	47%	17%	4%	4%	4%
Transformer V.A. rating						
Primary	$1.23P_{d-c}$	$1.23P_{d-c}$	$1.23P_{d-c}$	$1.05P_{d-c}$	$1.05P_{d-c}$	$1.28P_{d-c}$
Secondary	$1.75P_{d-c}$	$1.23P_{d-c}$	$1.50P_{d-c}$	$1.05P_{d-c}$	$1.48P_{d-c}$	$1.82P_{d-c}$
Max theoretical efficiency	81.2%	81.2%	96.5%	99.8%	99.8%	99.8%
P.I.V.	$3.14E_{d-c}$	$1.57E_{d-c}$	$2.09E_{d-c}$	$1.045E_{d-c}$	$2.09E_{d-c}$	$2.09E_{d-c}$

* Assuming tube drop and transformer leakage reactance both negligible in effect.
E_m is the peak value of voltage to neutral of anode voltage.
I_{d-c} is the average load current.

duction angle, resulting in blocks of current of maximum value $I_{\text{d-c}}$, as illustrated in Fig. 12-32 for an m-phase rectifier.

In such a general m-phase rectifier having a large inductance in the load, it can be seen by analogy that

$$E_{\text{d-c}} = \frac{m}{2\pi} \int_{\pi/2-\pi/m}^{\pi/2+\pi/m} E_m \sin \omega t \, d\omega t = E_m \frac{m}{\pi} \sin \frac{\pi}{m}. \quad (12\text{-}54)$$

Since the current in a diode at any instant is $I_{\text{d-c}}$, the a-c power input to the rectifier from the transformer secondaries is

$$P_{\text{a-c}} = \frac{m}{2\pi} \int_{\pi/2-\pi/m}^{\pi/2+\pi/m} I_{\text{d-c}} E_m \sin \omega t \, d\omega t = I_{\text{d-c}} E_m \frac{m}{\pi} \sin \frac{\pi}{m}. \quad (12\text{-}55)$$

The maximum theoretical efficiency can then be obtained as

$$\max \eta_R = \frac{P_{\text{d-c}}}{P_{\text{a-c}}} = \frac{I_{\text{d-c}} E_m \dfrac{m}{\pi} \sin \dfrac{\pi}{m}}{I_{\text{d-c}} E_m \dfrac{m}{\pi} \sin \dfrac{\pi}{m}} \times 100\% = 100\%. \quad (12\text{-}56)$$

The theoretical value of rectification efficiency has been raised to 100 per cent for all rectifiers by the addition of an inductance in the load that is sufficiently large for constant current to flow. This result should be expected, since with constant current no harmonic currents are present to represent power output not usable as d-c power.

The effective current per diode for this rectifier is

$$I_{\text{rms}} = \sqrt{\frac{1}{2\pi} \int_{\pi/2-\pi/m}^{\pi/2+\pi/m} I_{\text{d-c}}^2 \, d\omega t} = \frac{I_{\text{d-c}}}{\sqrt{m}}. \quad (12\text{-}57)$$

The a-c volt-ampere input for all m secondaries is

$$\text{sec. V.A.} = \frac{E_m}{\sqrt{2}} \frac{I_{\text{d-c}}}{\sqrt{m}} m = \sqrt{\frac{m}{2}} E_m I_{\text{d-c}}, \quad (12\text{-}58)$$

and the secondary utilization factor is

$$\text{sec. U.F.} = \frac{I_{\text{d-c}} E_m \dfrac{m}{\pi} \sin \dfrac{\pi}{m}}{\sqrt{\dfrac{m}{2}} I_{\text{d-c}} E_m} = \frac{\sqrt{2m}}{\pi} \sin \frac{\pi}{m}. \quad (12\text{-}59)$$

This expression is considerably simpler than that of Eq. 12-52 and may be readily maximized mathematically, showing that the secondary U.F. is a maximum at $m = 2.7$, or between the two-phase and three-phase conditions. For circuits in which the d-c components cancel in a transformer secondary, such as the single-phase full-wave and bridge, and the three-phase bridge and zigzag of those discussed, the primary effective current per phase consists of two pulses leading to a value of

$$\text{pri. } I_{\text{rms}} = \frac{\sqrt{2}\, I_{\text{d-c}}}{\sqrt{m}}.$$

The total primary volt-amperes are obtained by multiplying by m/n, where n is the ratio of secondary phases to primary phases. Then

$$\text{pri. V.A.} = \frac{E_m}{\sqrt{2}} \frac{\sqrt{2}\, I_{\text{d-c}}}{\sqrt{m}} \frac{m}{n} = \frac{\sqrt{m}}{n} E_m I_{\text{d-c}},$$

and the primary utilization factor is

$$\text{pri. U.F.} = \frac{E_m I_{\text{d-c}} \dfrac{m}{\pi} \sin \dfrac{\pi}{m}}{\dfrac{\sqrt{m}}{n} E_m I_{\text{d-c}}} = \frac{n\sqrt{m}}{\pi} \sin \frac{\pi}{m}. \qquad (12\text{-}60)$$

Calculated utilization factors and transformer ratings for rectifiers with rectangular current pulses are given in Table 11. It may be noted that for rectifiers having values of $m = 3$ or higher, there is negligible difference in performance and in transformer ratings between rectifiers with and without inductance filters. In such rectifiers, the current wave forms are close approximations to the rectangular without any filter present.

TABLE 11

TRANSFORMER UTILIZATION FACTOR—RECTIFIERS WITH INDUCTIVE FILTER*

Rectifier Rating	1ϕ Full-wave	1ϕ Bridge	3ϕ Half-wave	3ϕ Bridge	6ϕ Half-wave
m................	2	2	3	6	6
Pri. U.F..........	0.90	0.90	0.827	0.955	0.780
Pri. V.A. rating....	$1.11P_{\text{d-c}}$	$1.11P_{\text{d-c}}$	$1.21P_{\text{d-c}}$	$1.05P_{\text{d-c}}$	$1.28P_{\text{d-c}}$
Sec. U.F..........	0.637	0.90	0.675	0.955	0.552
Sec. V.A. rating....	$1.57P_{\text{d-c}}$	$1.11P_{\text{d-c}}$	$1.48P_{\text{d-c}}$	$1.05P_{\text{d-c}}$	$1.82P_{\text{d-c}}$

* Based on theoretically infinite inductance.

12-20. Rectifier Circuit Selection

Many other circuits are available for rectifier service. These circuits, although more complex, may be analyzed by the general methods discussed previously.

Transformer costs and low ripple are major items in rectifier circuit engineering. Zigzag windings to avoid d-c saturation, and poor utilization factors increase the transformer cost. Large numbers of phases may increase the transformer cost but they reduce ripple and telephone interference, and permit using many more tubes to raise the total rectifier output. A complete cost analysis of various circuits is needed to provide the economic factors, which may then be balanced against engineering performance.

In general three major tube ratings must be individually checked to make certain that a given type of rectifier service exceeds none of them. These ratings are the average current per tube or anode, the peak current per anode, and the peak inverse voltage rating of the tube or rectifier. Any one of the three may provide a limit to the amount of power obtainable from a given rectifier in a certain service.

Of the circuits discussed, the single-phase circuits suffer from high ripple percentage and low ripple frequency, making filtering expensive if large amounts of power are to be handled. The full-wave circuit also has low secondary utilization. The three-phase half-wave circuit has poor transformer utilization, and to avoid saturation must make use of the zigzag winding, thereby increasing transformer cost. The three-phase bridge circuit has excellent transformer utilization and low inverse voltage per tube. Although conduction through two tubes in series reduces the over-all efficiency, the circuit is frequently used for high-voltage output. The six-phase half-wave circuit has such low utilization factors that it is not frequently used for high power output. The three-phase double-Y circuit overcomes the poor utilization factor of the six-phase circuit but adds the cost of the interphase reactor. This item is not large and the circuit is frequently employed.

12-21. Over-All Efficiency

Although maximum theoretical efficiency of rectification has been discussed as a criterion of rectifier performance, no rectifier can ever operate in that manner.   Actual efficiencies of rectification are always less owing to tube losses.

The over-all efficiency, defined as the ratio of d-c output to a-c input to the transformer primary (and including filament and heater power, vacuum-pump power, control circuits, and so forth) is the actual measure of rectifier performance.   The efficiency of the rectifier is so high that even when the transformer and auxiliary losses are included, over-all rectifier efficiencies will usually be above those

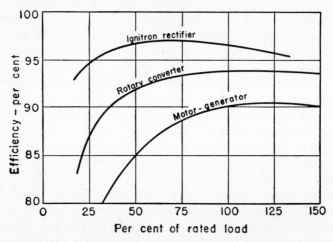

Fig. 12-33.   Relative efficiencies of ignitron rectifiers vs rotating machines, for 1500-kw, 600-v service.

possible for any rotating form of power conversion.   This is especially true at loads below 50 per cent of rated value.   Typical performance at 600 v direct current is shown in Fig. 12-33.   At higher voltages the advantage of the electronic rectifier is even more pronounced.

12-22. Glow Tubes

The normal glow region of the cold-cathode gaseous-discharge characteristic of Fig. 11-5 is employed in certain two-element tubes called *glow tubes*.   By reference to this figure, it is seen that after the breakdown voltage is reached, the voltage across the discharge falls and becomes constant over a considerable range of current, with currents of milliampere order flowing.   The voltage across the tube in normal-glow operation is determined by the material of the cathode and the gas or gases used. The cathodes are usually of nickel and are coated with oxides for easier emission by positive-ion bombardment. The gases used are normally neon, argon, or helium, or mixtures of argon with the other two. The presence of the argon lowers the breakdown voltage of the gas.

The maximum current ratings are dependent largely on the cathode area. In the normal-glow region, the current density at the cathode remains substantially constant, and the area of cathode covered by the glow increases with current through the tube. The cathode area must be sufficiently large to carry the desired current. Maximum ratings are of the order of 30 to 50 ma.

The tube voltages with various gas mixtures are in the range of 75 to 150 for different tube types. The voltage maintained across a given tube may increase slightly with life, partly because of loss of gas into the glass walls and metal tube elements, and partly because of loss of cathode-emitting material by bombardment.

A typical tube for use as a constant-voltage regulator has a cylindrical cathode and central wire anode. A short wire stub extends from the cathode to a point close to the anode, thereby raising the value of the electric field produced by a given voltage and lowering the voltage required for breakdown. The breakdown voltage is always higher than the voltage maintained across the tube in the normal-glow discharge, so that circuit voltages

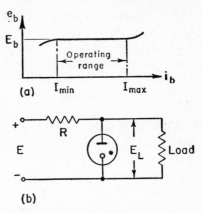

Fig. 12-34. (a) Volt-ampere characteristics of a voltage-regulator tube in the useful range; (b) circuit for a glow-tube voltage regulator.

higher than the value to be maintained must be available for starting. The breakdown varies from 50 to 100 per cent above the rated, constant operating voltage.

A circuit for operation of such a tube as a voltage regulator is shown in Fig. 12-34(b). At normal load current, the regulator tube should draw a current in the middle of its operating range, at (a).

The sum of the load and regulator current will be sufficient to provide a voltage drop in R equal to the difference in supply and tube voltages. A decrease in load current will cause a corresponding increase in tube current to maintain the drop in R and voltage E_L constant. A change in supply voltage will require a change of regulator current for readjusting the drop in R in order again to equal the difference between supply and regulated voltages.

If E is the d-c supply voltage and I_{max} the maximum rated tube current, the resistor R may be calculated by Ohm's law as

$$R = \frac{E - E_L}{I_{max}}.$$

The tube has some rated minimum current I_{min}, and the load may draw any current from zero to a value $(I_{max} - I_{min})$ without passing outside the operating range of the regulator tube.

Voltage-regulator (VR) tubes may be connected in series for higher controlled voltage. The regulated voltage may be expected to remain constant within 1 or 2 per cent as long as current ratings are not exceeded. Since the action of the regulator in adjusting glow area on the cathode is quite rapid, instantaneous voltage changes are wiped out. When used across the output of a rectifier, a glow tube is quite efficient as a filter in reducing the percentage of ripple present.

Very small neon glow tubes with ratings of 0.25 to 3 w are available in a slightly different form for use either as low-current regulators or as small light sources. They are constructed with various electrode forms, and for light sources use the light given off by the cathode glow. When so used, they require a series resistor to limit the current and to avoid damage. This resistor for some types is mounted inside the tube base, making a convenient form of low-intensity lamp for use at normal voltages and in conventional sockets. When they are to be used as voltage regulators, they can be obtained without the series resistor. Their operation is then like that described above for the larger tubes, though with much-reduced current ratings.

Both the VR tubes and the neon glow lamps have had application as voltage-reference sources in regulated d-c power supplies. The constant voltage across the tube is compared with a portion of the power supply output voltage, any difference or error being amplified and applied to other tubes serving as control amplifiers which adjust the output voltage back to the desired value. The small neon lamps have also been extensively used as indicators of circuit condition, that is, as current-flow indicators in computers, counters, and other electronic devices.

12-23. Gaseous-Discharge Light Sources

The glow in the plasma of a gaseous discharge is used in certain special electron tubes as a source of light. Gaseous-light sources are finding many applications, largely as a result of efficiencies of light production above that possible with incandescent lamps. The increased efficiency is possible because the emission of radiant energy occurs directly by transformation of electric energy, without going through the intermediate transformation of energy to heat. As a result, gaseous-light sources are frequently referred to as *cold-light* sources. Efficiencies possible with certain types are from two to four times those of tungsten-filament sources—30 to 80 lumens per watt, compared with 15 to 20 lumens per watt for the ordinary tungsten incandescent lamp.

Luminous-tube lighting of the type used in advertising signs is also employed because of the unique shapes and forms in which the light may be obtained. The discharge occurs between cold electrodes in a gas at a low pressure, and the light comes from the atomic spectra emitted in the plasma of the arc. Neon, most commonly employed, gives the typical red-orange glow. Helium provides a yellow, and mercury a blue, glow. By using colored glass tubing, other colors can be obtained.

Since each tube may be many feet in length, a high voltage, running several hundred volts per foot of tubing, is required to break down the gas and initiate the discharge. A high-voltage transformer of 10,000 to 15,000 v, with very poor voltage regulation, is employed so that at breakdown a high voltage is available, but in operation the voltage is low. The current taken depends on the size of the tubing but may be 15 to 30 ma. A large advertising sign may be divided into many separate circuits, each length of tubing being approximately of the same length and being separately supplied by an individual transformer.

Sodium-vapor lamps are employed in highway lighting. The distinctive yellow color of the sodium D lines (5890 and 5896 A) falls very close to the region of maximum sensitivity of the eye, thereby resulting in maximum efficiency of vision at low illumination levels. The lamps have a heated cathode and are filled with neon as well as with sodium. Since sodium has such a low vapor pressure, the discharge at first is a neon arc with the typical red color. As the lamp warms up, sodium is vaporized, and at full operating temperature the glow becomes a mixture of the sodium and neon spectra, with the intensities of the sodium lines predominant. To aid in maintaining the necessary sodium-vaporizing temperature, the lamp is usually assembled inside a vacuum bottle to reduce thermal conduction losses.

The strong sodium lines are produced in a transition of an electron in the atom from the 2.11-v level to the normal state, whereas the first neon excitation level requires 16.6 v energy. The plasma contains many more electrons with energies capable of exciting the sodium atom than electrons with energies sufficient to excite a neon atom; the production of sodium lines is therefore much more probable than the neon spectra lines. Since efficiencies may be 50 lumens per watt, the lamp is highly advantageous in lighting of heavily traveled roadways, where the ability to see transcends any need for true color rendition.

The mercury-vapor lamp, first developed as the Cooper-Hewitt lamp, is one of the oldest forms of gaseous-light source. Although the original lamps employed liquid mercury cathodes, these have been superseded by metallic electrodes giving thermal emission, with the temperature maintained by ionic bombardment. Lamps are started with neon or argon, and as the electrodes warm up, the mercury is vaporized and the discharge takes on the typical blue-green mercury hue. Although these lamps are frequently undesirable owing to this color, they have the advantage of efficiency and excellent visual properties.

Much of the energy of the mercury spectrum, especially the strong 2537-A line, is wasted because it is in the ultraviolet region. With increase in operating gas pressure and temperature, more of the energy appears in the visible spectrum, and the color becomes *whiter*. Consequently, development has centered on units operating at high pressures. To raise the pressure requires that the gas chamber be small and the arc concentrated in a very narrow tube.

The 1000-w type operates in a quartz tube, and the whole lamp is about the size of a cigarette. Water cooling is needed to remove the heat generated. Quartz is used as a bulb material because of the high temperatures and pressures, the latter running over 1000 lb per square inch. The high-pressure mercury lamp is a source of extreme brightness, approaching that of the sun, and is largely applied as a projection source.

The most common application of gaseous lighting is the fluorescent lamp. As mentioned above, much of the energy of the low-pressure mercury discharge is radiated in the invisible ultraviolet region. The fluorescent lamp acts as a frequency changer, absorbing the energy radiated in the ultraviolet and reradiating this same energy in the visible spectrum. The luminous, or visual, efficiency is thereby considerably increased.

A fluorescent lamp may be built with either cold or heated cathodes, usually one at each end of the tubular lamp, that take turns in acting as cathodes on alternating current. The gas employed is usually mercury vapor. The inside of the glass tubing is coated with a thin layer of fluorescent material which, upon being irradiated with the ultraviolet in the mercury discharge, emits colors in the visible spectrum which are characteristic of the material. A wide variety of materials and colors is available.

A fluorescent lamp requires a reactance or resistance in series in the circuit to control the current flowing, since the discharge has an arc volt-ampere characteristic. In a unit operating directly on an a-c line, a series reactor ballast is used, whereas when the unit is connected through a transformer, a high-leakage reactance transformer is used to give high voltage for starting and current-limiting for operation. A starting switch is also needed in some types to provide time for the cathodes to heat before the arc is initiated, and to provide a voltage surge to initiate the arc.

Life of the lamps is a function of the emitting material on the cathodes, and operating at too high or too low voltage can increase the rate of loss of the material. Each high-voltage surge on starting of the heated-cathode type causes some sputtering of cathode material, so that tube life of the hot-cathode type is dependent on the number of starts.

Luminous efficiencies depend on the phosphor material used, or the color of the lamp, but run from two to five times those of incandescent lamps. This has permitted higher lighting levels without increase in electric power loads in many applications.

A great advantage of all gaseous lamps, except the high-pressure mercury, is that they are sources of large area and low brightness, in contrast to the small-area, high-brightness incandescent lamps. Accordingly, the gaseous lamps produce fewer shadows, are much more free of glare, and when used in large numbers (as permitted by the low power requirements) can serve as large luminous panels and ceilings, thereby producing nearly ideal seeing conditions. A considerable disadvantage has been their ability to generate high frequencies which cause radio interference.

For some applications, mercury discharges are operated in quartz bulbs or other glass capable of transmitting ultraviolet light. The ultraviolet light then becomes available for therapeutic and germicidal applications, the strong 2537-A mercury line lying in the range of maximum germicidal effectiveness.

PROBLEMS

12-1. An FG-32 mercury-vapor diode is used in a single-phase half-wave circuit to supply a 50-ohm resistive load from a 50-v rms a-c supply. Assume the tube drop is 12 v. Find:

(a) The direct current.

(b) The peak anode current.

(c) The d-c load voltage.

(d) The efficiency of rectification.

(e) The power loss in the tube.

(f) The non-d-c power loss in the load.

(g) The peak inverse voltage on the tube.

(h) Plot to scale the wave forms of anode current, supply voltage, and tube voltage.

12-2. For the previous problem, calculate the reading obtained on a d-c voltmeter connected directly across the tube. Can the tube drop be measured in this way?

12-3. A single-phase full-wave rectifier uses a type 83 tube. This tube contains two mercury-vapor diodes rated at 0.675 amp peak plate current per diode, and 0.225 amp average current per diode. The transformer voltage to center tap is 300 v rms and the load is 2000 ohms. If the tube drop is 10 v, find:

(a) D-c load current.
(b) D-c power output.
(c) Total anode loss.
(d) Peak inverse voltage.
(e) A-c power input from the transformer.
(f) Efficiency of rectification.

12-4. A mercury-vapor rectifier rated at 5 amp peak current, 1.5 amp average current, is used in a single-phase half-wave circuit to charge a 6-v storage battery having 0.02-ohm internal resistance. The a-c supply is a 15-v rms source. Assume that the breakdown and tube-drop voltages are equal at 10.

(a) What value of resistor will be needed in the circuit to prevent exceeding the peak current rating?

(b) What is the value of battery-charging current with this resistor in the circuit?

12-5. The 866 mercury-vapor diode is rated as follows:

10,000 v P.I.V.	15-v tube drop
1.0 amp peak plate current	2.5 filament v
0.25 amp average plate current	5.0 filament amp

(a) What is the maximum d-c power which two of these tubes might supply to a resistance load in a full-wave rectifier circuit, a very large inductance being in series with the load?

(b) What is the over-all efficiency while this load is being rectified, if the power and filament transformers are 96 per cent efficient?

12-6. A mercury-vapor diode is used in a half-wave circuit to supply direct current to a 15-ohm load. The source has a voltage of 12 rms. If breakdown is at 15 v and the arc drop is 12 v, find:

(a) The peak load current.
(b) The average load current.
(c) Angles at which conduction starts and stops.
(d) The a-c load current (rms).
(e) Efficiency of rectification.
(f) Per cent ripple in the load.

12-7. An FG-104 mercury-vapor phanotron, rated 3000 v peak inverse, 40 amp peak anode current, and 6.4 amp average anode current, is used in a single-phase half-wave circuit. Neglecting tube voltage drop, find:

(a) The maximum possible d-c current, without exceeding ratings.
(b) The maximum possible d-c voltage.
(c) The a-c transformer voltage (rms) required for (b).
(d) The a-c input power, if (a) and (b) occur simultaneously.

12-8. Two mercury-vapor diodes, rated at 5 amp peak plate current each, are used in a full-wave single-phase circuit to supply a total of 6 amp direct current at 600-v to a resistance load. If tube drop is negligible, find:

(a) Rms a-c voltage required for each half of the transformer secondary.

(b) Direct current per tube.

(c) Whether tubes are operated within the peak rating.

(d) Efficiency of rectification, if tube drop is 15 v.

12-9. Two FG-32 phanotrons rated at 2.5 amp average anode current are used in a single-phase full-wave circuit. The a-c supply to neutral is 300 v. Neglecting tube drop, find:

(a) Maximum current per tube, if operated at rated direct current.

(b) Load resistance required.

(c) D-c load voltage.

(d) A-c power input from the transformer secondary.

12-10. Starting with the instantaneous current wave forms, Eqs. 12-18 and 12-19, for the full-wave rectifier, develop Eq. 12-21 for the d-c load voltage.

12-11. A full-wave rectifier employing tubes rated at 6.4 amp average, 40 amp peak, is used to charge a 75-v storage battery having a resistance of 0.6 ohm. The a-c secondary voltage of the transformer is 220 v with a center tap.

(a) What series resistance must be used to limit the charging current to tube ratings? Neglect tube drop.

(b) What is the length of time required to raise the charge of the above battery by 120 amp-hr, using the series resistor of (a)?

12-12. By accident the battery in the above circuit is connected with reverse polarity. Determine the peak and average currents which will flow, and the conduction angle.

12-13. A full-wave single-phase rectifier, with inductance in the load, has tubes with unequal tube drops. As a result the load current has the wave form shown in Fig. 12-35.

(a) Find the d-c load voltage if the load is 25 ohms.

(b) Find the ripple percentage in the load.

12-14. A six-anode mercury-arc rectifier is operated from a transformer having a 230-v delta-connected primary and star-connected secondary. It is to supply 200 amp at 600-v direct current. Assuming that the arc drop is 25 v and that transformer leakage reactance is negligible, find:

(a) Current and voltage ratings of the transformer secondary windings.

(b) Current and voltage ratings for the primary of the transformer.

(c) If the transformer is 97 per cent efficient, the total power and volt-ampere input to the rectifier.

12-15. A rectifier using a 220-v delta-connected transformer primary and

1100-v star-connected three-phase secondary employs three hot-cathode mercury-vapor diodes rated as follows:

12.5 amp avg   5 filament v

75   amp peak   20 filament amp

3500   P.I.V.   12-tube voltage drop

If the efficiency of both anode and filament transformers is 96 per cent, find

(a) D-c current in the load of 50 ohms.

(b) D-c output power.

(c) Kva rating of anode transformer secondaries (total).

(d) P.I.V.

(e) Over-all rectifier efficiency.

12-16. A three-phase full-wave rectifier is to use a mercury-vapor tube rated as follows.

75 amp avg   5 filament v

450 amp peak   65 filament amp

16,000 P.I.V.   10-tube drop v

(a) Without exceeding any rating, find the maximum direct current, voltage, and power which may be obtained from this rectifier.

(b) State primary- and secondary-transformer ratings for voltage and volt-amperes. Primary service is to be 440 v, three-phase.

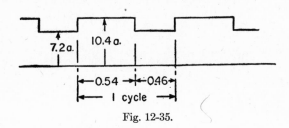

Fig. 12-35.

12-17. A three-phase, half-wave, gas-tube rectifier, using a large inductance in the load, is to be designed to furnish 750 v, 6 amp, d-c. Neglecting tube drop, determine:

(a) Transformer secondary voltage (rms).

(b) Primary and secondary kva ratings of the transformer bank.

(c) Average current rating per tube.

(d) Peak current rating per tube.

12-18. For the m-phase rectifier without filter, derive the general expression for the ripple factor.

12-19. Maximize the expression of Eq. 12-52 for secondary U.F., without filter, and find the value of m at which this factor is maximum.

12-20. You have a number of mercury-vapor hot-cathode tubes rated as follows.

$$2500 \text{ P.I.V.} \qquad \text{Tube drop} = 12 \text{ v}$$
$$I_{\text{peak}} = 15 \text{ amp} \qquad I_f = 18 \text{ amp}$$
$$I_{\text{av}} = 5 \text{ amp} \qquad E_f = 5.0 \text{ v}$$

(a) Find the maximum d-c power available in the following service to a resistance load: one-phase, full-wave; three-phase, half-wave, zig-zag; six-phase, half-wave.

(b) The tubes cost $125. Find the tube cost per d-c kw output in each case in (a).

(c) Transformers cost $15 per kva. Including filaments, find the transformer cost for each rectifier, based on secondary ratings.

(d) Find the total tube and transformer cost per d-c kw output for each rectifier.

(e) The transformers are 94 per cent efficient (filament transformers 86 per cent). If a return of 12 per cent must be paid for depreciation and interest on investment in equipment, and the rectifiers are used 4000 hours per year, find the cost of d-c power per kwhr from each rectifier, if the input a-c power costs 2c per kwhr.

12-21. Calculate the primary utilization factor of the circuit of Fig. 12-22 if the primary is Y-connected instead of delta-connected.

12-22. The circuit of Fig. 12-28 is to supply a load requiring 160 v and 1000 amp, d-c.

(a) If the tube drops are 12 v, specify the voltages and rms current ratings of all transformer windings.

(b) Compute the total secondary and primary volt-ampere ratings if the primary supply is at 440 v, 3-phase.

12-23. (a) Using the principles of Fig. 12-28, develop a 12-phase circuit.

(b) If the load takes 300 amp, 1200 v d-c, specify the volt-ampere rating of each transformer winding, neglecting tube drops.

(c) Find the primary volt-ampere rating under the above load, with supply at 440 v, 3-phase.

(d) Compute the ripple percentage.

12-24. Design a 200-kw, 600-v d-c rectifier system using the three-phase half-wave, zigzag connection. Calculate:

(a) Transformer secondary voltage for all windings.

(b) Direct current through each anode.

(c) Total heat to be dissipated by the cooling system if arc drop is 20 v and a mercury-pool cathode tube is used.

(d) Rms current through each anode.

(e) The kva rating of the transformer secondary.

12-25. A transformer having a 3000-v center-tapped secondary is used to supply either a single-phase full-wave or bridge rectifier. Find the ratio of the d-c power output in full wave to that in the bridge circuit for equal volt-ampere loading of the transformer. If the transformer can supply 500 va, give direct currents and voltages in each case.

12-26. A 10-kw, 600-v single-phase full-wave rectifier has an arc drop of 15 v for all resistance loads. Plot a curve of efficiency using points at 125 per cent, 100 per cent, 50 per cent, and 10 per cent load.

12-27. Find the efficiency of the above rectifier when supplying 50 amp at 100, 300, 600, and 1000 v.

12-28. A full-wave single-phase mercury-diode rectifier is supplied from an unbalanced transformer giving 120 v and 108 v, respectively, on each side of the center tap. If the breakdown and tube drops are 15 v, find $I_{d\text{-}c}$, $E_{d\text{-}c}$, tube loss, and efficiency of rectification.

12-29. Neglecting tube drops, find the secondary utilization factor of a 12-phase star-connected rectifier. Repeat for 18 and for 24 phases.

REFERENCES

1. Hull, A. W., "Gas-Filled Thermionic Tubes," *Trans. AIEE*, **47**, 753 (1928).

2. Koller, L. R., "Cathode Sputtering in Arc Discharges," *Physics*, **7**, 225 (1936).

3. Slepian, J., and Ludwig, L. R., "A New Method for Initiating the Cathode of an Arc," *Trans. AIEE*, **52**, 693 (1933).

4. Dow, W. G., *Fundamentals of Engineering Electronics*, John Wiley & Sons, Inc., New York, 1937.

5. Marti, O. K., and Winograd, H., *Mercury Arc Rectifiers—Theory and Practice*, McGraw-Hill Book Company, Inc., New York, 1930.

6. Cobine, J. D., *Gaseous Conduction*, McGraw-Hill Book Company, Inc., New York, 1941.

7. Chin, P. T., "Gaseous Rectifier Circuits," *Electronics*, **18**, 138, April; 132, May (1945).

8. Winograd, H., "Development of the Excitron-Type Rectifier," *Trans. AIEE*, **63**, 969 (1944).

9. "Standards for Pool Cathode Mercury-Arc Power Converters," American Standards Association Standard C34.1, 1949.

10. AIEE Committee Report, "Mercury-Arc Power Converters in North America," *Trans. AIEE*, **67**, 626 (1948).

CHAPTER 13

GASEOUS CONTROL TUBES AND CIRCUITS

The vacuum tube, although providing excellent control of the current flowing, is an inefficient power device that can operate only with relatively large anode voltages. Addition to the gas diode of the starter electrode by D. D. Knowles, and of the grid by I. Langmuir and A. W. Hull, allowed limited control of the current in gaseous discharges and retained the high power-handling capabilities and power efficiency of the gas tube. Later an electric starter was added by J. Slepian to the pool-cathode rectifier, as another form of current control in the gas tube.

These three developments opened the way to a whole new branch of power electronics where close control of alternating and rectified current is required, as in welding, lighting control, motor control, and voltage regulation and control of rectifiers. The gaseous control tube performs all these operations efficiently and with low tube voltages.

13-1. Action of the Grid—the Grid Ion Sheath

A grid structure may be placed between the anode and cathode of a hot-cathode gas diode to form a fairly complete electrostatic screen. At a nominal value of positive anode voltage, with a large potential on the grid negative to the cathode, electric flux lines emanating from the positive anode end on negative charges on the grid. Only a few flux lines succeed in penetrating the holes in the grid and reaching the cathode. With highly negative grid voltage, therefore, the positive effect of the anode potential on the electric field near the cathode is negligible when compared with the negative field due to the grid. Electrons emitted from the hot cathode face a repelling field and are unable to reach the anode through the grid openings.

As the grid voltage is made less negative, the anode field at the holes in the grid becomes stronger in proportion to the grid field. At some value of grid voltage, a few of the electrons having highest energies of emission in the anode direction may succeed in passing through the grid holes. These electrons are then accelerated toward the anode and receive enough energy so that upon collision with a gas atom, ionization may take place. The resulting positive ions neutralize some of the negative grid field near the grid holes, thereby further reducing the electron-repelling field. More electrons pass through the holes and are accelerated, more ions are produced, and the grid field is further neutralized; and since the process is cumulative, an arc discharge forms from cathode to anode. *The value of the grid potential then becomes the determining factor in the starting of the discharge.*

After ionization begins (the whole process takes only 10 to 20 μsec), positive ions are attracted to the negative grid and the cathode. A positive-ion sheath forms around the grid, or around any negative electrode. Electric flux lines, due to negative charges on the grid, terminate on positive ions nearby, whereas were the ions not present, the flux lines would terminate on charges at the cathode or anode and would influence the fields there.

The positive-ion sheath becomes so complete that all electric flux lines from the grid terminate on nearby ions, and the grid becomes completely shielded from the discharge. Changes in grid potential change the number of ions, or the thickness of the ion sheath, but because of the ionic shielding, the changes have no effect on the discharge beyond the sheath. Therefore, *after the start of the discharge and formation of the sheath, the grid potential has no effect on the value of current flowing to the anode.* As an arc, the discharge current is controlled solely by the external anode circuit resistance.

The grid may control the *time of ignition* of the arc, but then it loses control and cannot vary the current magnitude or stop the arc. The only means by which the arc can be extinguished is by removal of the positive anode potential. This is in marked contrast to the grid action in a vacuum tube where the value of the current can be controlled at any instant and cut off at will. *The vacuum tube may be looked upon as a form of variable resistance, the gas tube with grid being considered a relay.*

Before the start of the arc, current flow to the grid consists of a few electrons with emission energies sufficient to overcome the negative grid field. The grid current will be in the order of microamperes. After ionization takes place, the current to the grid reverses, because positive ions from the sheath reach the grid and are discharged. The positive-ion current may become quite large at high negative grid potentials, and resistance must be placed in the grid circuit to limit the current flow and to protect the tube and circuit elements.

13-2. The Thyratron, or Hot-Cathode Gas Triode

The *thyratron*, meaning "door tube," was developed from the hot-cathode gas diode by the addition of a grid structure to form an all most complete electrostatic shield between cathode and anode. By placing proper potentials on the grid, the starting time of the anode current may be controlled.

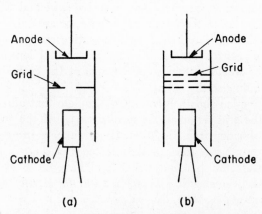

Fig. 13-1. Cross sections of electrode structures: (a) negative-grid thyratron; (b) positive-grid thyratron.

Cross sections of typical thyratrons are shown in Fig. 13-1. The cathodes are heat-shielded, filamentary or indirectly heated, and the anodes are simple nickel plates or graphite blocks. The grid is a sheet-metal cylinder usually surrounding both anode and cathode and with one or more baffle plates intervening. The baffle plates are pierced with holes, the size and number of which determine the effectiveness of the grid screening and the tube characteristics.

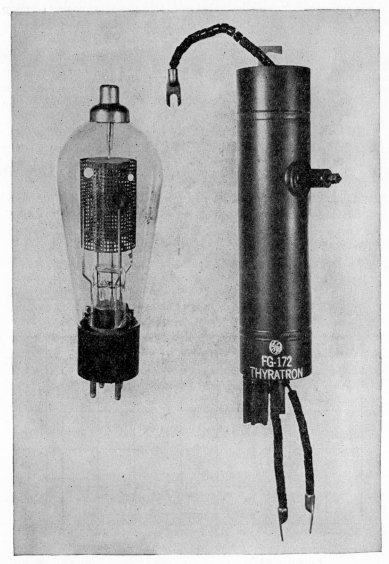

Fig. 13-2.   Glass- and steel-enclosed thyratrons.   Left, rating 2 amperes average; right, rating 6.4 amperes average.

Some thyratrons are made entirely of steel, the steel casing forming the grid or acting as an auxiliary electrode. Photographs of several thyratrons are shown in Fig. 13-2.

Because of the almost complete shielding of the cathode from the anode by the grid and the closeness of the grid to the cathode, small negative voltages on the grid can suppress the effects of much larger positive voltages on the anode. A few volts negative on the grid may prevent the starting of the arc even with several hundred or several thousand volts on the anode. The grid does not have gradual control of the current, as is the case in a vacuum triode: if the grid is more negative than a certain critical value, no current flows; if the grid is less negative than this critical potential, conduction takes place. The value of grid voltage which just prevents ignition of the arc in a thyratron is called the *critical grid potential*.

A curve relating the critical grid potential and the anode potential is known as the *critical grid characteristic*. Such a curve may be plotted by maintaining the tube, if it is a mercury-vapor type, at a constant temperature. A desired value of d-c anode voltage is set with the grid highly negative, and the grid voltage is gradually made less negative until the tube fires. The anode circuit is then opened

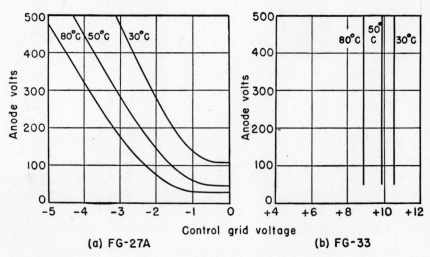

Fig. 13-3.   Critical grid characteristic curves for: (a) negative-grid tube; (b) positive-grid tube.

and the grid-cathode voltmeter is read to obtain the value of grid voltage present at the moment of ignition. This is the critical grid voltage for the anode voltage used. The performance may be repeated for other anode voltages, resulting in curves as given in Fig. 13-3.

In Fig. 13-3(a) are shown the critical grid characteristics for an FG-27A tube with the curves lying predominantly in the negative grid-voltage region. Tubes with characteristics of this type are called *negative-grid* tubes. A negative grid voltage must be applied at all times to *prevent* the discharge. The negative-grid tube has a fairly open grid structure as shown in (a), Fig. 13-1, giving the anode potential considerable chance to influence the field at the cathode. That it does so is shown by the slope of the curves of Fig. 13-3(a).

The critical grid characteristics for a positive-grid tube are shown at (b), Fig. 13-3. These curves lie entirely in the positive grid-voltage region, and a positive grid voltage must be applied to *make* the tube conduct. In certain types of service this requirement leads to a safer type of operation, inasmuch as a circuit failure in the grid circuit leaves the tube idle and inoperative. The positive-grid tube has a grid of very close mesh or small holes. The anode voltage has very little effect on initiation of the arc, or contributes practically zero accelerating field at the cathode. The grid is required to accelerate the electrons and produce the initial ionization. Thus the critical grid voltages are in the neighborhood of the mercury ionizing potential.

It may be noted that the critical grid-voltage curves are functions of condensed mercury temperature in mercury-vapor tubes. The condensing temperature must be controlled or the circuits must be designed to be noncritical of control voltage if the thyratrons are to fire at a desired instant. Hence a mercury-vapor thyratron should not be looked upon as a precision device. Some types of thyratrons are available with hydrogen, helium, argon, or other gas filling. Since the gas pressure in tubes of this nature is not greatly affected by temperature, their critical grid-voltage curves are practically the same for all temperatures. Tubes with inert gas filling may be used where characteristics must be independent of temperature, although the tube drop is usually larger than with mercury-vapor tubes.

13-3. Deionization

The arc discharge in a thyratron can be stopped only by removing the positive anode voltage. Either opening the anode circuit or driving the anode negative, as with applied a-c potential, will suffice to stop the generation of positive ions, after which the arc cannot be maintained. The grid can then regain control as soon as the positive ions in the sheath are removed from the space around the grid. The length of time which is required for the ions to be removed and for the grid to regain control is called the *deionization time*.

The deionization time varies with tube structure and depends on electrode arrangement and the amount of electrode surface on which recombination can take place. The time varies in different tube types from about 10 to 1000 μsec, with high gas pressures and currents increasing the deionization time.

When a thyratron is used on an alternating voltage, it is desired that the grid have control of the starting time in each cycle. To achieve this requires that the grid sheath be completely dissipated during the negative half cycle of anode voltage or that the deionization time of the tube be less than one half cycle of the a-c voltage applied. This requirement fixes an upper frequency limit for thyratron operation.

13-4. Thyratron Control of Alternating Current

With an a-c voltage applied to the anode of a thyratron, the arc is extinguished on each negative half cycle, and the grid may reinitiate the arc at any time desired in each succeeding positive half cycle. If the alternating anode potential e is plotted, as in Fig. 13-4(a), the critical grid voltage for the anode voltage at any instant may be read point by point from a critical grid-voltage curve and plotted as a critical curve for that particular anode-voltage wave form. At a voltage of E_b', the critical grid voltage is e_{c1} volts plotted negative, for a negative-grid tube. If the grid voltage is set at e_{c1} volts negative to the cathode, as in Fig. 13-5, conduction of current will start at θ_1, as indicated in Fig. 13-4. Conduction will continue until the circuit voltage falls below the maintaining, or tube-drop, voltage at θ_2, since the grid loses all control as soon as sufficient positive ions are generated to form the grid sheath. If the tube deionization time is less than the length of a half cycle, the operation is repeated in each successive positive half cycle.

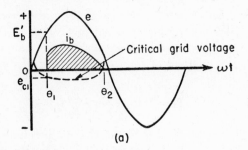

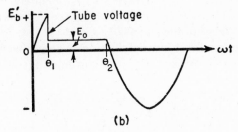

Fig. 13-4. (a) Plot of the critical grid-curve for a sine wave of applied anode potential; (b) the cathode-anode voltage wave form corresponding to the conditions in (a).

The value of anode current during the conduction angle can be written by inspection of the circuit as

$$i_b = \frac{E_m \sin \omega t - E_0}{R}. \tag{13-1}$$

The firing or ignition angle, θ_1, can be obtained by determining from the critical grid curve the value of anode voltage E_b' at which the tube will fire for a given grid voltage e_{c1}. The angle θ_1 may then be defined as

$$\theta_1 = \sin^{-1} \frac{E_b'}{E_m}. \tag{13-2}$$

As shown in (b), Fig. 13-4, the tube voltage at breakdown drops abruptly to the normal tube voltage drop, and the excess circuit

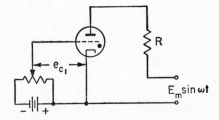

Fig. 13-5. Simple thyratron circuit with load R.

voltage, $E_b' - E_0$, causes the current to rise abruptly. If inductance is present in the load, the current rise is slowed.

Conduction continues until the tube voltage can no longer be maintained by the circuit or *until the numerator of Eq. 13-1 goes to zero*. This fixes θ_2 as

$$\theta_2 = 180° - \sin^{-1}\frac{E_0}{E_m}, \tag{13-3}$$

for a resistance load. It may be noted that the current wave form of a thyratron having a resistance load is definitely nonsinusoidal, being a sinusoid with E_0/R units sliced off the bottom and with the left side cut off over to the angle θ_1.

The average or direct current flowing in the circuit, as read by a d-c ammeter, may be calculated as the average of the instantaneous current over a cycle:

$$I_{\text{d-c}} = \frac{1}{2\pi}\int_0^{2\pi} i_b \, d\omega t = \frac{1}{2\pi}\int_{\theta_1}^{\theta_2} \frac{E_m \sin \omega t - E_0}{R} \, d\omega t$$

$$= \frac{E_m}{2\pi R}\left[\cos \theta_1 - \cos \theta_2 - \frac{E_0}{E_m}(\theta_2 - \theta_1)\right].$$

From the definition of θ_2, this may be written as

$$I_{\text{d-c}} = \frac{E_m}{2\pi R}\left[\cos \theta_1 + \sqrt{1 - \frac{E_0^2}{E_m^2}} - \frac{E_0}{E_m}(\theta_2 - \theta_1)\right]. \tag{13-4}$$

If the tube drop E_0 is small with respect to E_m, Eq. 13-4 reduces to a simpler form

$$I_{\text{d-c}} \cong \frac{E_m}{\pi R}\frac{(\cos \theta_1 + 1)}{2}. \tag{13-5}$$

The *average* value of the anode current may be varied from a maximum given by $E_m/\pi R$ to zero by variation of the angle θ_1 at which the tube fires. *In a gas tube the grid can control only the average current value, whereas in a vacuum tube the grid can control the instantaneous current value.* This is a difference of fundamental importance.

Thyratron control circuits, then, must provide a simple means of shifting the point in the cycle at which the grid voltage becomes more positive than the critical value. Control of the average value of current produced by an applied a-c voltage can then be achieved, providing a smooth, stepless, and practically lossless method. Three basic control circuits have been developed and will be discussed in succeeding sections.

Analysis of such circuits will follow in general the methods developed for gas rectifiers in the preceding chapter. Because of the complexity of Eq. 13-4, it will usually be found simplest and most convenient to integrate each problem individually. Likewise, calculations for I_{rms}, load $E_{d\text{-}c}$, tube loss, power input to the circuit, and so forth, may be integrated directly from fundamental processes introduced in Chapter 12, with the appropriate angles θ_1 and θ_2 used as limits.

13-5. Bias or Amplitude Control

The grid-bias voltage of a thyratron may be varied by a potentiometer, as in Fig. 13-5. By use of this control and an alternating anode supply, conduction will start at the point at which the grid-bias voltage is more positive than the critical grid-voltage curve, as shown for bias E_{c1} in Fig. 13-6. The angle θ_1 is, therefore, fixed by

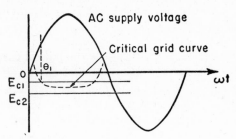

Fig. 13-6. Operation of the bias control circuit for two values of E_{cc}. For E_{c1} conduction starts at θ_1. For E_{c2} no conduction is possible.

E_{c1} and the critical curve. At the second intersection of the bias line and critical grid curve, the tube is conducting, the grid sheath is in existence, and the tube is totally unaware of any particular grid-voltage value, with conduction continuing in the cycle until θ_2 is reached. If E_{c1} is made more negative, angle θ_1 is increased, or the firing of the tube is delayed. If the grid bias is made more negative than the minimum of the critical curve, as with a value E_{c2}, at no time in the cycle is the bias more positive than the critical grid-voltage curve and the tube is unable to fire.

The grid-bias line becomes tangent to the critical curve at an angle of 90°, or $\pi/2$, so that control of the firing angle is possible only from zero to 90° of the cycle. The variation of average anode current with bias value is shown for an FG-27A thyratron in Fig. 13-7. Considerable instability exists at the 90° point, where a

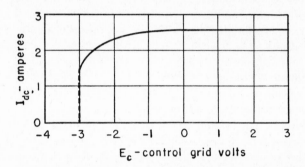

Fig. 13-7. Variation of anode current with grid bias when using the bias control circuit on an FG-27A thyratron with resistive load.

given grid bias sometimes just exceeds the critical curve, and sometimes does not quite reach it, since the a-c supply voltage may vary slightly with time. The value of anode current can be controlled only over a range from maximum to about one-half of the maximum value by the bias-control method. This is a serious limitation of the method.

The critical grid-voltage curve is a function of the temperature of the condensing mercury, so that if the temperature varies, another curve will be obtained; this will lie above or below the critical curve of Fig. 13-6 as the temperature falls or rises. The firing angle θ_1 then will not be a constant for a given value of E_c but will be different for different temperatures. Some value of grid bias which, for a given temperature, makes $\theta_1 = 60°$, say, may not fire the tube at all with a lower mercury temperature. Some other bias that is set negative enough to prevent the tube from firing may permit operation if the temperature rises, thereby dropping the critical curve to more negative values. Consequently, the bias-control method is not precise; it is a function of tube operating temperature and may vary considerably in characteristics from tube to tube. This is a second disadvantage of the method.

Despite these serious shortcomings the method is used, but usually only in applications where the thyratron is to operate as an *on-off* switch and where control of average current value is not desired. To ensure absolutely certain operation, a considerable excess of grid voltage is used. If under all operating voltages and temperatures the most negative value of the critical grid-voltage curves is −7 v, then to ensure that the conduction will be stopped at all times desired, a grid bias of −25 or more volts may be applied for *off* operation. Likewise, to ensure that the tube will turn on under all conditions, a grid bias of zero or possibly +20 v might be used for the *on* operation. By such excesses in grid voltage, the thyratron becomes certain and safe in operation.

A resistor large enough to limit the grid current to a safe value must always be in series in the grid circuit.

13-6. Phase-Shift Control

Another method of controlling the point of intersection of the actual grid voltage and the critical grid-voltage curve of a thyratron is by application of alternating current to the grid, with the phase of the grid voltage variable with respect to the anode voltage. If the grid voltage is made to lag the anode supply voltage by an angle θ, the grid-voltage wave, if plotted as in Fig. 13-8, will cross the critical breakdown curve at angle θ_1 just before rising to zero. If

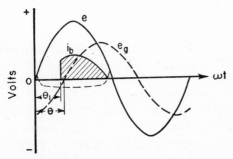

Fig. 13-8. Phase-shift control of a thyratron, with grid voltage e_g lagging the anode voltage e by an angle θ, with resistive load.

the amplitude of the grid voltage is large compared with any voltage on the critical curve, the firing angle θ_1 is approximately equal to θ, the angle of lag of grid voltage. This amounts to saying that the critical grid-breakdown voltage is zero for all anode voltages, which is a minor assumption for large values of a-c grid voltage.

By allowing the a-c grid voltage to vary in phase, the arc may be established at any point in the cycle from zero to 180° for lagging grid voltages. If the grid voltage leads the anode-supply voltage, the grid will always be positive at $\omega t = 0$ of the anode wave, and conduction will start approximately at that point and continue throughout the half cycle, so that leading grid voltage provides no control. The variation of the anode current with grid phase angle,

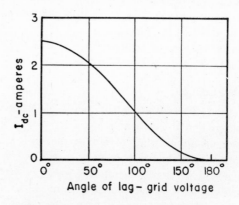

Fig. 13-9. Variation of average anode current with angle of lag of the grid voltage, for phase-shift control and resistive load.

assuming $\theta_1 = \theta$ and $E_0 \ll E_m$, is plotted in Fig. 13-9 by use of Eq. 13-5. This curve shows that control may be obtained over the whole positive half cycle of anode-supply voltage, and the average current may be varied in magnitude from 100 per cent to zero in a smooth manner. This is an important advantage of the phase-shift method over bias control.

If the a-c grid voltage is large, the slope with which it crosses the critical grid-breakdown curve is quite steep. Small shifts up or down in the critical curve, due to variations in tubes, grid characteristics, or condensed mercury temperature, can make only a very slight change in the firing angle θ_1.   For this reason, alternating volt-ages of 25 to 50 peak are ordinarily used, making the control of thyratrons more precise and independent of temperature.

For cases of small a-c anode supply voltage or small a-c grid volt-age, where the assumptions of $\theta_1 = \theta$ and $E_0 \ll E_m$ are not valid, the firing angle can best be determined by making a scale drawing of the voltage wave forms and plotting the critical curve.

13-7. Bias-Phase Control

For certain applications a variable direct voltage is available, but it is inconvenient to develop a source of variable-phase alternating voltage for thyratron grid control.   To avoid the difficulties which would arise if bias control were used, a combination of bias and phase-shift control may be used, called *bias-phase control*.   Variable d-c bias is used in series with a large a-c grid voltage lagging in phase

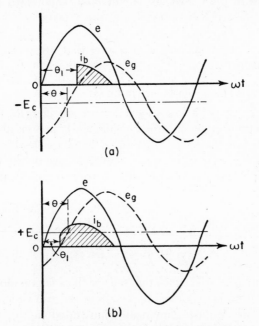

Fig. 13-10.   Control of current in a thyratron with resistance load by the bias-phase method with $\theta = 60°$: (a) negative d-c bias; (b) positive d-c bias.

by a fixed angle, usually between 45° and 90°. If the critical grid curve is assumed at zero volts, the situation may be pictured as in Fig. 13-10. At (a), the bias has a negative value $-E_c$, and the a-c grid voltage has been plotted with an angle of lag $\theta = 60°$. The firing angle θ_1 is then approximately 90°.

If the bias is made more negative, the whole a-c grid wave will move downward, thereby cutting the zero axis, or critical grid curve, and firing the tube, at progressively later angles in the cycle. If the bias is increased to a negative value equal to the peak of the a-c grid voltage, the tube will fire at 150°. Any further increase will lower the a-c grid-voltage wave below the critical grid curve, or zero axis, and the tube will not fire at all.

The bias may be increased to zero or to a positive value as at (b). The firing angle moves forward in the cycle, and with sufficient positive bias the tube may be made to fire at the beginning of the cycle.

Control with the bias-phase circuit may be obtained over almost the entire positive half cycle with a direct voltage as the variable. In addition, the circuit affords the advantages of freedom from temperature variations and of precision that are possible with the phase-shift circuit.

13-8. Delayed Firing with Inductive Loads

Inductance may be introduced into a rectifier load circuit to achieve filtering action, or it may be inherently present in the leakage inductance of the supply transformer, or in the load. The action of this inductance will cause the current flow to lag the applied voltage, and if delayed firing of the gas triode is added, the situation is no longer simple.

If the tube drop is assumed negligible, the circuit of Fig. 13-11(a) may be seen to lead to the circuit equation

$$\frac{di}{dt} + \frac{Ri}{L} = \frac{E_m}{L} \sin \omega t, \tag{13-6}$$

which is similar to that in Section 6-6 for the vacuum diode rectifier.

The thyratron is to be fired by action of the grid circuit at a firing angle θ_1. This is diagrammatically illustrated in (b), Fig. 13-11. The complete solution for Eq. 13-6 may be written

$$i_b = A\epsilon^{-R\omega t/\omega L} + \frac{E_m}{\sqrt{R^2 + \omega^2 L^2}} \sin(\omega t - \phi), \tag{13-7}$$

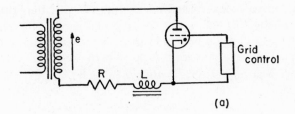

(a)

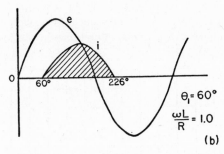

$\theta_1 = 60°$

$\dfrac{\omega L}{R} = 1.0$

(b)

Fig. 13-11.   (a) Thyratron circuit with inductive load.   (b) Current wave form for $\theta_1 = 60°$, $\omega L/R = 1.0$.

where
$$\phi = \tan^{-1} \frac{\omega L}{R}. \tag{13-8}$$

Since negative currents are impossible, due to the rectifying action of the tube, it is necessary to restrict the use of Eq. 13-7 to the time interval

$$\theta_1 < \omega t < \omega t_2,$$

where θ_1 is the firing angle and ωt_2 is the angle at which conduction ceases.

Discontinuous current is usual in half-wave circuits and thus $i_b = 0$ at $\omega t = \theta_1$ and the constant A may be determined as

$$A = -\frac{E_m}{\sqrt{R^2 + \omega^2 L^2}} \epsilon^{R\theta_1/\omega L} \sin(\theta_1 - \phi),$$

so that

$$i_b = \frac{E_m}{\sqrt{R^2 + \omega^2 L^2}} \left[\sin(\omega t - \phi) - \epsilon^{-(R/\omega L)(\omega t - \theta_1)} \sin(\theta_1 - \phi) \right]. \tag{13-9}$$

A typical current wave form for i_b is drawn in (b), Fig. 13-11 with $\theta_1 = 60°$, and $\omega L/R = 1$.

The current will again be zero at the angle of cutoff, ωt_2. Then by setting Eq. 13-9 equal to zero it is possible to obtain

$$\sin (\omega t_2 - \phi) = \epsilon^{-(R/\omega L)(\omega t_2 - \theta_1)} \sin (\theta_1 - \phi),$$

from which

$$\sin (\omega t_2 - \phi)\epsilon^{R\omega t_2/\omega L} = \sin (\theta_1 - \phi)\epsilon^{R\theta_1/\omega L}. \qquad (13\text{-}10)$$

This is a transcendental relation which can be solved graphically, and results for ωt_2 are given in Fig. 13-12 in terms of parameters θ_1 and $\omega L/R$ of the circuit. An interesting observation which can be made from this curve is that, with inductance in the load circuit,

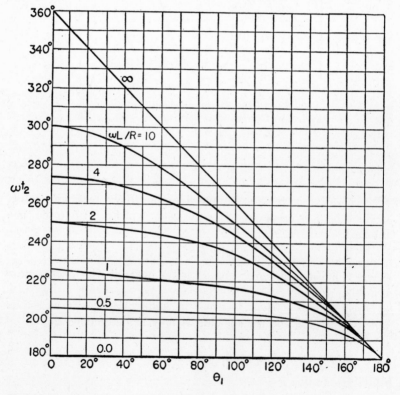

Fig. 13-12. Variation of cutoff angle ωt_2 with delay angle for various values of $\omega L/R$.

cutoff occurs earlier in the cycle for later firing angles. Thus the average value of the current is reduced through later firing angles, and also through the earlier value of cutoff angle.

The d-c or average current value can be obtained by integration of the current wave form over the conduction interval from $\omega t = \theta_1$ to $\omega t = \omega t_2$. Thus

$$I_{\text{d-c}} = \frac{E_m}{2\pi\sqrt{R^2 + \omega^2 L^2}} \int_{\theta_1}^{\omega t_2} [\sin(\omega t - \phi) - \epsilon^{-(R/\omega L)(\omega t - \theta_1)} \sin(\theta_1 - \phi)]d\omega t$$

$$= \frac{E_m}{2\pi\sqrt{R^2 + \omega^2 L^2}} \left[-\cos(\omega t_2 - \phi) + \cos(\theta_1 - \phi) \right.$$

$$\left. - \frac{\omega L}{R} \sin(\theta_1 - \phi) + \frac{\omega L}{R} \sin(\theta_1 - \phi)\epsilon^{-(R/\omega L)(\omega t_2 - \theta_1)} \right]. \quad (13\text{-}11)$$

By use of Eq. 13-10 and relations derived from Eq. 13-8 as

$$\cos\phi = \frac{R}{\sqrt{R^2 + \omega^2 L^2}} \qquad \sin\phi = \frac{\omega L}{\sqrt{R^2 + \omega^2 L^2}}$$

a value for $I_{\text{d-c}}$ can be obtained as

$$I_{\text{d-c}} = \frac{E_m}{\pi R}\left(\frac{\cos\theta_1 - \cos\omega t_2}{2}\right). \quad (13\text{-}12)$$

This equation is illustrated as a set of curves in terms of parameters θ_1 and $\omega L/R$ in Fig. 13-13. It is interesting to compare this result with that for the controlled rectifier with resistive load. It can be seen that Eq. 13-12 reduces to the form of Eq. 13-5 when $\omega L/R = 0$, giving $\omega t_2 = 180°$, and this is the result that would be expected.

In the case of the full-wave rectifier the current flow is usually continuous, and the effect of the inductance is largely that of producing this continuous flow. The results may be derived with proper attention to limits, and to the fact that the current value at angle θ_1 is equal to that at angle $\theta_1 + \pi$. The direct current may then be found to be

$$I_{\text{d-c}} = \frac{2E_m}{\pi R} \cos\theta_1 \quad (13\text{-}13)$$

when current flow is continuous.

The action of the controlled gas tube is seen to be dependent on the type of load supplied. These effects may be of considerable

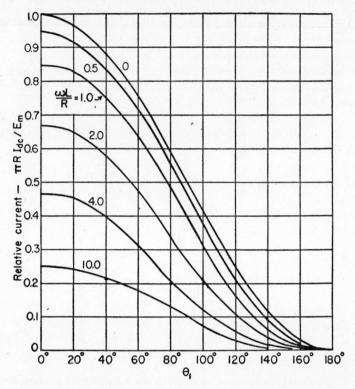

Fig. 13-13.   Relative current with inductive load and delay θ_1, for various $\omega L/R$ ratios.   Plot of the bracketed portion of Eq. 13-12.

importance in rectifiers supplying filters, or those supplying d-c motor loads.

13-9. Thyratron Firing Circuits

A simple device for varying the phase of an alternating voltage is the wound-rotor phase shifter (*Selsyn, Autosyn*).   This device has a single-phase rotor and a three-phase stator.   If the stator is connected to a three-phase system of voltages, a single-phase voltage will be induced in the rotor, the phase of this voltage depending on the rotor position with respect to the phase windings on the stator.   By consideration of the fields set up, it can be seen that rotation of the rotor will vary the phase of its voltage, but not the magnitude.

The rotor voltage can then be used as thyratron control voltage by the phase-shift method.

For polyphase rectifier operation, a wound-rotor induction motor may be used. With the stator excited, a rotating magnetic field is set up; and since the rotor may be held in any position, its three-phase induced voltages will vary in phase as its position is changed. Three-phase voltages may then be obtained from the rotor for control of polyphase rectifiers.

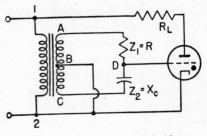

Another circuit for producing a phase shift in a single-phase voltage is the phase-shift bridge, shown in Fig. 13-14 as applied to control of a thyratron. By proper choice of the impedance elements Z_1 and Z_2, variation of either or both can be made

Fig. 13-14. The phase-shift bridge applied to control of a thyratron.

to shift the phase of the cathode-to-grid voltage with respect to the cathode-to-anode voltage. If the transformer is so connected that the polarity 2-1 of the primary is the same as the polarity C-A of the secondary, the voltage of point A is in phase with the anode voltage. Voltage C-A may be drawn as a vector with B as the mid-point, as in Fig. 13-15.

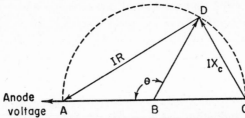

Fig. 13-15. Circle diagram for the phase-shift bridge of Fig. 13-14. Angle θ is the angle of lag of grid voltage behind anode voltage.

It is known that the voltage drops $IZ_1 = IR$ and $IZ_2 = IX_c$ must vectorially add to the applied voltage CA, and likewise it is known that voltages IR and IX_c are mutually at right angles. By reference to a well-known theorem in geometry, the locus of point D is on a semicircle having CA as a diameter. Vectors IR and IX_c may be drawn with appropriate voltage scales to meet in a right angle at any point on this circle. The vector BD then is the cathode-to-grid voltage; and since BA has been placed in phase with the cathode-to-anode voltage, the angle θ is the angle of lag of grid voltage behind anode voltage.

Variation of either R or X_c can be used to shift the angle θ. At $R = 0$ the phase angle is zero, and the thyratron will fire at the beginning of the cycle. At $R = \infty$ the phase angle will be 180°, and the thyratron will be completely cut off. For use at 60 cycles, resistance is usually chosen as the variable, since variable capacitances of sufficiently low reactance at that frequency are difficult to obtain. The lag angle may be computed from circuit constants.

It can be seen that

$$\theta + \angle DBC = 180°;$$

but because triangle DBC is isosceles,

$$\angle DCB = \angle BDC,$$

and

$$\angle DBC + 2 \times \angle DCB = 180°,$$

from which

$$\frac{\theta}{2} = \angle DCB$$

and

$$\theta = 2 \tan^{-1} \frac{Z_1}{Z_2} = 2 \tan^{-1} \omega CR. \tag{13-14}$$

It should be noted that the output voltage magnitude of the phase-shift bridge is constant and independent of the phase angle.

If R and X_c are interchanged, the circle of Fig. 13-15 will be thrown below the axis, making θ an angle of lead. This would not be usable for control of the thyratron because the tube would conduct for all values of θ.

Impedances Z_1 and Z_2 can be selected as resistance and inductance, if Z_1 is chosen inductive and Z_2 resistive. Variable inductors having suitable values of reactance at power frequencies are readily available, so that either R or L may be the variable element. The circle diagram of Fig. 13-15 is again obtained, with inductive voltage drop replacing the resistive drop and resistive drop replacing the capacitive drop. The angle for Z_1 inductive and Z_2 resistive can then be obtained as

$$\theta = 2 \tan^{-1} \frac{Z_1}{Z_2} = 2 \tan^{-1} \frac{\omega L}{R}. \tag{13-15}$$

It is frequently convenient to employ a *saturable reactor* as the variable-inductor element of a phase-shift bridge, as in Fig. 13-16. The variation is easily obtained by control of a small direct current supplied to the coil on the center leg of the device. The bridge alternating current flows through coils 1 and 2 of the reactor, so connected that their a-c fluxes add in the outside path of the core structure and, therefore, oppose in the center leg 3. Since these coils are on a closed iron core, their reactance is high and the grid phase angle will be that produced with large L.

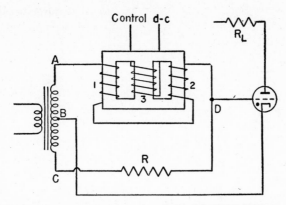

Fig. 13-16. Saturable reactor in a phase-shift bridge.

As direct current is supplied to coil 3, d-c fluxes are set up in the outer legs of the inductor. The operating point on the magnetization curve is moved toward the saturation region, or a point of lower slope on this curve. Since reactance is $2\pi f N\, d\phi/di$, and $d\phi/di$ is the slope of the magnetization curve, it can be seen that the reactance of the a-c coils is reduced by the direct current in coil 3, and the phase of the bridge output voltage will thus shift as the direct current is varied. Since coil 3 can be wound with many turns of fine wire the phase shift can be produced by direct currents of a few milliamperes, possibly varied by control of a vacuum tube. The inductance can be shifted over a range of possibly 20 to 1.

The saturable reactor is also employed in a nonelectronic device known as the magnetic amplifier, where control of considerable amounts of electric power is desired.

13-10. The Peaking Transformer

To increase the precision of thyratron firing, a peaking transformer is sometimes inserted in series with a resistor in the B-D connection of the bridge of Fig. 13-14. The transformer may be designed to have a large leakage reactance, in which case the series resistor is not necessary. The leakage reactance, or resistor, being effectively in series with the primary, serves to produce a large voltage drop at the peak of the magnetizing current, distorting and flattening the peak of the voltage wave applied to the primary and resulting in a primary flux wave as shown in Fig. 13-17. The flux changes appreciably only at the beginning and end of the half cycles. The secondary emf then consists of sharp peaks occurring at each 180° of the cycle, and these are applied to the grid-cathode circuit of the thyratron.

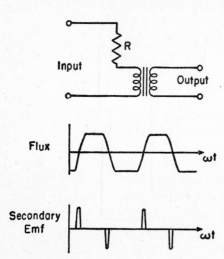

Fig. 13-17. Flux and secondary voltage waves in the peaking transformer circuit.

By shifting the phase of the primary voltage with the bridge, the secondary peaks may be made to occur at any point in the anode cycle. The sharp peak of grid voltage definitely fires the thyratron, and the firing angle is almost completely independent of tube characteristics or temperatures.

13-11. Shield-Grid Thyratrons

In the thyratron the grid is large and is exposed to the emission from the cathode. Even though the grid is negative before breakdown, some electrons gain sufficient energy to reach the grid, and as the point of breakdown is approached, the number of electrons reaching the grid increases. Even though this current is in microamperes, an appreciable voltage drop may be produced in high impedances in the grid control circuit. The drop is of such polarity as to make the grid more negative, delaying and in some cases preventing the firing of the tube. To avoid this difficulty, only relatively low-impedance control circuits can be employed with the three-element thyratron.

A second grid may be introduced in such a way that the control grid is almost completely shielded from both anode and cathode. This grid is called the *shield grid*. The control grid then may be only a sleeve or wire ring, enclosing the electron path between cathode and anode, as seen in Fig. 13-18. Electrons leaving the cathode before breakdown strike the shield instead of the control grid, so reducing the control-grid current that impedances up to 100 megohms may be used in the control circuit. Although the shield grid is ordinarily operated at cathode potential, it may have voltages applied in order for it to aid or oppose the effect of the control grid in preventing breakdown. If the shield grid is made positive, the tube takes on the characteristics of a negative-grid thyratron, whereas if negative shield voltages are used, the tube develops positive-grid characteristics.

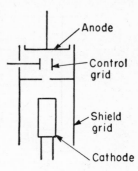

Fig. 13-18.   Shield-grid thyratron construction.

The input capacitance of the grid in the shield-grid tube is of the order of a fraction of a micromicrofarad, whereas the unshielded type has a capacitance of several micromicrofarads. The reduction in capacitance raises the grid input impedance and improves the tube response to short voltage pulses.

13-12. Thyratron Applications

In addition to being suitable for use in controlled rectifier service, in which they can operate in any of the basic circuits described in Chapter 12, thyratrons have been applied in a great many other ways. One basic application of thyratrons has been as a rheostat to control the flow of alternating current. To do this, it is necessary to circumvent the rectifying properties of the thyratron by some circuit arrangement. A second fundamental form of application has been as a switch in generating and shaping unusual wave forms and pulses needed in other electronic circuits for oscillography, television, and radar.

One large-scale application of thyratrons in the control of alternating current has been in light-dimming circuits for theaters and special illumination effects. The d-c output of the thyratron controls the value of alternating current in the lamp circuit by use of a saturable reactor (Section 13-9) as shown in Fig. 13-19. The lamp alter-

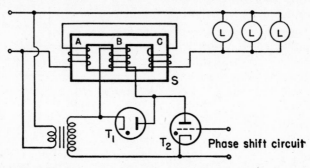

Fig. 13-19.   Thyratron light-dimming circuit with a saturable reactor S.

nating current flows through the a-c coils and varies as the reactance of the coils is changed by the direct current supplied to the center leg. As the direct current is increased the reactance drops and the lamp current and brilliancy increases.

The gaseous diode T_1 is used to provide almost continuous current flow in the d-c coil without need for a second thyratron and full-wave circuit. In each cycle, while the current in coil B is increasing, the anode of T_1 is maintained negative by the $L\,di/dt$ voltage of the coil; but when the current starts to decrease, the sign of the $L\,di/dt$ voltage reverses and T_1 conducts during the negative half cycle when T_2 is inoperative, or until the energy stored magnetically in coil B is dissipated. The circuit is simplified and made less expensive by the use of T_1 in place of the second tube of a conventional full-wave rectifier.

Thyratron control of lamps provides stepless variation of illumination, high efficiency because there are no rheostatic power losses, and reduction of the theater switchboard to a few small knobs and dials. The same circuit has been applied to modulating control of the temperature of large electric furnaces that are rated in hun-

dreds of kilowatts.   Control of alternating current with thyratrons
and saturable reactors permits handling large amounts of a-c power
with expenditure of only 1 or 2 per cent in the control circuit.   Disadvantages are poor power factor of the a-c circuit at light loads and
distortion of the alternating voltage wave form on the load.

A second basic circuit for the control of alternating current with
thyratrons is shown in Fig. 13-20.   This is an *inverse-parallel* or
back-to-back connection of two thyratrons so that one tube handles
each half wave, and alternating current is transmitted.   The thyratrons then act as switches, or under grid control as series variable
impedances.

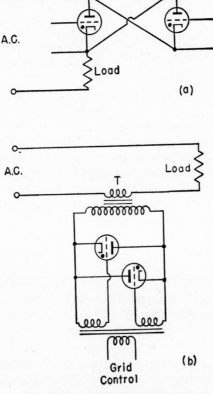

Fig. 13-20.   Methods of controlling
alternating current with thyratrons.

In Fig. 13-20(a) the tubes are required to handle the full value of load current. Since tube current ratings are limited the circuit at (b) is sometimes used for higher line currents. The transformer T has a primary rated for line voltage and a step-up turns ratio such that with normal load current flowing, full rated thyratron current will flow in the secondary. As long as the thyratrons are inactive, the reactance of the primary as an unloaded transformer is so high that negligible voltage appears across the load. When grid control is applied the thyratrons conduct, one on each half cycle, effectively short-circuiting the series transformer and placing substantially full voltage on the load. The load current is greater than the tube current by a factor equal to the transformer turns ratio.

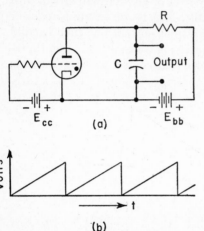

Fig. 13-21. Thyratron sweep circuit for cathode-ray oscillographs.

In the wave-generating and -shaping field for thyratrons, a common application is that of the sweep oscillator for a cathode-ray tube, shown in Fig. 13-21. A thyratron is set with a grid bias so that it will fire at some relatively low anode voltage that is also the voltage on capacitor C. The capacitor charges through a high resistance R from a d-c source, the voltage across the capacitor being given by

$$e_C = E_{bb}(1 - \epsilon^{-t/RC})$$

When e_C reaches the thyratron breakdown voltage, the tube fires and the capacitor discharges through the thyratron. When the voltage e_C falls below the arc-maintaining voltage, the thyratron ceases conduction because R is large and is unable to recharge the capacitor rapidly. The tube deionizes, the grid regains control, and the capacitor charges again until the action is repeated.

The first few per cent of rise in the voltage e_C is practically linear, so that if the thyratron breakdown voltage is low with respect to the value E_{bb}, the voltage across the capacitor will be a saw-tooth, with nearly linear rises, and rapid drops. This wave form is that desired to sweep the beam across the cathode-ray-tube screen as a linear function of time. The period of sweep can be varied by change of R or C.

If a more linear rise of voltage be desired the capacitor may be charged with a constant current, rather than a constant voltage, since e_C is proportional to the capacitor charge. A constant charging current can be obtained by replacing R with a vacuum pentode operating so that its current is independent of applied voltage, which in this case is $E_{bb} - e_C$. The frequency of oscillation may then be varied by changing the grid bias of the pentode, and thus the capacitor charging rate.

13-13. Thyratron Motor Control

The thyratron rectifier is a valuable tool for supplying power to a d-c motor from an a-c line. It is readily possible to control the thyratron grids so that the motor current may be limited to achieve constant acceleration, to prevent motor and tube overloads on starting, and to give essentially constant speed. A simple circuit for supplying the rectified alternating current is shown in Fig. 13-22. The motor shunt field may also be supplied by a separate rectifier so that a complete a-c operated package is obtained. Complex control circuits are used to shift the phase of the grid voltage to achieve the forms of current control mentioned above.

It should be noted that the current flow indicated in the figure is discontinuous, and the presence of inductance in the motor armature is indicated by values of ωt_2 exceeding 180°. An additional factor is the presence of the counter emf of the motor when operating. During starting conditions this emf is absent, and since the armature current is given by the usual motor relation

$$I = \frac{E - kN\phi}{R},$$

the current will reach excessive values on starting. In the above equation E is the applied voltage, N the speed, ϕ the motor flux, k a constant of proportionality, and R the armature resistance. To protect the motor from excessive starting current, and the tubes from excessive peak current, it is necessary to retard the firing angle of the thyratrons on starting.

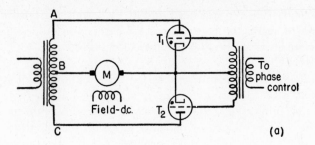

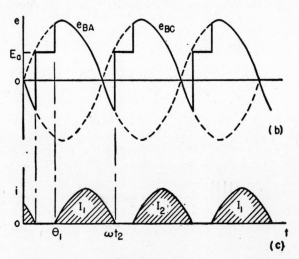

Fig. 13-22. (a) Thyratron motor-control circuit. (b) Voltage wave form applied to motor. E_a is counter emf. (c) Motor current wave form.

Normal operation will permit advancing the firing angle because of the counter emf term, $kN\phi = E_a$, which will aid in limiting the current. Since the speed is given by

$$N = \frac{E - IR}{k\phi},$$

it is possible to vary the motor speed by adjustment of the average voltage applied, or by advancing or retarding the thyratron firing angle.

Motor heating will be greater than when the motor is operated on smooth d-c sources, due to the greater value of the effective current flowing. This may at times require an oversize motor. The fact that the torque is developed in pulses is not important since the armature and connected load will have sufficient inertia to filter out the pulsations.

13-14. Grids in Mercury-Pool Cathode Tubes

The individual anodes in the large multianode steel-tank rectifiers are frequently provided with grids for control. Since ionization is present in such tubes at all times while they are in operation, the space around a negative and nonconducting anode cannot be sufficiently deionized to allow the grid to obtain control unless the anodes are well baffled and shielded from each other.

In a more advanced form each anode is contained in a separate water-cooled steel cylinder with its individual mercury-pool cathode. Six, twelve, or more of these rectifiers are assembled in a unit. Mechanical means of starting the arc are usually provided, and auxiliary arc-holding electrodes and circuits are needed to maintain the cathode spot. Baffles around the grid are needed to aid it in deionizing during the negative anode period, but the baffling is not so complete as in the multianode tank. A major advantage of the individual anode assembly is that in case of failure of an anode, a replacement unit can be quickly installed without shutdown of the whole rectifier, as would be required by the multianode tank.

The grids are used to provide firing delay in each anode conduction period, the delay then being varied to provide voltage regulation of the d-c output. By ingenious control circuits, overcompound, flat compound, or undercompound characteristics can be obtained, as desired. The grids may also be connected into the protection circuits and act to cut off the rectifier in a fraction of a cycle in event of a circuit fault, thus aiding the circuit breakers in interrupting the fault current.

13-15. The Ignitron

In 1933, Slepian showed that a cathode spot could be initiated on a mercury pool by use of a special ignitor electrode. From this has been developed the *ignitron* (ĭg-nĭ′tron) class of mercury-vapor tubes. A cut-away view of a WL-652 ignitron is shown in Fig. 13-23.

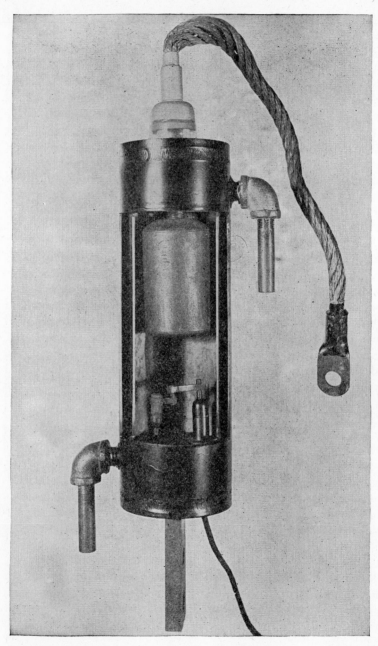

Fig. 13-23.   Cut-away view of a WL-652 ignitron showing internal construction, water jacket, ignitor, and anode.

These tubes are usually steel-enclosed and water-jacketed for cooling, and employ mercury-pool cathodes and graphite anodes. In the photograph, the large cylindrical block in the upper part of the tube is the anode. The mercury-pool cathode is located in the bottom of the tube, connection being made to the heavy copper bar. The steel enclosure is at cathode potential, with the anode insulated by a short glass seal.

Since the ignitron is a mercury-pool tube, it does not suffer from limitations on emission current as do the hot-cathode thyratrons. Accordingly, tubes have been developed with peak anode-current ratings as high as 2000 amp and with average ratings of 300 amp and over. Some of these tubes may carry surge currents of 12,000 amp for a fraction of a second without damage, which is an impractical value of surge current for a heated cathode. Internal heating is the limiting factor in ignitron current ratings.

The feature that distinguishes the ignitron from the mercury-pool diodes of Chapter 12 is the starter electrode, or electric ignitor. This electrode, shaped somewhat as shown in Fig. 13-24, dips into the mercury-pool cathode. The starter is made of a refractory semiconductor, materials used being silicon carbide or boron carbide. It must be nonwetting in mercury, or mercury should form a meniscus when in contact with the rod material.

The ignitor is operated and the tube is fired by passing a current from ignitor to mercury pool. The exact mechanism that produces the cathode spot is still obscure, but it is believed that the first spark appears when the potential gradient in the gas layer surround-

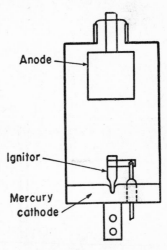

Fig. 13-24. Internal construction of a sealed-off ignitron, showing the ignitor.

ing the unwetted starter rod in the mercury exceeds a critical value. The small spark developed at the junction of the rod and mercury quickly grows into a full cathode spot capable of emitting many amperes. The ignition process takes only a few microseconds.

The electric ignitor permits starting of the arc at any desired point in each cycle, a feat not possible with the mechanical forms of starters. By control of the point in the cycle at which the ignitor is operated, the ignitron may be used to vary the average anode current flowing, in the same manner as with the thyratron.   The ignitron then becomes an electric control tube with a heavy-duty mercury-pool cathode.   Most ignitrons are suited to low-voltage operation only, but higher-voltage types are being developed.

The current required to operate the ignitor may be 10 to 30 amp at 50 to 200 v.   Although the instantaneous power is large, circuits are usually designed so that the current flows for a very short interval, and the average power requirements are then small.

The cathode spot on a mercury-pool cathode becomes unstable and may not maintain itself throughout a positive half cycle if the current falls below 3 amp.   An auxiliary anode, supplied from a

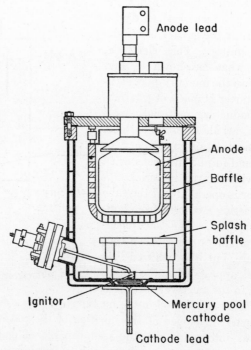

Fig. 13-25.   Cross section of a large single-anode ignitron.

separate a-c source, is provided in many ignitrons to furnish a minimum load on the cathode spot.

Ignitrons are made in larger sizes in single-anode units which are assembled into multianode rectifiers. These tubes are in steel and are connected to automatically controlled vacuum pumps to maintain the vacuum, since complete exhaust is difficult in the large sizes, and occluded gases may be released during the life of the tube. The internal construction of such a single-anode unit is shown in Fig. 13-25. Multiple-unit ignitron rectifiers of this nature operate in the circuits described in Chapter 12, with control circuits to provide voltage regulation. In this service they are built to rectify thousands of kilowatts for the electrochemical industries. An ignitron-rectifier assembly rated 3225 kw, 645 v, is shown in Fig. 13-26.

The ignitron, although similar to the thyratron in performance,

Fig. 13-26. An ignitron rectifier assembly for aluminum reduction, with 12 anodes. Rated 3225 kw, 645 v. (Courtesy of General Electric Co.)

is fundamentally opposite in operation. In the thyratron the grid *prevents* the arc, whereas in the ignitron the ignitor *causes* the arc. The ignitron has a heavy-duty mercury-pool cathode compared to the somewhat limited thermionic cathode of the thyratron. However, in the thyratron's favor is the very small grid power required with high grid impedance, compared with the low ignitor impedance and large, instantaneous ignitor current required by the ignitron.

13-16. Ignitron Circuits

Although the ignitron is suitable for almost any type of a-c control service, it has been specifically developed for two main applications: as a synchronous a-c contactor in resistance welding and as a rectifier. For these applications, two main types of ignitor firing circuits have been developed. These are the self-excitation and the separate-excitation circuits of Fig. 13-27. Self-excitation is the simpler system and is used in most welding applications, whereas separate excitation is usually preferred for rectifier service.

A rectifier is used in series with the ignitor rod to cut off the ignitor current after ignition, and to prevent damaging reverse cur-

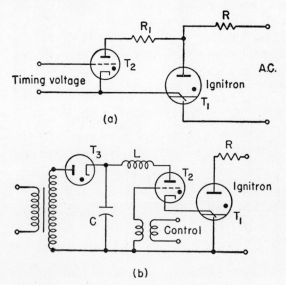

Fig. 13-27. (a) Self-excitation firing circuit for the ignitron; (b) separate excitation circuit.

rents in the ignitor on the negative half cycle. If it is desired to
control the firing angle in the cycle, the rectifier diode is changed
to a thyratron, which, by means of grid control, can fire the ignitron
at the selected angle. In (a), Fig. 13-27, with the ignitron and
thyratron anodes positive, the control circuit fires the thyratron T_2,
usually through a peaking transformer from a phase-shift bridge.
Since the whole supply voltage is across the thyratron, it conducts
and passes its load current through the ignitor to the mercury-pool
cathode. This fires the ignitron, and its cathode-anode voltage becomes the arc drop of 10 to 20 v. The arc-drop voltage is also across
the thyratron and ignitor, and is less than the voltage required to
maintain the thyratron current in this circuit. Thus the thyratron
fires the ignitron and is itself almost instantaneously extinguished.
The ignitor current flows only long enough in each cycle for the ignition process to take place, usually less than 100 μsec, and the
average ignitor power is low.

In (b), Fig. 13-27, the capacitor C is charged by the separate
a-c source and rectifier T_3 during the half cycle in which the ignitron
anode is negative. At the desired instant in the next half cycle
the thyratron grid is excited, usually by a pulse, and the capacitor
discharges through the thyratron T_2 and the ignitor, firing the
ignitron. The thyratron and ignitor cease conduction as soon as
the energy in the capacitor is dissipated, giving a very short, high

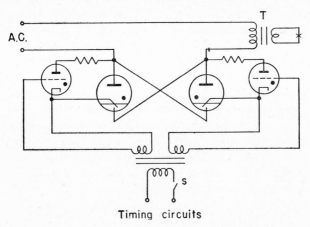

Timing circuits

Fig. 13-28. Ignitron synchronous switch used for control of
a resistance welder.

current pulse to the ignitor. The operation is repeated in each cycle. The inductance L is used to limit the thyratron peak current to a safe value.

When ignitrons are used as a synchronous relay as for welding service, the circuit may appear as in Fig. 13-28. The two ignitrons are connected in parallel opposing, so that a full a-c wave is passed. The tubes may be fired at will and controlled to pass any number of integral cycles desired. The circuit is also of use when ignitrons are employed to replace switches or contactors in duty such as *on-off* control of electric furnaces where maintenance of ordinary contactors is very high. The circuit may be used as a high-speed circuit breaker, since the ignitrons can be turned off within a half cycle, whereas mechanically operated circuit breakers may take several cycles to clear a short circuit.

For applications such as *on-off* switches where no control of the average current value is desired, the control thyratrons may be replaced by cheaper diodes or copper-oxide rectifiers. The ignitors then carry current from the beginning of the positive half cycle until the tube fires.

13-17. Ignitron Ratings

For rectifier service the ratings of ignitrons are essentially the same as for gas diodes, with the addition of maximum allowable voltage and current for the ignitor. The ignitor ratings are unusual in that a large voltage with a low current or a large current with a low voltage will fire the tube. The relation is illustrated in Fig. 13-29, a curve of minimum ignition requirements for the FG-238 tube.

When ignitrons are used in welding-contactor or other highly intermittent service, they are rated in terms of maximum average anode current and maximum kilovolt-ampere demand, with the time of averaging the anode current specified. The kilovolt-ampere demand is determined by the rating of the load or welder controlled. The average current per cycle can be calculated from the demand kilovolt-amperes and the supply voltage:

$$I_{\text{line}} = \frac{\text{V.A.}}{E_{\text{line}}}; \quad \text{average tube current per cycle} = \frac{\sqrt{2}\, I_{\text{line}}}{\pi}. \quad (13\text{-}16)$$

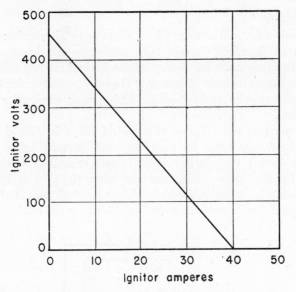

Fig. 13-29.   Minimum ignitor voltage and current requirements for firing the FG-238 ignitron.

The rated ampere-second capacity of the tube is the maximum rated average current, max $I_{\text{d-c}}$, times the time of averaging, t_a, or

$$\text{rated ampere-seconds} = \max I_{\text{d-c}}t_a. \tag{13-17}$$

The permitted time of conduction t_c for a particular load may then be found from

$$\max I_{\text{d-c}}t_a = \frac{\sqrt{2}\,I_{\text{line}}}{\pi}\,t_c,$$

or

$$t_c = \frac{\pi \times \max I_{\text{d-c}}t_a}{\sqrt{2}\,I_{\text{line}}}, \tag{13-18}$$

and the allowable duty is

$$\text{per cent duty} = \frac{t_c}{t_a} \times 100\% = \frac{\pi \times \max I_{\text{d-c}}}{\sqrt{2}\,I_{\text{line}}} \times 100\%. \tag{13-19}$$

This determines the allowable percentage of *on* time during any given averaging period, to avoid tube overload and overheating.

13-18. Inverters

A circuit that will change direct current to alternating current is called an *inverter*. Vacuum-tube oscillators are, in general, inverters, but they have low power efficiencies and are not suitable for handling large amounts of power. Thyratrons and ignitrons used in inverter circuits make possible high power efficiencies at low frequencies.

Since inverter operation of gas control tubes is with d-c anode potential, circuits must be used that will develop transients capable of driving the anode voltage to zero or negative values long enough for the space to deionize and allow the grid or ignitor to regain control. A capacitor-and-resistor network may be used to set up the desired transient, as in Fig. 13-30, by use of the principle

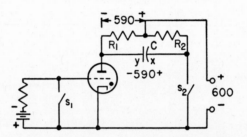

Fig. 13-30.   Basic circuit for cutting off the anode current of a thyratron operating with d-c anode voltage.

that the charge on a capacitor cannot change instantaneously in a resistive network.

Suppose switch S_1 to be closed to start current flow in the thyratron, S_2 being open. The voltage drop across R_1 charges the capacitor C to a voltage equal to the d-c supply voltage minus the tube drop, and of polarity as indicated. For illustration, assume the d-c supply to be 600 v and the tube drop 10 v; then, when the steady state is established, there will be 590 v across R_1 and 590 v across C, since no current will flow in R_2. The left plate Y of the capacitor C is then 590 v negative with respect to the right plate X. If switch S_2 is closed and S_1 opened, the potential of plate X is changed from +600 v to zero instantaneously. The charge on C cannot change instantaneously; and since $E = Q/C$, the potential cannot change, so that plate Y must still be 590 v negative with respect to plate X immediately after the switch operation.   Plate X is at zero, however, so that plate Y and the anode must instantaneously be at -590 v. Since a finite time is required for the charge to leak off and the potential of the left plate Y to become positive, the anode may be held negative a sufficient time to deionize the space and allow the grid to regain control, and thus the arc will not restrike when the anode again becomes positive.

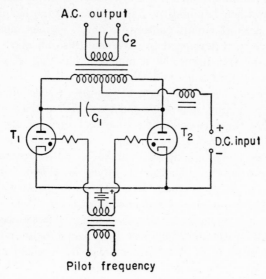

Fig. 13-31.   Separately excited parallel-type inverter
circuit using thyratrons.

The parallel-type inverter, as drawn in Fig. 13-31, replaces the switch S_2 with another thyratron.   If T_1 is turned on by a positive grid pulse, capacitor C_1 charges, and current flows through the transformer primary to T_1.   The grid of T_2 is at the same time negative; but on the next half cycle of the pilot frequency, the grid of T_2 fires this tube and lowers the potential of the right end of C_1 to near zero, capacitor C_1 instantaneously drives the anode of T_1 negative, and T_1 deionizes, allowing its grid to regain control.   Current then flows to T_2 through the other half of the transformer.   The cycle of operation is repeated every cycle of grid voltage, each tube kicking the other tube off in turn. The transient currents in the output transformer primary flow alternately in opposite directions, thereby inducing an a-c voltage in the secondary. Capacitor C_2 shapes the output a-c wave form to approximate sinusoidal shape.

Large values of capacitance C_1 and C_2 improve the certainty of current interchange or commutation between the tubes, and make the wave form more sinusoidal. The time constants of the circuits must be such that during a half cycle the current can build up only to the safe maximum value for one of the tubes. Should one tube fail to start when required, or fail to turn off, the circuit becomes essentially a short circuit on the d-c line. Various more complex circuits have been developed to overcome this difficulty.

If the grid transformer is eliminated, blocking capacitors are placed in each grid lead, and these grid leads are connected, the two-tube circuit becomes a form of gas-tube trigger circuit. With one tube conducting, a positive pulse applied to the common grid lead will fire the nonconducting tube and turn off the other. A second pulse will restore the original conditions. If a counter is placed in one anode circuit, the number of pulses recorded will be one-half the number applied, or the circuit is said to *count down* by a factor of 2. If the output transformer is replaced with resistors and an output is taken from one anode through a blocking capacitor to the grids of a similar circuit, a particular tube in the second circuit will fire once for each four pulses on the original input and will count down by a scale of 4. The system may be repeated any desired number of times, for higher count-down ratios.

13-19. Cold-Cathode Gas Triodes

Another basic type of gas triode is built with a nickel cathode coated with barium and strontium, somewhat as for an oxide-coated thermionic cathode. In an argon or argon-and-neon mixture, the initial ions are formed by applying greater-than-breakdown voltage to a starter electrode, and the arc is maintained by secondary emission from ionic bombardment of the cathode.

The anode may be a wire or a metal plate. The control, or starter, anode is a wire or metal plate placed close to the cathode surface and so arranged that the breakdown voltage between cathode and starter is lower than the breakdown from cathode to anode. A voltage applied to the starter may break down the starter gap, and if the

anode is positive and the ionization due to the starter current sufficiently intense, the arc will transfer to the anode. After the transfer, the starter no longer has any control of the current until the
anode voltage is removed and deionization has taken place. The
anode voltage required to make the arc transfer to the anode is a
function of starter current; the greater the starter current and ionization, the lower is the anode transfer voltage. The starter current
is in microamperes, so that very small excitation energies are required.

The OA4-G tube is an example of this type. Although the maximum current is limited to milliamperes, tubes of this nature find
many applications because no cathode heating power is required.
Their uses include small sensitive relays, small carrier-current relays,
and telephone applications.

PROBLEMS

13-1. (a) The rated deionization time of an FG-41 thyratron is 100 μsec.
What is the highest frequency at which it is usable?

(b) The FG-41 is rated at 75 amp peak, 12.5 amp average. What is the
greatest delay in the angle of firing which may be used, if rated direct current flows into a resistive load.

13-2. (a) Using the characteristics of the FG-27A thyratron in Fig. 13-3,
at 50°C condensed mercury temperature, for what percentage of the total
time of a cycle will current flow through such a tube if it is operated at 500
peak sinusoidal anode volts and grid volts of −4? Assume that tube drop
is 10 v, that breakdown equals tube drop, and the load is resistive.

(b) With the 10-v tube drop, what value of direct current will flow through
a 200-ohm load resistor in the anode circuit?

(c) How much heat will be produced in the resistor of part (b)?

(d) What is the power loss in the anode in part (b)?

13-3. Assuming the critical grid voltage for a thyratron is zero for all
anode voltages, find the average value of plate current for a tube with plate
voltage of 220 v rms, 60 c, applied through a 100-ohm resistor, with grid
voltage of 20 v rms, 60 c, lagging the plate voltage by 60°. Assume 10-v
tube drop and breakdown.

13-4. An ignitron with anode supply of 100 v rms, 60 c, applied through
a 200-ohm resistor, is fired at 50° of the anode cycle. If tube drop is 12 v,

(a) Find the average current flowing.

(b) Draw the current wave form.

(c) Draw the tube-voltage wave form.

(d) Find the power input and the efficiency.

13-5. An FG-41 thyratron has a critical grid characteristic given by the following data:

E_b (v)	E_c (v)	E_b (v)	E_c (v)
500	+4	3,800	−3
1000	+2	6,400	−4
1800	0	10,000	−5

(a) Plot the critical grid characteristic.

(b) Plot the critical grid curve as a function of time for an anode voltage of 600 v rms, showing also the anode voltage to a different scale.

(c) Graphically determine the time of firing if a grid voltage of 10 v rms lagging 90° is used.

13-6. The tube drop in an ignitron is 15 v. If the anode supply is 55 v rms and the load a resistance of 10 ohms, find:

(a) The average current when the tube fires at 135°.

(b) The average current when the tube fires at 45°.

(c) The average current when the tube fires at 0°.

(d) The heat loss in the tube for each of the above.

13-7. Two FG-27A tubes operated at 50°C mercury temperature are used in a full-wave rectifier circuit with a transformer having a 440-v primary and ratio of 1 : 2 primary to total secondary. Find:

(a) The value of grid bias needed to set the firing angle to 30° behind the anode voltage.

(b) The value of load resistance to limit average anode current per tube to 2.5 amp, if tube drop is neglected.

(c) The d-c output voltage.

(d) The peak inverse voltage.

(e) The power input, if the transformer is 95 per cent efficient, tube heaters take 5 v at 4.5 amp each, and tube drop is 15 v.

13-8. Plot the load current wave form in a half-wave rectifier with applied alternating voltage of 250, if the tube drop is neglected, load $\omega L/R = 7.5$ and $R = 100$ ohms, and the tube fires at 65°.

13-9. Starting with Eq. 13-11, develop Eq. 13-13 for the full-wave circuit, with continuous current flow in a load containing resistance and inductance.

13-10. A thyratron with critical grid voltage equal to zero for all anode voltages has a peak current rating of 2.0 amp and a tube drop of 15 v. It is supplied by a sinusoidal voltage of 100 v rms, with a load of 20 ohms resistance in series with an inductance L. Find the value for L if the peak current rating is not to be exceeded when the tube is fired at 45° of the anode voltage wave. The supply frequency is 60 c.

13-11. A certain 10-kw, 300-v rectifier may operate at 15 per cent load for 14 hr and at 80 per cent load for 10 hr each day. Three thyratrons to handle the load have heaters taking 5 v, 20 amp each, and tube drops at all currents of 12 v.   Three ignitrons capable of handling the load have tube drops of 18 v each with negligible ignitor losses.   The circuit is three-phase half-wave.

(a) If power costs 4 cents per kwhr, which type of tube will be the cheapest to operate in this rectifier over the time of one year?

(b) How much is the saving?

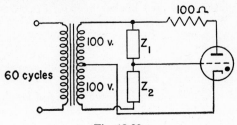

Fig. 13-32.

13-12. The thyratron of Fig. 13-32 is to be phase-shift-controlled by Z_1 and Z_2.   A 10-h inductor and 5000-ohm variable resistor are available. Neglect tube drop and assume critical grid voltage as zero.

(a) Which is to be Z_1 and Z_2?   Prove your choice by drawing a vector diagram of the voltages.

(b) What are the maximum and minimum values of anode current obtainable?

(c) Plot a curve of anode current against the value of resistance used.

13-13. Repeat Problem 13-12, using a 1-μf capacitor in place of the 10-h inductor.

13-14. A full-wave single-phase thyratron rectifier is used to charge a 120-v storage battery of 0.5 ohm resistance.   The tube drop may be neglected.   If the transformer supplies 220 v rms each side of the center tap. and a 10-ohm resistance is in series with the battery, plot a curve showing the charging rate of the battery as a function of the firing angle θ_1.

13-15. A three-phase half-wave ignitron rectifier supplies power to a 15-ohm load from a 330-v rms three-phase transformer.   The tubes are fired at 80° of each anode voltage wave.   The tube drops are all constant at 20 v.   Find:

(a) The reading of an a-c ammeter in series with the load.

(b) The load direct current.

(c) The reading of a d-c voltmeter across any tube.

(d) The reading of a wattmeter in circuit with the load, its voltage coil across the load.

(e) The total tube power loss.

(f) The average power supplied by the source.

(g) The efficiency of rectification.

13-16. A small thyratron in the circuit of Fig. 13-21 is biased to fire at an anode voltage of 65 v. If R is 250,000 ohms, find the value of C required to produce a saw-tooth voltage frequency of 1200 c, with $E_{bb} = 250$ v. Neglect the tube-maintaining voltage, and assume that the discharge time of capacitor C is negligible. Plot the wave form of voltage obtained.

13-17. Two ignitrons are used in the circuit of Fig. 13-28 to supply a resistance-welder load demand of 500 kva at 240 v rms, 60 c. The tubes to be used are rated at 30 amp average current each, with an averaging time of 18 sec.

(a) Find the total number of cycles of conduction time permissible in any averaging period.

(b) How much would the average current rating of an ignitron have to be increased to permit two *on* periods of 3 sec each in any averaging period?

(c) If the tube voltage drop is taken as 16 v and cooling water at 15°C is supplied to each tube at the rate of 2 gpm, what temperature rise will occur in the water for continued operation under (a), above? Tubes may be considered as firing at 0° of the cycle.

13-18. A spot welder is rated at 250 kva, 440 v single phase, 60 c. An ignitron contactor for this welder has a duty cycle of four 10-c *on* periods, separated by 20-c *off* periods, ending with an 80-c rest period. Total time of the duty cycle is 180 c, or 3 sec.

(a) What must be the average current rating of the two tubes in the contactor, if they are rated for a 5-sec averaging period?

(b) What should be the maximum instantaneous current rating of each tube?

13-19. A resistance load which takes 180 amp rms at full load is to be controlled by a series transformer in the circuit of Fig. 13-20(b). If the a-c supply is at 220 v, 60 c, if the series transformer causes a 200-v drop with open secondary, and if the tubes are rated at 7500 v P.I.V., find:

(a) Series-transformer voltage ratio.

(b) Average-current tube rating.

(c) Transformer kva rating.

REFERENCES

1. Hull, A. W., "Gas-Filled Thermionic Tubes," *Trans. AIEE*, **47,** 753 (1928).

2. ———, "Hot Cathode Thyratrons," *Gen. Elec. Rev.*, **32,** 213, 390 (1929).

3. Slepian, J., and Ludwig, L. R., "A New Method of Initiating the Cathode of an Arc," *Trans. AIEE*, **52,** 693 (1933).

4. Willis, C. H., Bedford, B. D., and Elder, F. R., "Constant Current D-C Transmission," *Elec. Eng.*, **54,** 102 (1935).
5. Marti, O. K., "Excitron Mercury-Arc Rectifiers," *Trans. AIEE*, **59,** 927 (1940).
6. White, A. B., *et al.*, "The Strobotron," *Electronics*, **12,** —— February, (1937).
7. Marshall, D. E., and Rigrod, W. W., "Characteristics of Resistance Ignitors," *Electronics*, **20,** 122 (May 1947).
8. Cobine, J. D., *Gaseous Conductors*, McGraw-Hill Book Company, Inc., New York, 1941.
9. Engineers of the Westinghouse Electric Corp., *Industrial Electronics Reference Book*, John Wiley & Sons, Inc., New York, 1948.
10. Myers, H. C., and Cox, J. H., "Excitation Circuits for Ignitron Rectifiers," *Trans. AIEE*, **60,** 943 (1941).
11. Tompkins, F. N., "The Parallel Type of Inverter," *Elec. Eng.*, **52,** 253 (1933).
12. Moyer, E. E., "Electronic Control of DC Motors," *Electronics*, **18,** 98, May; 119, June; 118, July; 133, Sept.; 128, Oct. (1943).
13. Chute, G. M., *Electronics in Industry*, McGraw-Hill Book Company, Inc., New York, 1946.

CHAPTER 14

PHOTOELECTRIC CELLS

Adaptation of photoelectric emission to commercial and industrial uses has been slow. At first this effect was regarded as a laboratory curiosity, and practical applications had to await the development of the triode vacuum tube for amplification of the output currents. It was not until the advent of sound motion pictures in 1927 that the use of photoelectric cells became general. Industrial counters and controls, printing-register controls, and photographic and color-measuring equipment soon came into general use.

14-1. Photoelectric-Cell Classification

All photoelectric cells convert light energy directly into electric energy. They are classified according to the manner in which the electric-energy output of the cell is made available in the electric circuit.

Photoemissive Cells (Phototubes). In photoemissive cells the energy of the light beam causes emission of electrons from a metal surface. The output of the cell is then in the form of an electric current of minute value. The photoemissive cell is enclosed in an evacuated or gas-filled bulb of glass, or of quartz for ultraviolet light transmission. This type is treated in this chapter.

Photovoltaic Cells. In the photovoltaic cell the radiant energy striking the cell surface causes generation of an emf. The emf may be applied to an external circuit, and with proper design the current resulting in the external circuit may be made directly proportional to the light intensity striking the cell. These cells consist of oxides or compounds coated on metal plates, and need not be used in a vacuum. The photovoltaic cell is also known as a *barrier-layer* cell, and is considered in Chapter 15.

Photoconductive Cells. The photoconductive cell varies its electric resistance in accordance with the light intensity received. It consists of a thin coating of selenium or a metallic oxide between two electrodes on a glass plate and may be used in an electric circuit as a variable resistance. The selenium cell of the early experimenters was a photoconductive cell. This type will also be treated in Chapter 15.

The photoemissive and photovoltaic cells may also be classified as *high internal impedance* and *low internal impedance*, respectively. The difference in impedances restricts the choice of instruments and circuits and somewhat determines which type of cell will be the most suitable for a given application.

14-2. Sensitivity Definitions

The sensitivity of a photoelectric cell is most accurately stated in terms of current per unit of radiant power striking the cell surface. This is usually stated in terms of microamperes per microwatt of incident power at a certain specified color or wavelength of light. The latter specification must be added because of the changes in conversion efficiency at different wavelengths of incident light. A

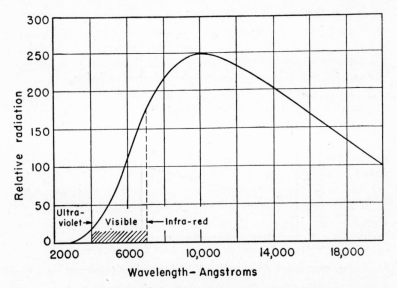

Fig. 14-1.   Relative radiation from a tungsten filament operating at a color temperature of 2870° K.

standard source for comparison purposes is frequently a tungsten-filament lamp operating at a temperature such that its spectrum of radiant energy is that of a black body operating at 2870°K. The relative distribution of energy at different wavelengths for a tungsten filament operating at this *color temperature* is shown in Fig. 14-1. For a photocell having most of its sensitive region in the visible or ultraviolet, sensitivity would mean little without such an exact specification of a standard source.

Sensitivity may also be stated in terms of visible light only, in which case it is called *luminous sensitivity* and is stated in terms of microamperes per lumen of incident light. The *lumen* is a measure of the *visible stimulus* given to the human eye by the incident radiation. Because of the color selectivity of photosensitive surfaces, specification of luminous sensitivity should be accompanied by a statement of the source used.

To convert the candlepower rating of a point source to lumens, the following relation may be used:

$$L = \frac{CA}{d^2} \tag{14-1}$$

where L is the intensity in lumens on A sq ft from a point source of candlepower C at a distance of d ft.

14-3. Photoelectric Cathode Materials

From the Einstein equation for photoelectric emission,

$$hf = eE_w + \frac{mv^2}{2}, \tag{14-2}$$

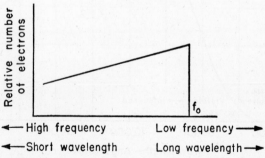

Fig. 14-2. Theoretical number of photoelectrons emitted for equal incident energy at different frequencies.

it might be assumed that the value of the emitted current would depend wholly on the number of photons striking the surface per second. For a constant total energy per unit area of surface, the number of photons decreases linearly with increase in frequency, since the energy per photon increases. If it were assumed that the efficiency of emission, or number of photons needed to emit one electron, were constant, the number of photoelectrons emitted would vary with frequency or wavelength according to Fig. 14-2. Actually, no surface emits numbers of electrons varying in this manner with frequency, since variation with frequency is not regular and approaches the threshold asymptotically, not abruptly.

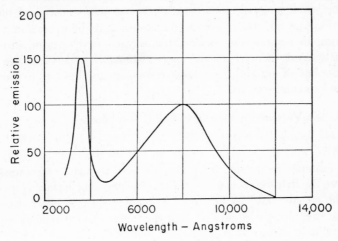

Fig. 14-3.   Relative photoelectric sensitivity, Cs-CsO-Ag surface.

It seems that some other unexplained phenomena enter and vary the efficiency of emission, or the number of photons striking the surface per electron emitted, with changes in the frequency of the incident light. Consequently, irregularities appear in curves where the current emitted is plotted against frequency of the incident light. A curve for a typical cesium on cesium oxide on silver surface is shown in Fig. 14-3. The threshold frequency is evidently at 0.25×10^{15} cycles or 12,000 A wavelength in the infrared. At frequencies above the threshold, the emission varies considerably.

It would be expected from the theory that each cathode material would exhibit a definite and typical spectral sensitivity curve, but with thin films only a few atoms deep the curves may be greatly modified, not only in shape but also in threshold frequency. It is apparent that in thin films surface forces are present which alter the value of the work function.

The most common materials used for photoemissive cathodes are the alkali metals because their threshold frequencies lie in, or at frequencies below, the visible spectrum. The preparation of surfaces of these materials usually involves sputtering or evaporation of the metal in vacuum to produce condensation of the very thin, usually monatomic, film on the cathode. Films of oxygen or hydrogen have marked effects on sensitivity and color response.

The whole process of preparation is not well understood but is practiced as an art. Cesium, potassium, rubidium, sodium, and lithium, in combination with either oxygen or hydrogen, are frequently used. Choice of the proper material makes possible the production of phototubes whose responses are limited to certain desired spectral regions.

14-4. The Vacuum Photoemissive Cell (Phototube)

A photoemissive cell consists of a cathode, coated with the light-sensitive material, and an anode to collect the emitted electrons. The cathode is frequently a semicylindrical surface arranged to receive the light on its concave face. The emitting surface is formed on the concave face by heating a bead of cesium or other material in the vacuum system and causing the metal vapors to condense on the cathode surface in a layer only one or two atoms thick. The anode may be a straight wire, a wire ring, or a metal plate mounted so as not to cast a shadow on the cathode. The anode and cathode are assembled in a glass or quartz bulb, as is shown by two types of construction in Fig. 14-4.

With light of appropriate color to cause emission striking the cathode, a small voltage may be applied across the tube, causing a small current to flow. As the voltage is increased, the current rises rapidly, being limited by space charge at small potentials on the anode. Further increase in potential causes the value of current obtained to level off, as is shown in Fig. 14-5. This indicates that saturation has been reached, or that all the electrons emitted for a particular light intensity are being attracted to the anode. For a

Fig. 14-4.   Photoemissive cells, approximately full size.

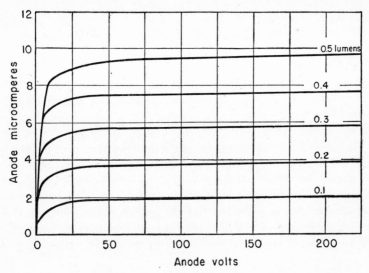

Fig. 14-5.   Volt-ampere curves for a type 922 vacuum phototube.

higher value of light intensity, saturation would occur at a higher current. Owing to saturation, the current is almost entirely independent of the applied emf above values of 20 v. The very slight slope of the characteristic curves is probably due to the Schottky effect, which reduces the work function of the surface at higher potentials.

A replot of the data of Fig. 14-5, with light flux used as an independent variable and with the anode potential held constant at 100 v, yields the curve of Fig. 14-6. The output current of a vac-

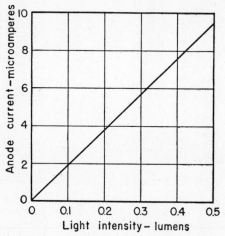

Fig. 14-6. Variation of current with light flux for a vacuum photoemissive cell.

uum photocell, operated in the saturation region, is seen to be linear with light intensity. This confirms the Einstein equation and the theory advanced in Chapter 4. Independence of applied voltage value and linearity of output are valuable properties of the vacuum photoemissive cell.

The slope of the volt-ampere curve is the conductance of the photocell. Measurements of the slope indicate that the vacuum photocell has a very low plate conductance or an extremely high internal resistance of the order of hundreds of megohms. The flatness of the volt-ampere curves indicates that the output current is almost entirely independent of voltage, and allows the vacuum photoemissive cell to be considered a constant-current generator. The value of constant-current output is a function of light intensity only, in the saturation region.   If a parallel form of equivalent circuit is considered as applying to the cell, the value of plate resistance is so large in comparison with any practical load which may be connected that the effect of the plate resistance may be neglected.   Consequently, the equivalent circuit becomes that of a constant-current generator connected to a load resistor.

It would seem that with a constant-current generator a larger load should result in a higher output voltage.   This is true, but increase of the load resistor beyond a certain limiting value becomes impractical owing to leakage currents that may be present.   If a load equal to the internal resistance of some hundreds of megohms were used, it would be found that the leakage-current paths in parallel with the load, over the phototube surface and insulation, would shunt out the load and reduce the effective load resistance to a much lower value.   In industrial practice, owing to moisture, dirt, and unavoidable insulation leakage, the upper limit for the load resistance is usually considered 10 to 20 megohms.   In laboratory apparatus, with carefully controlled humidity conditions and cell leakage reduced by coating the glass bulb with special waxes, loads of several hundred megohms may be satisfactorily used.   Insulation leakage, and capacitance effects if rapidly varying light intensities are used, prevent the use of any appreciable length of cable for electric connection in the cell circuit, and require that the photocell be closely connected with its associated equipment.

14-5. The Gas-Filled Phototube

By introduction of a small and carefully controlled amount of argon or other inert gas into a phototube, a considerable increase in sensitivity, or in current carried by the phototube for a given illumination of the cathode, can be achieved.   The emitted electrons, in moving to the anode, collide with gas atoms, producing ionization. The electrons knocked out of the atoms join in the electron flow to the anode, thereby increasing the anode current above the value emitted.   The positive ion, upon arrival at the negative cathode, may add to the emitted current by causing secondary emission from the cathode surface.   In this manner the anode current obtained for a given illumination may be increased four to seven times over that possible in an equivalent high-vacuum cell.

The increase in the current due to the presence of gas is called the *gas-amplification factor*. Attempts to increase the gas amplification above about 10 usually result in ionization so intense that a visible glow discharge forms. Bombardment of the cathode by the positive ions then may be so severe as to damage the surface irreparably and destroy the cell sensitivity. Such damage is prevented by keeping the voltage across gas-filled cells below 90 v. Limitation of maximum light intensities may also be necessary.

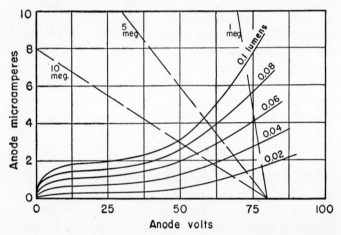

Fig. 14-7.   Volt-ampere curves for a type 921 gas-filled phototube.

Volt-ampere characteristics of a gas-filled Type 921 photocell are drawn in Fig. 14-7. The curves are of the same shape as for the vacuum cell in Fig. 14-5 until the ionization potential of the gas is reached at about 20 v. The current obtained from the gas tube then rises with increased anode voltage owing to the electrons added to the original current by ionization and secondary emission. For all anode potentials above 20 v, the gas-filled cell is seen to have a sensitivity exceeding that of the vacuum cell. Since the Types 922 and 921 cells of Figs. 14-5 and 14-7, respectively, are identical in type of surface and cathode area of 0.4 sq in., the gas-amplification factor at any desired voltage may be computed. For 75 v and 0.1 lumen per square foot applied to the cell, the gas amplification can be obtained as 4.2.

The variable spacing of the volt-ampere curves shows that above the voltage at which ionization takes place, the current output of the cell is no longer strictly linear with light intensity. This is one disadvantage of the gas-filled cell, although it is not serious for small variations in light intensity. Gas-filled cells may be used for reproduction from sound motion pictures without serious distortion, owing to the small light variations employed.

An additional difficulty encountered when the gas cell is used in sound reproduction is a loss of sensitivity for high-frequency light variations. This loss is due to the time lag between a change in light intensity and the corresponding change in current, which in turn is caused by the slowness of the positive ions in reaching the cathode and producing the secondary-emission component of the current. Output currents of a gas cell are reduced at frequencies above 2000 cycles per second, thereby causing frequency distortion, although compensating circuits may be introduced to eliminate most of the distortion.

14-6. Calculation of Output

A load line for the load-circuit equation

$$i_b = \frac{E_{bb}}{R_L} - \frac{e_b}{R_L} \tag{14-3}$$

may be drawn on the volt-ampere characteristics of a photocell, as was done for the diode and triode. When drawn through the intercept $e_b = E_{bb}$ and with slope of $-1/R_L$, it allows prediction of performance of the photocell with a particular load R_L. Figure 14-8(a) shows load lines for 5 and 20 megohms drawn on the volt-ampere characteristics of the Type 922 cell for $E_{bb} = 200$ v. The current flowing in the load for a particular value of light flux input can be found from the intersection of the load line with the volt-ampere curve for that light input. Changes from one value of light intensity to another then will result in current changes, as given by the intersections. The voltage change across the load is then just the change in IR voltage drops.

Sinusoidal or other regular variations of intensity of light from a mean value can be analyzed by considering the mean value as fixing a Q point. For the Type 922 cell with the 20-megohm load and a Q point fixed at 0.3 lumen per square foot, a sinusoidal variation having a peak-to-peak light-intensity change of 0.2 lumen will pro-

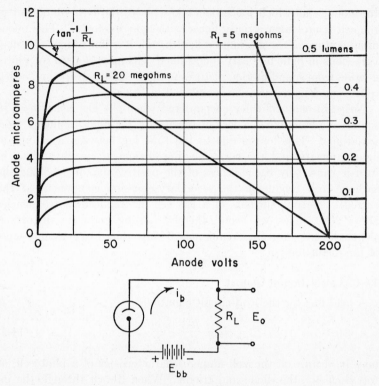

Fig. 14-8.   (a) Load-line calculation of output for a photoemissive cell;
(b) photoemissive-cell operating circuit.

duce an output voltage across the load of 75 v peak to peak, or
26.5 rms volts.   Owing to the linearity of the vacuum cell, linear
interpolation for values of light intensity that are intermediate to
those of the curves can be readily practiced.

The load-line method is applicable to the gas cell in an exactly
similar manner.   Owing to the nonlinearity of the gas cell, interpolation of the intensity curves cannot be so readily performed.

A circuit of unusually high sensitivity is shown in Fig. 14-9(a).
This utilizes two photocells in such a way that one becomes the load
for the other.   Developing that idea further, the curve for T_1 in (b)
is that of the usual vacuum photocell for some particular light
intensity.   The load is T_2; and although it does not have a linear

volt-ampere characteristic as a resistor, it has a volt-ampere curve like T_1 (at equal light intensities), and this curve is drawn in (b) in exactly the manner a normal linear load line would be drawn. With the T_2 characteristic as a load line the operating point is at A, where the two solid curves intersect.

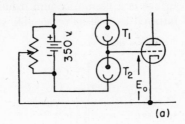

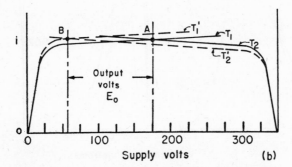

Fig. 14-9. (a) A phototube circuit of considerable sensitivity; (b) load-line calculation for the circuit of (a).

If the exciting light beam is arranged to shift such that an increase on T_1 causes a decrease on T_2, then after a small change of light intensity in this manner the two cells will have characteristics given by the dashed curves for T_1' and T_2'. The point of intersection and operation is now at B, giving for the case under consideration an output voltage change of 118 v. This is much larger than could be obtained across any reasonable value of external resistance load for a similar small change in light intensity.

14-7. Color Response of Typical Surfaces

Considerable color selectivity is desirable in photoemissive cells to permit operation with different colors of light or with different types of light sources. For some uses the cell should have a color sensitivity approximating that of the human eye.

Variation of cathode material and methods of treatment allows a considerable variety of spectral sensitivity curves to be obtained. Curves of spectral response for typical surfaces are given in Fig. 14-10. The S-2 surface is a cesium-cesium oxide surface with high sensitivity in the infrared as well as reasonable sensitivity through-

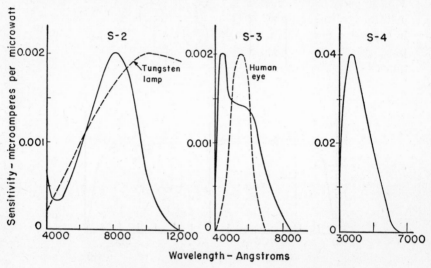

Fig. 14-10.   Color sensitivity of various photoemissive surfaces.

out the visible region (4000-7000 A). A comparison of the S-2 curve with that of the radiation from a tungsten filament at 2870°K is given in Fig. 14-10, and it can be seen that the S-2 surface is well adapted for use with a tungsten lamp as a source. The S-3 surface employs rubidium, with sensitivity largely confined to the visual region, and having its greatest sensitivity in the blue (short wavelength) end of the spectrum. The S-4 surface of cesium is highly sensitive, having a peak response 20 times greater than the peak of the S-3 surface. Besides these commercially available surfaces, many others, especially those having sensitivities in the ultraviolet, are available for special purposes.

In application, it is important to select a cell having a high response in the spectral region in which the source has high output. The S-4 surface would be of little use with a tungsten-filament source. Considerable color selectivity can also be obtained through the use of optical light filters.

14-8. Photoemissive Cell Applications

The phototube, either gas or vacuum, has a very high internal resistance and provides a high voltage and very low current output. This property makes it unsuited to the direct operation of relays and instruments that require appreciable current, or to circuits of low impedance. Since the grid circuit of a vacuum tube is of high impedance, the vacuum-tube amplifier is a satisfactory relay and impedance reducer for the photocell.

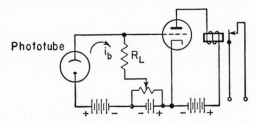

Fig. 14-11. Circuit of a phototube and vacuum-tube relay.

A typical combination is shown in Fig. 14-11. Choice of R_L for such a circuit may be limited somewhat by grid current produced by stray electrons in the triode, and choice of the vacuum tube should be made to permit as high a value of grid resistor as possible. Medium-μ triodes are the most satisfactory and permit grid resistors as high as 10 to 15 megohms. The potentiometer in the grid circuit may be used to adjust the plate current to a minimum, with zero light. Then, when light strikes the cell, the grid of the triode becomes more positive owing to the drop across R_L, and the plate current increases and operates the relay. For applications in which the light is varied by the sound track of sound motion-picture film, the relay may be replaced by a conventional coupling circuit and followed by additional amplification.

All types of phototubes, except those having S-4 surfaces, are limited in ambient operating temperature to about 100°C. The S-4 surface must not be used over 50°C. This figure includes any temperature rise of the cathode due to radiant heat from the source. Heat-absorbing filter glass is available to limit this heating in extreme cases.

In choosing between the vacuum and gas cells for a particular application, the following characteristics may be considered. The vacuum cell is linear with light and independent of applied voltage variations when used at voltages over 20. It is relatively stable in sensitivity over long periods. The gas cell is less linear, less stable in sensitivity, and is highly dependent on the value of applied voltage. The gas cell is four to seven times more sensitive than the vacuum cell but cannot be used at full sensitivity at frequencies above about 2000 cycles. The decision as to which cell should be used, therefore, hinges largely on the sensitivity required, at least for the lower frequencies.

14-9. Photoelectric Electron Multipliers

The currents expected in photoemissive cells under low light conditions are extremely small. Without some form of interrupter or light chopper they are direct currents as well, and difficult of amplification. The amplification problem, however, has been overcome by application of principles of secondary emission in a device known as the *secondary-emission multiplier*.

If the secondary-emission coefficient is greater than unity, it is possible to achieve amplification of the original beam current, or *multiplication* of the electrons. For example, if on the average the secondary-emission coefficient is 5, or each primary electron releases 5 secondaries, then if an incident current of 1 μa strikes the surface, a current of 5 μa may be attracted from the surface as secondary electrons. The original input electron current may originate from any source, but usually it will be a photoelectric current. The design of a tube may take the form of either single-stage multipliers, producing amplification due to bombardment of one surface, or multistage multipliers, with the total amplification due to a number of surfaces in cascade.

Figure 14-12 shows the basic design of all multistage multipliers, in which a series of electrodes, all surface-treated with secondary-emitting materials, are operated at successively higher positive potentials. For each electron leaving the source S, δ electrons are emitted from target T_1. These are attracted to target T_2 by the positive potential thereon, and since each of the electrons reaching T_2 causes δ electrons to be emitted, then δ^2 electrons leave T_2 and are attracted to T_3.   The number of electrons leaving T_3 is δ^3, and the number of electrons leaving the nth electrode, or the current multiplication or gain of the multiplier, is

$$\text{gain} = \delta^n, \tag{14-4}$$

where n is the number of electrodes on which secondary emission is employed.   With δ frequently in the range of 9 to 10, and as many as 10 stages used, gains of several million are possible in a single tube.

Although in theory the multiplier of Fig. 14-12 would operate satisfactorily if source S were made a photoelectric cathode, certain

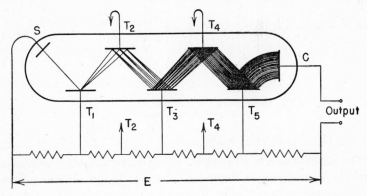

Fig. 14-12.   Principle of the multistage secondary-emission multiplier.

difficulties would arise.   Many electrons would pass straight down the tube under the attraction of the potential on the collector C, thereby reducing the gain.   Also, owing to the mutual repulsion of the electrons in the beam passing from target to target, the beam would spread out and many electrons would miss targets T_4 and T_5 and become lost.   As a result, development has been directed to types of multipliers in which the electrons are focused successively on one target after another, thus preventing spreading of the beam, and maintaining the full theoretical value of gain.   The focusing can be achieved by electric or magnetic fields, or by combinations of the two.

Work on electric-field focusing arrangements has been done by tracing electron trajectories for various electrode arrangements, and the methods of the electrolytic tank or the rubber-sheeting model have been extensively used.   Figure 14-13 shows one result of this development.   The targets, called *dynodes*, have been so shaped as to provide curved electric fields which give a focusing effect for electrons proceeding from one target to the next.   One form of such a tube is built with a photoelectric cathode and nine dynodes and has an over-all gain of 2,000,000.   The applied voltage totals 1250 v, divided equally between the nine dynodes and the collector anode.

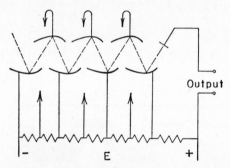

Fig. 14-13.   Curved electrode multiplier using electric-field focusing.

14-10. Noise in Electron Multipliers

The possible gain in a multiplier is limited by the *noise*, or random variations of current in the output circuit.   If the currents become small enough or the number of electrons passing is greatly reduced, even the smoothest direct current is found to have variations due to random behavior of the individual electrons.   The primary current to a multiplier will usually be quite small, in fractions of microamperes, and fluctuation may show up in the electron actions.   This fluctuation, when amplified, appears as noise or random current variations in the output.   The noise currents in the output of a multiplier are due to two causes:

1. The random currents in the primary electron beam.
2. Variation or fluctuation of the secondary-emission coefficient from electron to electron.

On the assumption that the input noise is amplified by subsequent multiplier stages just as a signal is, and that ordinary statistical laws of variation apply to fluctuations in the secondary-emission coefficient, it can be shown (Ref. 7) that the signal-to-noise ratio is modified, because of the presence of the multiplier, by a factor

$$\sqrt{\frac{\delta - 1}{\delta}}. \tag{14-5}$$

If δ is large, the signal-to-noise ratio in the output is nearly that due to the original input variations only. This shows that variations in numbers of secondaries produced, from electron to electron, average out very closely, and the secondary-emission multiplier produces almost zero random-current noise.

Although the input noise sets the fundamental limit on input sensitivity and gain, there are two other factors limiting the sensitivity: thermionic emission from the targets and the effect of positive gas ions present because of imperfect vacuum. Although the targets operate close to ambient temperature, thermionic emission is possible because of the extremely low work functions of the surface materials.

The secondary-emission multiplier has also been applied to amplification of thermionic currents, wherein, if g_m is the transconductance of the thermionic tube, $\delta^n g_m$ is the over-all transconductance of a combination of a thermionic tube and a multiplier.

PROBLEMS

14-1. (a) Plot a current-vs-illumination characteristic for the type 921 photocell with a load of 1 megohm if the voltage supply is 80 v.

(b) Repeat for a load of 10 megohms, and voltage of 60 v.

14-2. Three applications for photocells are as follows:

(a) A device to count opaque objects passing on a conveyor belt. The light source is able to provide 0.5 lumen per sq ft on the cell.

(b) A colorimeter in which a color is to be matched to a standard by light transmission. The light source must be low enough in intensity that materials are not heated.

(c) An illumination-measuring instrument, in which values are to be read from a calibrated dial. Line voltage variations may be ±10 per cent. Specify which applications should employ gas cells and which vacuum cells.

14-3. The S-2, S-3, and S-4 photosurfaces of Fig. 14-10 have threshold frequencies at 12,000, 8200, and 6500 A, respectively. What are the values of the work functions of these surfaces?

14-4. A 32 cp lamp has its filament 6 in. from a lens of 1.5 in. diameter. All the light reaching the lens is caused to converge onto the cathode of a photocell with a sensitivity of 15 μa/ lumen. What is the current through the photocell?

14-5. A photocell receives a change in light flux from 0.15 to 0.37 lumen per sq ft. If the tube is a type 922 and has a load of 10 megohms and applied voltage of 150, find the change in voltage across the load.

14-6. An illumination control for a schoolroom employs the circuit of Fig. 14-11 with a type 922 photocell and a 6J5 tube. The photocell operates at 150 v with $R_L = 3$ megohms; the 6J5 tube has the grid bias adjusted for a plate current of 0.2 ma at $E_{bb} = 250$ v, with the resistance of the relay being 10,000 ohms. If the relay opens its contacts and turns off certain lamps at 4 ma coil current and closes the contacts at 1.8 ma, find the limits between which the room illumination will be allowed to vary. (*Hint:* the 922 cell is linear, so its characteristics may be interpolated.)

14-7. (a) A type 922 cell is used with a 15-megohm load and applied voltage of 150. Light striking the photocell changes sinusoidally from 0.07 to 0.11 lumen per sq ft. What is the rms voltage across the load?

(b) If this voltage is now applied to the grid of a 6J5 triode with $\mu = 20$, $r_p = 10,000$, and load of 20,000 ohms, what rms voltage will be developed across the 20,000-ohm load?

14-8. Draw the circuit and discuss the changes needed in the circuit of Fig. 14-11 to make the relay open its contact for minimum light and close for maximum light. Describe the adjustment of the slider on the bias-control potentiometer.

14-9. A secondary-emission multiplier having dynodes whose surfaces have the characteristic of curve (a), Fig. 4-16, has eight stages of multiplication and a collector anode. The over-all voltage applied to the tube is 1350, evenly divided between the dynodes and collector. If the input photoelectric current is 0.015 μa, find the output current.

14-10. A tetrode having g_m of 1500 μmhos is followed by four stages of current multiplication having $\delta = 3.4$. Find the output-current change expected because of a 1-v rms signal on the tetrode grid.

14-11. A conventional photocell produces a change in output of 1 μa for a given change in light intensity. If a nine-stage multiplier having $\delta = 8$ follows this photocell, what is the change in output current of the multiplier?

14-12. A 50-cp lamp is used as a point source for a type 921 cell in a circuit with a 5-megohm load and 80 v applied. How far away can the source be and still produce a current of 4 μa in the load? The area of the cell surface is 0.4 sq in.

REFERENCES

1. Metcalf, G. F., "Operating Characteristics of Photoelectric Tubes," *Proc. IRE*, **17**, 2064 (1929).

2. Zworykin, V. K., and Ramberg, E. G., *Photoelectricity and Its Applications*, John Wiley & Sons, Inc., New York, 1949.

3. Richter, W., *Fundamentals of Industrial Electric Circuits*, McGraw-Hill Book Company, Inc., New York, 1947.

4. Shepard, F. H., "Some Unconventional Vacuum Tube Applications," *RCA Rev.*, **2**, 149 (1937).

5. Farnsworth, P. T., "Television by Electron-Image Scanning," *J. Franklin Inst.*, **218**, 411 (1934).

6. Zworykin, V. K., Morton, G. A., and Malter, L., "The Secondary-Emission Multiplier," *Proc. IRE*, **24**, 351 (1936).

7. Pierce, J. R., and Shockley, W., "A Theory of Noise for Electron Multipliers," *Proc. IRE*, **26**, 321 (1938).

8. Pierce, J. R., "Electron-Multiplier Design," *Bell Labs. Record*, **16**, 305 (1938).

9. Zworykin, V. K., and Rajchmann, J. A., "Electrostatic Electron Multiplier," *Proc. IRE*, **27**, 558 (1939).

10. Wagner, H. M., and Ferris, W. R., "Orbital-Beam Secondary-Electron Multiplier," *Proc. IRE*, **29**, 598 (1941).

11. Muller, R. H., Garman, R. L., and Droz, M. E., *Experimental Electronics*, Prentice-Hall, Inc., New York, 1942.

CHAPTER 15

SOLID-STATE ELECTRONICS

In recent years a number of devices have been developed which depend upon the nonlinear voltage-current relations, power control, and energy-transformation properties of certain materials broadly classified as semiconductors. These devices, utilizing the phenomena of electric conduction through certain solids, such as silicon, germanium, selenium, or some of the metallic oxides, do not strictly fall within the group of electronic devices as defined in Chapter 1. However, the basic processes employ theory similar to that underlying electron emission and charge movement, and the nonlinear characteristics and applications are similar to those of electron tubes. Semiconductor devices are extensively used for measurement, control, and rectification, often in close association with vacuum tubes, so that the research and development workers of the electronic field are also those most interested in the new devices.

15-1. Semiconductors

In general, it may be said that a semiconductor is a material having quite poor electric conductivity, although this conductivity value differs from that of insulators by many orders of magnitude. A semiconductor may also exhibit polarity effects in the resistance between the semiconductor and a contacting metal, and over considerable temperature ranges will have a negative temperature coefficient of resistance.

In Chapter 4 the Fermi-Dirac distribution of energy among the electrons of a metal was discussed. A diagram of this energy distribution, indicating the relative number of electrons in a metal having given amounts of energy, E, at 0°K, is reproduced in (a), Fig. 15-1. There are many available energy states above E_M into which electrons are free to move when given increased energy, as by applica-

tion of heat or of an electric field in the metal.   The existence of
these unfilled levels is indicated in the figure by the dashed extension
of the bounding curve from E_M to E_B.

The electron-energy distribution in insulators and semiconductors
is considerably different from that for metals.   In the former two
substances, the energy distribution takes the forms of (b) and (c),
Fig. 15-1.   Possible electron-energy levels are represented along the
horizontal scale, and the number of electrons having a given energy
are proportional to the vertical scale.   In semiconductors and insulators the energy distribution is found to have one or more low-
energy bands in which all available levels are filled, separated from a
normally empty higher band by an unallowed or forbidden band or
gap.   For insulators the width of this forbidden band, ΔE, is a few

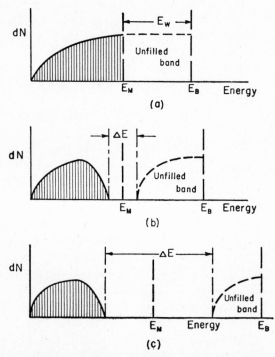

Fig. 15-1.   Density of electron energy states in (a)
a metal of good conductivity; (b) a pure semiconductor; (c) an insulator.

electron volts or more, whereas for semiconductors the width may approximate 0.5 ev.

The energy level shown as E_M was defined for metals (good conductors) in Chapter 4. It is generally known as the *Fermi characteristic energy*, which first appeared in Eq. 4-1. In metals the E_M level is always inside an allowed energy band. In semiconductors or insulators the Fermi level is always inside an unallowed region or gap. It is the magnitude of ΔE, or the large amount of energy required to raise an electron across the gap and produce conduction, that causes some materials to be classified as insulators.

15-2. Conduction in a Semiconductor

Quantum mechanics requires that when a band is completely filled, the electrons therein cannot contribute to the electric conduction. A pure semiconductor is an insulator at 0°K, because the lower band is filled and there are no electrons in the upper conduction band. As the temperature is raised, some electrons acquire sufficient thermal energy to raise them across the unallowed gap into the upper band, where they are then free to migrate from atom to atom under action of an electric field, and constitute a current. This is *intrinsic* conduction.

As the temperature rises, the number of electrons passing to the upper conductivity band increases rapidly and the conductivity increases, or the resistance falls. Thus the negative temperature coefficient typical of semiconductors is a result of the limitation on the available number of conductivity electrons, this number being a function of temperature.

The conductivity of a semiconductor is greatly affected by extremely small traces of impurities, and the impurities lead to two types of conduction: n and p. Two of the most common semiconductors are silicon and germanium, elements of the fourth group in the periodic table. Impurity traces of elements from the third group, such as boron, aluminum, and gallium, give p-type conductivity. Addition of traces of elements from the fifth group, such as nitrogen, phosphorus, antimony, and arsenic, lead to n-type conductivity.

An impurity atom may have a filled energy state located ΔE_1 ev below the unfilled semiconductor band as in Fig. 15-2. This electron can easily be raised from the impurity band into the allowed upper or conduction band of the semiconductor; these impurity atoms are spoken of as *donator* atoms. The raised electron is then able to take part in conduction, while the donator atom is a positive ion bound to a particular location and cannot contribute to the conductivity. Conduction is then by reason of these excess electrons, and is *n*-type.

In some impurities of the third group the atoms have an empty band located ΔE_2 ev above the top of the filled semiconductor band. These impurity atoms may take up or become *acceptors* of electrons which are taken from the top of the semiconductor filled band, thus leaving *holes* in the top of the lower band of the semiconductor. The hole or absence of an electron in a particular atom can be filled by passing an electron from a neighboring atom, under action of an electric field. This operation creates a new charge deficiency or a

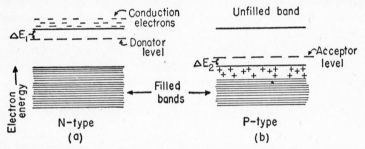

Fig. 15-2.　Energy levels in a semiconductor (a) *n*-type; (b) *p*-type. Energy plotted vertically.

new hole, and if it is successively repeated the hole appears to move along bucket-brigade style. The hole has a positive charge of absolute value equal to that of an electron but migrates much more slowly through the crystal. Such a conductor appears to conduct by positive charges or holes, and is said to be a *p*-type conductor.

15-3. Photoconductors

The earliest photocells were of the photoconductive type and consisted of a thin film of carefully prepared selenium, as a semiconductor, coated between electrodes on a glass plate. When this plate was placed in a strong light, the electric resistance was reduced to 20 per cent or less of the resistance when in the dark. The actual resistance was usually in the order of megohms.

The operation of semiconductor photocells involves the absorption of radiant energy to raise an electron from the top of the filled band, across the unallowed gap, into the conductivity band, Fig. 15-1. This electron then contributes to conduction through the crystal. When the electron is taken from the filled band a hole is left, and this may migrate as described in the previous section. Thus both the hole and the electron contribute to the photocurrent.

The energy which must be supplied by the radiation must be equal to the width of the unallowed band, or the gap energy, and this is of the order of 0.7 ev for germanium. The quantum of energy required to produce photoconductivity is smaller in size than that required for electron emission in photoemissive cells, wherein usual work functions approximate 1 ev. Hence photoconductivity can be excited by light of longer wavelength than that needed for photoemission.

Assume that the gap energy for germanium is 0.7 ev; then since $W = hf$ joules and

$$\lambda_0 = \frac{hc}{eE} \qquad \text{m,} \qquad (15\text{-}1)$$

the longest exciting wavelength or threshold is

$$\lambda_0 = \frac{6.55 \times 10^{-34} \times 3 \times 10^8}{1.60 \times 10^{-19} \times 0.7} = 17.5\mu = 17{,}500 \text{ A.}$$

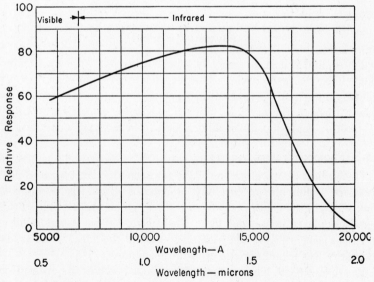

Fig. 15-3. Response of germanium as a photoconductive device.

This wavelength is in the infrared. A curve of relative output vs wavelength for germanium is given in Fig. 15-3. For comparison a cesium photoemissive cell has a peak output of only about 5 on this scale, at a wavelength of 8000 A. It cuts off completely at about 12,000 A.

A so-called coaxial type of unit is shown in Fig. 15-4. By forming the area around the point contact with passage of a momentary heavy current, an area of p-type material is apparently created under the contact. Although the mechanism is not yet clear, it appears that the holes released by the light form a positive space charge around the collector wire, thus making it easy for the electrons released by the light, or furnished by the supply, to pass through the surface barrier. Efficiencies in excess of the theoretical one electron per quantum of incident energy are obtained in such a unit by this means.

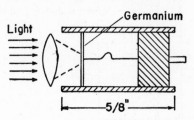

Fig. 15-4.   Coaxial phototransistor of germanium.

It is to be expected that some electrons from the impurity atoms would exist in the conduction band at normal temperatures, even when the cell is dark. These have been raised to the conduction band from donor impurities by thermal energies, and produce conductivity in the dark or "dark current." If there is a high impurity percentage, the dark current may be so large as to mask the photocurrent.

15-4. Semiconductor Rectifiers

It was discovered many years ago that certain semiconductor materials, notably silicon and germanium, exhibited polarity effects on their surfaces and thus were rectifiers. Because of the low shunt capacitance, making them suitable for high-frequency rectifiers, these materials have received much development work in recent years. Two types have been developed, the point-contact unit of Fig. 15-5, and the germanium junction type of Fig. 15-6. Both types are very small and light in weight.

By controlled diffusion of impurities into the germanium it is possible to form a portion of a single crystal in which one end is p-type and the other n-type as indicated in Fig. 15-7. Contact wires are fastened to the ends, and the unit becomes a rectifier of low forward resistance when the p portion is made positive. In (b) of the figure are energy level diagrams, as discussed with Fig. 15-2, for the two separate materials.

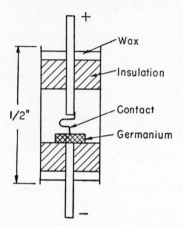

Fig. 15-5. Assembly of a germanium point-contact rectifier.

When the materials are joined, under thermal equilibrium conditions the Fermi levels, E_M, of the two materials must be equal across the junction as shown in (c). The filled energy levels in both portions are shaded, the charge-marked areas representing holes or electrons available for conduction, and the white area the unallowed gap.

A natural "energy barrier" is formed at the junction, which tends to keep the electrons and holes in their own material unless an external potential is applied to drive the charges over the hill, as it were. This barrier and transition layer is thin, of the order of 10^{-4} to 10^{-6} cm.

By connecting a battery, negative terminal to the n material, positive terminal to the p material, additional high-energy electrons are made available to the n material. Likewise the positive terminal extracts electrons from, or "injects holes" into, the p material. In effect, the energy pattern is distorted into that of (d), wherein the barrier is wiped out and electrons and holes are free to migrate as current across the junction. This is then the low-resistance direction.

If the battery polarity is reversed it can be reasoned that the barrier height is increased, current flow is extremely difficult, and this connection yields the high-resistance direction of the rectifier.

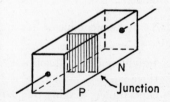

Fig. 15-6. Junction semiconductor rectifier.

In the manufacture of the point-contact units of Fig. 15-5, wherein a phosphor-bronze wire is used as a point contact on the n-type semi-conductor surface, a large current is passed through the point and the contact is "formed." It is now believed that in this forming operation a portion of the material under the contact is changed to p-type, and thus the theory of operation follows that given above.

A considerable variety of silicon and germanium rectifiers are

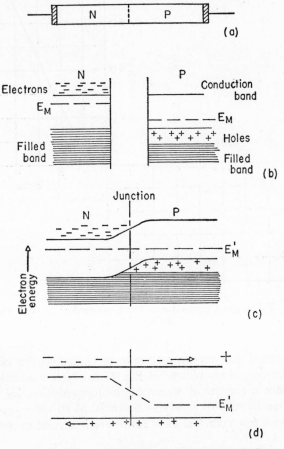

Fig. 15-7. (a) Junction semiconductor diode. (b) Electron energy levels in the n and p materials. (c) Energy levels under thermal equilibrium when the materials are joined. (d) Readjusted levels when p material is positive.

available, with various design features such as high back resistance, low forward resistance, low capacitance, high back voltage, and other capabilities. The capacitances, including mountings, are usually of the order of a few micromicrofarads, so that operation at frequencies of thousands of megacycles is possible.

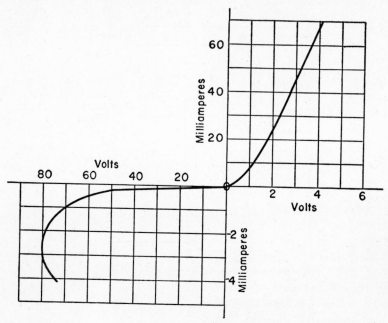

Fig. 15-8. Volt-ampere curve for a 1N34 germanium crystal diode. Note scale changes.

The forward and reverse volt-ampere characteristics of a 1N34 germanium crystal are plotted in Fig. 15-8. Note that only 3 volts will produce a current of 46 ma in the forward direction, whereas only 0.6 ma flows with a reverse potential of 60 volts applied. In fact, up to a few volts the back resistance is several megohms.

15-5. Transistors

A solid-state conduction triode has been named the *transistor*, combining the *trans*lational properties of the triode tube with the peculiar res*istor* properties of semiconductors.

As with semiconductor rectifiers, the transistor has been developed in both point-contact (Fig. 15-9) and junction forms (Fig. 15-10). The latter type may take the form of either *n-p-n* or *p-n-p* junctions, depending on the control used in manufacture. The junction type

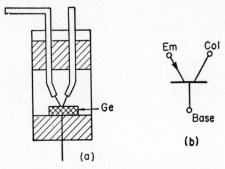

Fig. 15-9.   (a) Assembly of a point-contact transistor; (b) circuit symbol for a transistor.

appears as a lacquer-coated bead the size of a pea. Three wires are brought out, being connected as shown and called the *emitter*, the *base*, and the *collector* electrodes.

The theory of operation of an *n-p-n* transistor is illustrated in Fig. 15-11 wherein (a) illustrates the energy-level diagram under thermal equilibrium conditions. The electrons and holes are effectively trapped in their respective regions. At (b) is shown the circuit connection, and the energy-level diagram when arranged for control of the collector current, or for amplification. It may be noted that the collector is biased in the reverse or high-resistance direction.

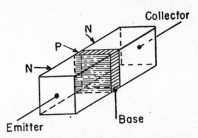

Fig. 15-10.   Schematic of a junction transistor.

Electrons in the emitter *n* region are urged by the applied potential to climb the small potential hill to the base or *p* region where it will then be possible for most of them to travel on and "slide" downhill under the influence of the collector potential and reach the collector. The flow over the hill depends on the hill height and this is varied by the variable potential signal introduced on the base. If the p region is thin, few electrons will be lost in traveling through and the efficiency will be high.

The emitter region may be considered as analogous to the cathode of a triode, the base or p region to the grid wires, and the collector to the anode. If the signal is applied to the base, the controlled current flowing through the p region may be very much larger than the base current, and the current amplification may be high.

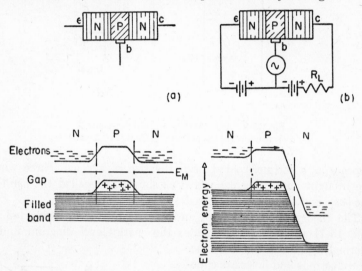

Fig. 15-11. *n-p-n* junctions (a) thermal equilibrium; (b) biased as an amplifier.

Even if the currents through the emitter and collector are merely equal, a large power gain is possible since the two circuits differ in resistance, with the output several orders of magnitude higher. Power gains of the order of 40 to 50 db are possible, since the input resistance has values from 200 to 600 ohms, and the output resistance may range from 20,000 ohms to over a megohm.

Point-contact units are made with either p or n germanium. The forming operation at the contact point is believed to produce a region of n or p characteristics, respectively, under the contacts, and the theory then follows that of the junction unit. The main advantage of the point-contact construction is reduced capacitance, as the power gain is only 20 to 30 db.

The current amplification is expressed as

$$\alpha = \frac{\Delta I_2}{\Delta I_1}.$$

In the *n-p-n* unit this can have a maximum value of unity, if all the emitter current reaches the collector, no electrons combining with

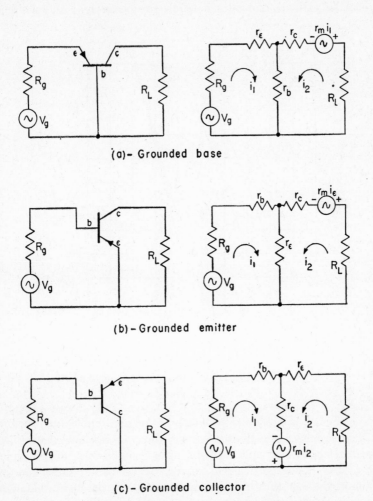

(a)- Grounded base

(b) - Grounded emitter

(c) - Grounded collector

Fig. 15-12. Transistor equivalent circuits: (a) grounded base; (b) grounded emitter; (c) grounded collector.

holes in transit. In practice the figure reaches 0.95 to 0.98. For
the *p-n-p* unit the values of α are in the range of 3 or 4.

Basic circuits, similar in performance to the three fundamental
circuits of vacuum tube practice are possible, and in fact the transistor
is the dual of the triode. The three fundamental circuit types are
illustrated in Fig. 15-12, where they correspond to the grounded grid,
grounded cathode, and cathode follower respectively. Actual circuit

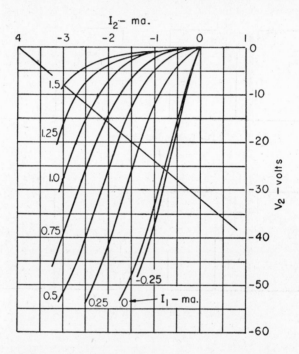

Fig. 15-13. Collector characteristics for a point-contact
transistor.

development is not quite as simple as merely duplicating vacuum
triode circuits, since the presence of the base resistance introduces
feedback in some circuits. Operating or Q points must be maintained
in terms of a constant current instead of a constant voltage, and this
is more difficult with usual power supplies. Variation of characteristics with operating temperature may also be a difficulty.

Performance characteristics may be plotted for transistors much as for vacuum tubes. A typical plate family for a point-contact unit is shown in Fig. 15-13, and a plate family for a junction unit in Fig. 15-14. Graphical methods for computing large signal outputs with a load line are similar to those for vacuum tubes.

The transit time of the electrons in the semiconductor is long compared to that in vacuum tubes and the transit times of the holes are even longer. This transit time is not a constant for all carriers, but there is considerable random variation, so that the charges

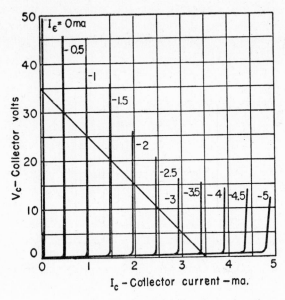

Fig. 15-14. Collector characteristics for a junction transistor, with 10,000 ohm load line.

corresponding to a particular part of the input wave do not all arrive at their respective terminals together. When this difference in arrival time corresponds to an appreciable part of a cycle, there is a tendency for some of the charge variations to cancel, and the frequency response begins to fall off.

Due to this dispersion in transit time, and also to the internal capacitances, frequency limits at present are 10 megacycles for junction units, and 70 megacycles for point-contact types. The internal noise or random current generated is also somewhat greater than that of vacuum tubes.

Limited to powers of about one watt at present, the chief applications lie in the area of small-signal amplification and in computers, where the lack of filament heating power, and small size and light weight are helpful. The field is in rapid development and improvements in performance are to be expected.

15-6. Large-Area or Blocking-Layer Rectifiers

Several semiconductor rectifiers that employ boundary-layer properties of selenium, copper sulfide, and cuprous oxide in large-area contacts have also been developed. These consist usually of a layer of the semiconductor bonded onto a metal base, with electric contact

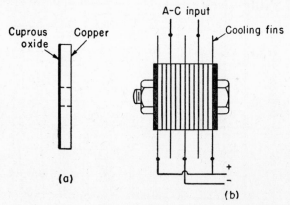

Fig. 15-15. (a) A single copper-cuprous oxide disk; (b) a complete bridge-connected rectifier having three disks in series in each arm.

being made to the whole surface of the semiconductor and to the metal base. Rectification depends on the development of a blocking layer at the junction of semiconductor and base metal. The easy movement of electrons in the units is from base metal to semiconductor; thus the low-resistance direction occurs with the semiconductor positive.

In the copper-cuprous oxide cell, developed by Grondahl in 1926, the cuprous oxide is formed on a copper washer by controlled oxidation at high temperature. The cuprous oxide surface is dusted with graphite to improve contact, and is stacked on an insulated bolt as part of a sandwich of copper, cuprous oxide, and a soft lead washer. A stack of many similar units is forced together under pressure for low forward resistance, as in Fig. 15-15 (b).

A typical volt-ampere curve for a copper oxide cell is shown in Fig. 15-16. Each disk is limited to about 8 to 10 v in the reverse direction, so that for higher voltages it is customary to stack units in series. Cells may be paralleled for higher currents. The back current is a function of temperature, so that operating temperatures are limited to about 45°C.

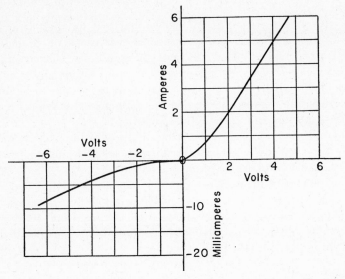

Fig. 15-16.   Volt-ampere curve of a single copper-cuprous oxide disk.

One difficulty with such units is that they tend to age or decrease in efficiency with time. Usual ratings are such that the effect of aging has been discounted, and a new unit will perform better than its rating would indicate.

The selenium rectifiers used in many small radio receivers are similar in principle and construction, the selenium being deposited on either iron or aluminum. It will withstand up to 25 v back emf per disk, and may be operated up to 75°C. This property allows the construction of units of considerably smaller size and weight for a given electric capacity than is possible with the copper-oxide units.

15-7. Thermistors

One device employing the negative temperature coefficient of resistance of semiconductors is the thermally sensitive resistor or *thermistor*. Basically it is a unit whose resistance drops rapidly with increasing temperature. It serves as an accurate and sensitive temperature-measuring unit or as a control device, since heat developed in a resistor in one circuit can be applied to a resistor in a second circuit, thereby changing the resistance of the second circuit. A time lag is, of course, introduced.

Mixtures of various metallic oxides are used for thermistors, to obtain resistors whose useful resistance variations lie in desired temperature ranges. For one type the resistance changes about 4 per cent per degree centigrade at room temperature, and over the range of 0° to 300°C the resistance may decrease by a factor of 1000. Over this same temperature range the resistance of a typical metal such as platinum will increase by a factor of 2.

Thermistors are made by sintering mixtures of the oxide powders which have been extruded or pressed into beads, rods, disks, or washers. Contact wires are fused or soldered on.

A resistance-vs-temperature plot for one mixture of manganese and nickel oxides is given in Fig. 15-17, with the resistance change plotted logarithmically. The range indicated is from 10,000,000 ohm-cm at −100° to less than 1 ohm-cm at 400°. It is found that these units seem to obey a law of the form

$$\rho = \rho_0 \epsilon^{(B/T - B/T_0)}$$

where

T = temperature (°C),

$\rho_0 = \rho$ when T is some temperature T_0 (ohm-cm),

B = a constant having dimensions of temperature.

For the material of Fig. 15-17, $B = 3920$°C, although this value will vary slightly with operating range chosen.

A steady-state voltage-current curve for a small bead of the material of Fig. 15-17 is shown in Fig. 15-18. Each time the current is changed, sufficient time is allowed for the voltage drop to reach a new steady value. For very small currents, the power dissipated is too small to heat the thermistor appreciably, and a linear relation is obtained. As the current is given larger values, the power dis-

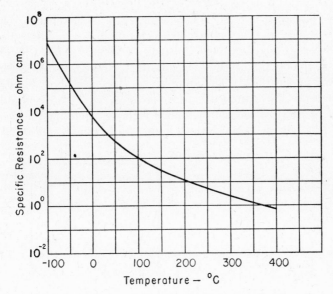

Fig. 15-17. Resistance of a semiconductor as a function of temperature.

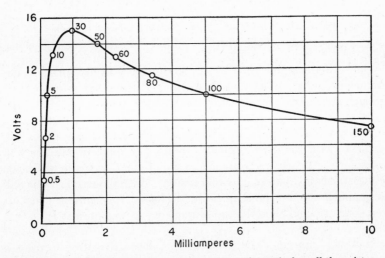

Fig. 15-18. Steady-state voltage-current curve of a typical small thermistor bead. Numbers on the curve are °C rise above ambient.

sipated increases and the temperature rises.   This change reduces
the resistance, and the voltage drop is less than it would have been if
the resistance had remained constant.   The curve shows that it is
possible to obtain a negative slope in the relation, this being of value
in some applications.   The numbers on the curve show the rise in
temperature above ambient in degrees centigrade.   Size and mount-
ing of thermistors, as well as applied voltage, determine the thermal
time-delay characteristics, which are useful in some applications.

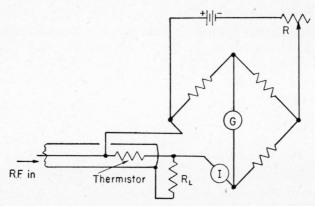

Fig. 15-19.   Thermistor bridge for measurement of radio-
frequency power in a coaxial line.

One valuable application of the thermistor is in measuring radio-
frequency power.   The thermistor bead is connected into a circuit
in such a way as to be heated by radio-frequency current, and at the
same time is connected in a d-c bridge circuit as in Fig. 15-19.   The
thermistor is maintained at constant temperature and constant resistance, with the d-c bridge circuits used to indicate constancy of
resistance.   At zero radio-frequency input the d-c circuit will cause
P_0 watts dissipation in the thermistor.   As radio-frequency power
is supplied the d-c input must be decreased to maintain constant
temperature, and thus the radio-frequency power present is

$$P_{rf} = P_0 - P_{d\text{-}c},$$

where $P_{d\text{-}c}$ is the d-c power input at time of measurement.   In order
to minimize skin effect, the beads have very small diameters.

When the thermistor is used for measurement of temperature in bridge circuits, it displays great sensitivity to temperature changes. With a good galvanometer the sensitivity may be as good as 0.0005°C, approximately 60 times better than that of a platinum thermometer. Although the stability of thermistors is not yet so good as that of the platinum thermometer, the units can be depended upon to about 0.01°C up to about 100°C. High-resistance thermistor bridges, operated from alternating current, may have their output amplified by vacuum tubes, thus eliminating delicate galvanometers.

15-8. Photovoltaic Cells

The mechanism discussed in Section 15-2 is found to explain the *generation of an emf* under illumination of the barrier layer. By reason of reception of light energy, electrons may be raised to the conduction band, and when the semiconductor is placed in contact with a metal, these high-energy electrons flow over into the metal from the semiconductor. At the same time a reverse flow from the metal is prevented by the surface barrier set up in the semiconductor. As long as the illumination continues there is a supply of these electrons and the current flow continues.

Two common types of self-generating, or *photovoltaic* cells using the barrier layer principle are the copper-copper oxide and the iron-

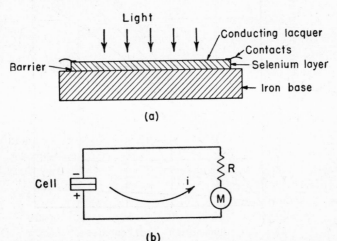

Fig. 15-20. (a) Assembly of a photovoltaic iron-selenium cell; (b) circuit for measurement of light received, as in a photographic exposure meter.

selenium cells.   The iron-selenium cell is a sandwich consisting of an iron base plate, covered by a thin film of iron selenide over which is sprayed a transparent film of a conducting metallic lacquer.   The iron plate forms one electrode and the conducting lacquer becomes the other.   The lacquer is contacted around the edge by bronze spring fingers.   This arrangement is diagrammed in Fig. 15-20.   At (b) is shown the simple operating circuit of the cell.   The action of the copper-copper oxide cell is similar.

The voltage generated is small, of the order of a few hundred millivolts in bright light, and the voltage is not a linear function of light intensity.   The cell internal resistance is found to be small, so that currents of quite a few hundred microamperes—and in sunlight currents of a few milliamperes—may flow.   The internal resistance varies proportionately with voltage in such a way that

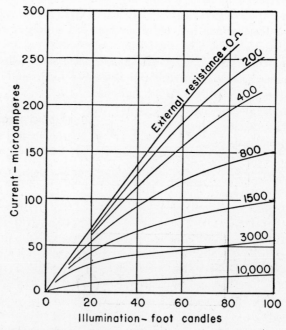

Fig. 15-21.   Current vs illumination for voltaic cell.
Area = 1.1 sq. in.

under short circuit or under zero external circuit resistance, the output current becomes almost linear with illumination. The characteristics of an iron-selenide cell with various external loads are shown in Fig. 15-21.

Cells of this nature are sensitive to temperature and will lose their sensitivity permanently if operated above 55°C. Below that limit, it is found that both emf and resistance are functions of temperature, but the short-circuit current is nearly independent of temperature.

Because of the stability with temperature and linearity with light intensity, photovoltaic cells are usually operated with very low external resistances, approximating short circuit. The current of a few hundred microamperes may be used to operate sensitive relays directly, forming simple illumination controls with no need for external voltage sources. In another important application the cell is directly connected to a low-resistance portable microammeter, calibrated directly in light intensity, to make light-measuring instruments and photographic exposure meters. Since the photovoltaic cell develops such a low voltage, direct amplification of its output by vacuum-tube amplifiers is not feasible. Erratic shifts in bias supply voltages may be greater than input voltages from the cell, completely masking the emf to be amplified.

The semiconductor film between the electrodes is quite thin, and the internal capacity of photovoltaic cells is high. Since this capacity appears directly in shunt with the cell, it effectively short-circuits any alternating current developed by the use of modulated light. Even at a 60-cycle variation frequency the response is less than one-half the output for a steady light source. Photovoltaic cells are, therefore, not well suited for sound reproduction from film.

Spectral response depends considerably on cell construction and treatment, but it may be made to approximate that of the human eye by use of a special filter which places the peak response in the yellow green at about 5500 A.

Photovoltaic cells may be connected in parallel to increase the current output when working into low-resistance loads, and in series when working into high-resistance loads. The short-circuit current is approximately proportional to the area of surface exposed to the light.

REFERENCES

1. Grondahl, L. O., and Geiger, P. H., "A New Electronic Rectifier," *J. AIEE*, **46**, 215 (1927).

2. Hamann, C. E., and Harty, E. A., "Fundamental Characteristics and Applications of the Copper Oxide Rectifier," *Gen. Elec. Rev.*, **36**, 342 (1933).

3. Seitz, F., *Modern Theory of Solids*, McGraw-Hill Book Company, Inc., New York, 1940.

4. Ramsey, G., "The Selenium Rectifier," *Elec. Eng.*, **63**, 425 (1944).

5. Cornelius, E. C., "Germanium Crystal Diodes," *Electronics*, **19**, 118, February (1946).

6. Lark-Horovitz, K., and Johnson, V. A., "Theory of Resistivity in Germanium Alloys," *Phys. Rev.*, **69**, 258 (1946).

7. Becker, J. A., Green, C. B., and Pearsons, G. L., "Properties and Uses of Thermistors," *Bell Syst. Tech. J.*, **26**, 170 (1947).

8. Bardeen, J., "Surface States and Rectification at a Metal-Semiconductor Contact," *Phys. Rev.*, **71**, 717 (1947).

9. Torrey, H. C., and Whitmer, C. A., *Crystal Rectifiers*, McGraw-Hill Book Company, Inc., New York, 1948.

10. Bardeen, J., and Brattain, W. H., "The Transistor, A Semiconductor Triode," *Phys. Rev.*, **74**, 230 (1948).

11. ———, ———, "Physical Principles Involved in Transistor Action," *Phys. Rev.*, **75**, 1208 (1949).

12. Ryder, R. M., and Kirchner, R. J., "Some Circuit Aspects of the Transistor," *Bell Syst. Tech. J.*, **28**, 367 (1949).

13. Bardeen, J., and Brattain, W. H., "Conductivity of Germanium," *Phys. Rev.*, **75**, 1216 (1949).

14. Becker, J. A., and Shive, J. N., "The Transistor—A New Semiconductor Amplifier," *Elec. Eng.*, **68**, 215 (1949).

15. Sweeney, J. H., "Use of Germanium Diodes at High Frequencies," *Elec. Eng.*, **69**, 217 (1950).

16. *Symposium on Electrical Properties of Semiconductors and the Transistor*, American Institute of Electrical Engineers, New York, 1950.

17. Shockley, W., Sparks, M., and Teal, G. K., "The p-n Junction Transistors," *Phys. Rev.*, **83**, 151 (1951).

18. Bell Telephone Laboratories, "The Transistor," Western Electric Co., New York, 1951.

19. Wallace, R. L., Jr., and Pietenpol, W. J., "Some Circuit Properties and Applications of n-p-n Transistors," *Proc. IRE*, **39**, 753 (1951).

APPENDIX

SELECTED VACUUM-TUBE CHARACTERISTIC CURVES AND DATA

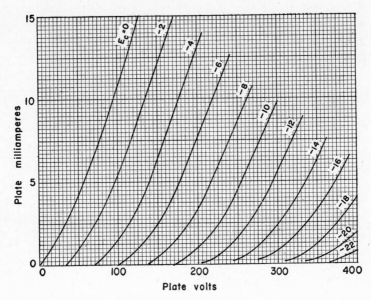

Fig. A-1.   Type 6J5 triode.

$$C_{gp} = 3.8 \ \mu\mu\text{f}; \qquad C_{gk} = 4.2 \ \mu\mu\text{f}; \qquad C_{pk} = 5.0 \ \mu\mu\text{f}$$

Maximum anode dissipation = 2.5 w

At recommended Q point:

$E_b = 250 \ \text{v}$	$\mu = 20$
$E_c = -8 \ \text{v}$	$r_p = 7700 \ \text{ohms}$
$I_b = 9 \ \text{ma}$	$g_m = 2600 \ \mu\text{mhos}$

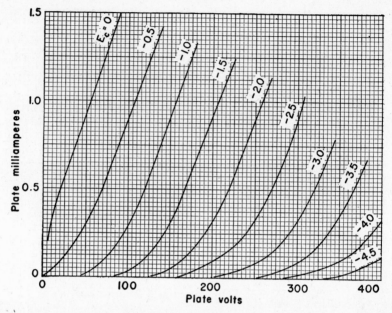

Fig. A-2.   Type 6SF5 triode.

$$C_{gp} = 2.4 \ \mu\mu\mathrm{f}; \qquad C_{gk} = 4.0 \ \mu\mu\mathrm{f}; \qquad C_{pk} = 3.6 \ \mu\mu\mathrm{f}$$

At recommended Q point:

$E_b = 250 \ \mathrm{v}$	$\mu = 100$
$E_c = -2 \ \mathrm{v}$	$r_p = 66{,}000 \ \mathrm{ohms}$
$I_b = 0.9 \ \mathrm{ma}$	$g_m = 1500 \ \mu\mathrm{mhos}$

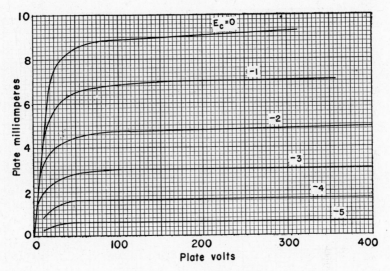

Fig. A-3.   Type 6SJ7 pentode.

$$C_{gp} = 0.005 \; \mu\mu\text{f}; \qquad C_{gk} = 6 \; \mu\mu\text{f}; \qquad C_{pk} = 7 \; \mu\mu\text{f}$$

Maximum anode dissipation = 2.5 w
Maximum screen dissipation = 0.3 w

At recommended Q point:

$$
\begin{aligned}
E_b &= 250 \text{ v} & I_b &= 3 \text{ ma} \\
E_{c1} &= -3 \text{ v} & I_{c2} &= 0.8 \text{ ma} \\
E_{c2} &= 100 \text{ v} & r_p &= 1 \text{ megohm} \\
E_{c3} &= 0 \text{ v} & g_m &= 1650 \; \mu\text{mhos}
\end{aligned}
$$

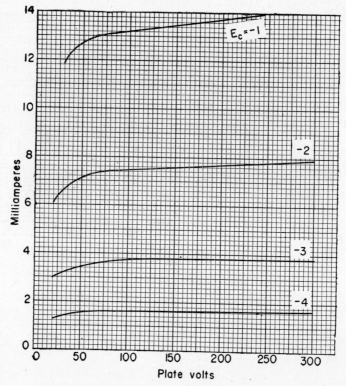

Fig. A-4.   Type 6AK5 pentode.

$$C_{gp} = 0.02 \; \mu\mu\text{f}; \qquad C_{gk} = 4.0 \; \mu\mu\text{f}; \qquad C_{pk} = 2.8 \; \mu\mu\text{f}$$

At recommended Q point:

$E_b = 180$ v $I_{c2} = 2.4$ ma

E_c thru 200-ohm resistor $r_p = 690,000$ ohms

$I_b = 7.7$ ma $g_m = 5100 \; \mu$mhos

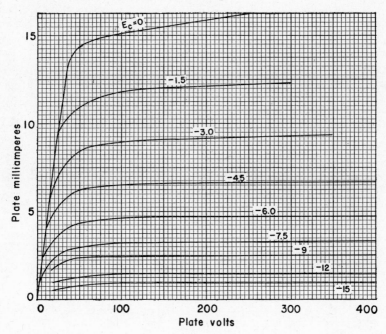

Fig. A-5.   Type 6SK7 variable-μ pentode.   Equivalent to type 6BD6 except for capacitances.

$$C_{gp} = 0.003 \ \mu\mu\text{f}; \qquad C_{gk} = 6 \ \mu\mu\text{f}; \qquad C_{pk} = 7 \ \mu\mu\text{f}$$

Maximum anode dissipation = 4 w

Maximum screen dissipation = 0.4 w

At recommended Q point:

$E_b = 250$ v	$I_b = 9.2$ ma
$E_{c1} = -3$ v	$I_{c2} = 2.6$ ma
$E_{c2} = 100$ v	$r_p = 0.8$ megohm
$E_{c3} = 0$ v	$g_m = 2000 \ \mu$mhos at grid bias of -3 v
	$g_m = 10 \ \mu$mhos at grid bias of -35 v

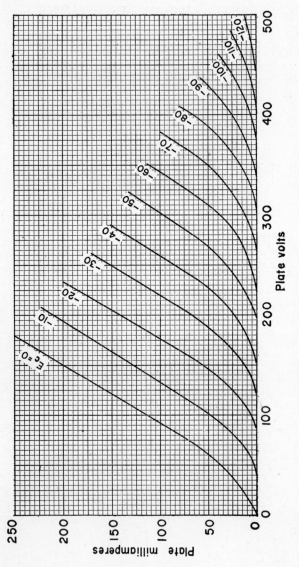

Fig. A-6. Type 2A3 triode power amplifier.

$C_{gp} = 16.5\ \mu\mu f;$ $\qquad C_{gk} = 7.5\ \mu\mu f;$ $\qquad C_{pk} = 5.5\ \mu\mu f$

Maximum anode dissipation = 15 w

At recommended Q point (Class A):

$E_b = 250$ v $\qquad \mu = 4.2$
$E_c = -45$ v $\qquad r_p = 800$ ohms
$I_b = 60$ ma $\qquad g_m = 5250\ \mu$mhos

494

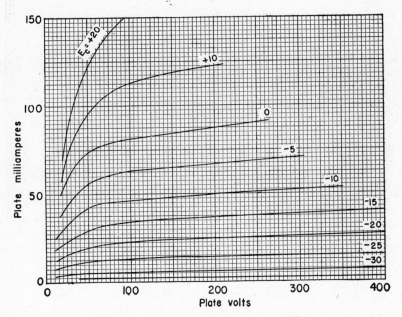

Fig. A-7. Type 6F6 pentode power amplifier.

$$C_{gp} = 0.2 \ \mu\mu f; \qquad C_{gk} = 6.5 \ \mu\mu f; \qquad C_{pk} = 13 \ \mu\mu f$$

Maximum anode dissipation = 11 w
Maximum screen dissipation = 3.75 w

At recommended Q point (Class A):

$E_b = 250$ v	$I_b = 34$ ma
$E_{c1} = -16.5$ v	$I_{c2} = 6.5$ ma
$E_{c2} = 250$ v	$r_p = 80,000$ ohms
	$g_m = 2500 \ \mu$mhos

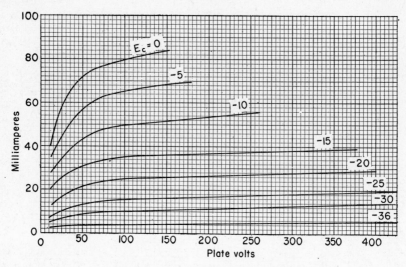

Fig. A-8.   Type 6AR5 power pentode.

Maximum anode dissipation = 8.5 w
Maximum screen dissipation = 2.5 w

At recommended Q point (Class A):

$$E_b = 250 \text{ v} \qquad I_b = 32 \text{ ma}$$
$$E_{c2} = 250 \text{ v} \qquad I_{c2} = 5.5 \text{ ma}$$
$$E_{c1} = -18 \text{ v} \qquad r_p = 68{,}000 \text{ ohms}$$
$$g_m = 2300 \text{ } \mu\text{mhos}$$

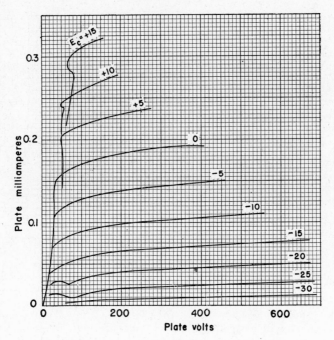

Fig. A-9. Type 6L6 beam-power tetrode amplifier.

$$C_{gp} = 0.9 \ \mu\mu\text{f}; \qquad C_{gk} = 11.5 \ \mu\mu\text{f}; \qquad C_{pk} = 9.5 \ \mu\mu\text{f}$$

Maximum anode dissipation = 19 w
Maximum screen dissipation = 2.5 w

At recommended Q point (Class A):

$$E_b = 350 \text{ v} \qquad I_b = 54 \text{ ma}$$
$$E_{c1} = -18 \text{ v} \qquad I_{c2} = 2.5 \text{ ma}$$
$$E_{c2} = 250 \text{ v} \qquad r_p = 33,000 \text{ ohms}$$
$$g_m = 5,200 \ \mu\text{mhos}$$

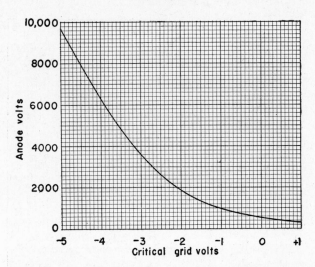

Fig. A-10. Type FG-41 thyratron—critical grid characteristics.

Average anode current = 12.5 amp (30 sec averaging time)
Peak anode current = 75 amp
Maximum peak inverse voltage = 10,000 v
Temperature limits = 40° to 65°C, condensed Hg
Deionization time = 100 μsec
Ionization time = 20 μsec
Cathode heater voltage = 5 v
Cathode heater current = 20 amp

INDEX

Date Due

DEC 1 7 1954		MY 30 62	
APR 3 1956		AP 3 '63	
		NO 18 64	
MAY 1 1956		AP 20 66	
DEC 4 1956		MY 11 68	
DEC 1 8 1956			
APR 8 1957			
APR 2 3 1957			
MAY 7 1957			
APR 2 3 1958			
	MY 19 60		
JUN 8 59			
	DEC		
AP 21 60	JA 24 60		
DEC 1 '61			
Demco 293-5